ILLUSTRATED FLORA OF MALLORCA

DR. ELSPETH BECKETT

ILLUSTRATED FLORA
OF
MALLORCA

Illustrations by the author

EDITORIAL MOLL
MALLORCA
1993

Primera edició: Juliol 1993

Dipòsit Legal: B-25.538-1993
ISBN: 84-273-0714-4
Imprès a: BIGSA
        C/ Manuel Fernández Márquez, s/n
        08930 Sant Adrià de Besòs

CONTENTS

Preface 7

Signs and Abbreviations 8

Some Notes on Mallorcan Flora 10

Some of the plant communities in Mallorca 10

Acknowledgements 13

Bibliography 15

Glossary 17

Index to Plates 23

The Plates 1 to 96 27

Index to Latin names of Families and Genera 221

PREFACE

This book is intended to be an easily accessible guide to the flowering plants of Mallorca. It is modelled on W. Keble Martin: *The Concise British Flora in Colour*, Ebury Press and Michael Joseph 1965.

It falls short of the model in very many ways. One is unavoidable. Not all the illustrations here are from Mallorcan specimens. Keble Martin lived mainly in industrial parishes, and his 'patch' was much larger, but it was more accessible than mine, and some of it could be reached for short excursions as well as longer holidays. My visits to Mallorca totalled 1-3 weeks per year until I retired recently and could go rather more. He also started when he was rather younger and spread his efforts over 60 years.

This does mean that some plants may look 'not quite right' to people who live in Mallorca. I have made it clear in the text when a non-Mallorcan specimen was used, usually for rarer plants. Occasionally I found something in Mallorca after painting it from a specimen from elsewhere. If it looked very different I repainted the page, otherwise I added a small supplementary illustration or a note in the text.

Like Keble Martin I was engaged for much of the time I was working on this project in another occupation. He was a parson, I was a GP. My first trip to Mallorca in 1976 was to take some of my children for a cheap sunny holiday. A lot of people go for the same reason. Some, sadly, never venture beyond the beaches, and so miss the best things — wild rugged mountains with spectacular rock formations, stony paths without a house in sight, nightingales singing, frogs croaking, and flowers everywhere.

Visitors to Mallorca cannot always depend on sun. It can rain heavily there at almost any time of the year, particularly in the spring. It is because of this that flowers can be found in plenty at almost any time, and the countryside may remain green and lush much later in the year than in other parts of the Mediterranean area.

The list of plants known to occur in Mallorca is derived from:

F. Barceló: *Flora de las Islas Baleares*. Palma de Mallorca 1879-1881.

F. Bonafè: *Flora de Mallorca*. Palma 1977-80.

J. Duvigneaud: *Catalogue Provisoire de la Flore des Baléares*, Liège, 2nd edition 1979.

Alfred Hansen: *Additions and corrections to J. Duvigneaud Catalogue Provisoire de la Flore des Baléares, 2. edition*. Copenhagen 1985 (privately circulated): also from correspondence with Dr Hansen.

H. Knoche: *Flora Balearica*. Montpellier 1921-23.

Lleonard Llorens et al. (1991) (unpublished at the time of writing).

Tutin et al.: *Flora Europaea*. Cambridge 1964-80.

Various papers mentioned in the text and in the bibliography.

A few were added from specimens and photos from members of the Botanical Society of the British Isles, and from my own 'finds' in Mallorca. I have tried to illustrate most of the flowering plants likely to be found now, excepting hybrids, and usually only including one subspecies if there is more than one. I had hoped at one time to include *all* flowering plants ever recorded for Mallorca, but this was a hope only a very inexperienced botanist could entertain. Gradually I came to realise that there was, as in other areas, a body of well established plants that fluctuates very little over the years, including some rare ones. But there are too records over 200 years or so of about the same number of marginally established species which come and go. These include some escaping from cultivation as crops or for ornament and some arriving as impurities in seed for cultivation, or carried by birds and other agencies (including botanists' socks?). There are also some very doubtful records where one plant has been recorded for another (for example *Hypericum elodes* for *H. tomentosum*). Because of my initial optimism some of the plates completed first include plants which have not been seen in Mallorca recently if ever (for example *Moluccella spinosa*). Their status should be clear from the text.

The illustrations are pen drawings coloured in watercolour. A sample of each plant is included, but not usually the whole plant. For most grasses I have shown only the flowering part. Live specimens or close-up photographs were used when possible, but some were done from herbarium specimens. I have tried to avoid numbering of details as much as possible as this tends to clutter up the page — the main number is usually placed between the main illustration and the corresponding details. Usually the main illustration is x 1 or slightly reduced, and the details more or less enlarged. Hairs are drawn in sepia ink like the main outline: this does not mean that they were this colour.

Each plant illustrated is described in a correspondingly numbered entry in the text. The descriptions are largely based on those in the Flora Europaea, to which a page reference is added wherever possible. Latin names used here without an authority are as used in the Flora Europaea (hereafter FE). I have used FE names whenever they approximate to the names used by Professor Llorens in his list, and in these cases I have not compared them with names in the Med-Checklist (see Bibliography). Where the FE name differs from Llorens' name I have given both names, giving priority to Med-Checklist name when this is available to me. I have given English names when I know a genuine one, but not when the only name is one recently contrived from the Latin.

The description is followed by the flowering time, usually after Knoche or from my own observation, and some indication of habitat and/or rarity.

Signs & Abbreviations

K, D, B, H, Ll...indicate that the plant is **listed for Mallorca** by Knoche (1921-23), Duvigneaud (1979), Bonafè (1977-1980), Hansen (1985) and Llorens (1991). (In a few cases I was unable to identify plants listed by Knoche with any certainty). For most plants I have only quoted the first two. B H and Ll are added where possible if the plant seemed rare or the record uncertain, or where they were the only sources.

K or **D** .....indicates that it was seen in the field **in Mallorca** by Knoche or Duvigneaud. (Knoche's symbol for plants he has seen in the field include those he has seen only in Minorca or Ibiza. His maps are sometimes not clear on this point).

(Ma, Mi, I) indicates records from Mallorca, Minorca, Ibiza — mainly after Duvigneaud and Llorens but also from other sources listed in the Bibliography and text.

Reference to the smaller islands (mainly Formentera off the coast of Ibiza, and Dragonera and Cabrera off the coast of Mallorca) is usually given only when the only station for the Balearic Islands is on one of these. **Ma** ....indicates that I have seen the plant growing in Mallorca.

When as far as I know a plant has not been seen in Mallorca recently (K, D or Ma not in bold type) I have attempted to date the source of the record. The information for this is mainly from Knoche (1921-1923), also from Hansen (1985) and Barceló (1879-1881). The dates only give an approximate idea of when the plant was seen, as some refer to the date of publication of the work in which the plant is listed, and some to the dates when the author was collecting. It seemed worthwhile to record the actual finding of live specimens in this way to give at least some idea of whether the plant is common, fairly common, rare or possibly extinct. However it is important to remember that many of the plants recorded as not having been seen in the field by Knoche, Duvigneaud or myself may have been seen in the field recently (and possibly frequently), and the finding either not published or published in some journal I have not seen. These plants are sometimes rare, or very like a commoner plant and therefore overlooked. Sometimes plants are under-recorded because they flower when not many people are looking for them, or because they are too dull for much consideration.

Where the FE does not record a plant as occurring in the Balearic Islands I have added 'Not Bl in FE'. 'Bl in FE' is recorded only where there seems some doubt about the occurrence of the plant here.

At the end of the text for each plate there is a list of other plants recorded for Mallorca. This includes any plants not illustrated, sometimes because of limitation of space (usually unimportant plants) or because the plant is very like another (illustrated) species, or because I didn't know about it at the time I was painting. Others are omitted because the records seem very old or dubious.

Following are records from the other islands. This is to help people who may use the book in Minorca and Ibiza. These records are listed without any reference to the source or critical evaluation of it, apart from a ? when I know it to be doubtful. These islands are strictly outside the scope of a book on the Flora of Mallorca.

Other signs and abbreviations

ca .... about (in measurements)
cf .... compare
subsp .... subspecies
X .... multiplied by: degree of (linear) magnification or reduction
< .... up to
> .... more than

SOME NOTES ON THE MALLORCAN FLORA

Islands well separated from the mainland tend to have an interesting flora which has evolved in isolation. Also there may be relics of an older flora whose survival has somehow been facilitated, for instance by the non-occurrence of a competitor. *Hypericum balearicum* is such a a survivor from a group which has disappeared from the mainland. There are also 30 to 40 species and subspecies endemic to Mallorca (and others to the Balearic Islands) and many plants here show the beginnings of speciation in minor but significant variation from mainland populations.

There is at least one monotypic genus on the island which is confined to the Western Mediterranean, the minute Umbellifer *Naufraga balearica*. *Femeniasia balearica* (Rodr. Fem.) Susanna, local in Minorca and once recorded from Mallorca, has recently been separated from *Centaurea* because of its distinctive features.

Other plants here are outposts of the African flora. *Silene pseudatocion* seems to be increasing here, its only station outside Africa. *Helianthemum caput-felis* and *Tamarix boveana*, also African species, have a very local foothold on the Spanish mainland too.

Some of the absences are interesting. They include *Juniperus communis, Urtica dioica, Pastinaca sativa, Bellis perennis* and probably *Sagina procumbens* and *Cerastium fontanum*. Some people eat *Urtica dioica* and it is said to be good for butterflies, but for me any place without it deserves extra points, not because it stings (so does the remarkable *Urtica atrovirens* subsp. *bianorii* Knoche), but because of the aggressive way in which it has cashed in on the surplus nitrogen in British hedgerows, to the great impoverishment of the countryside.

Some of the plant communities in Mallorca

Pinewoods

Many areas of the coast and lower slopes of the mountains are covered in woods of *Pinus halepensis*. Except where these are too dense there is an understory of shrubs such as *Pistacia lentiscus, Cistus monspeliensis, Juniperus oxycedrus, Fumana thymifolia, Dorycnium hirsutum, Phillyrea angustifolia, Smilax aspera* and *Ruscus aculeatus*. Occasionally the spectacular purple spikes of *Limodorum abortivum* may be found here.

Where the wood is thinner or recently burnt, *Cistus salvifolius* may replace *Cistus monspeliensis*, with some *Cistus albidus*. Herbaceous plants may include *Lotus tetraphyllus, Linum trigynum, Rubia peregrina, Dorycnium pentaphyllum* and *Blackstonia perfoliata*.

Dry open habitats not under pines

These are often dominated by the pampas-like grass, *Ampelodesmos mauritanica*, often with *Rosmarinus officinalis, Hypericum balearicum, Astragalus balearicus* and *Cneorum tricoccon*. In other places broom-like shrubs predominate, *Calicotome spinosa*, mainly in the north and west, and *Genista lucida*, mainly in the east. Other shrubs which occur locally in dry open scrub are *Chamaerops humilis, Arbutus unedo* and *Euphorbia dendroides*.

Herbaceous plants which often grow in these habitats are *Orchis pyramidalis*, *Rumex intermedius*, the huge yellow umbellifer *Ferula communis*, a smaller endemic yellow umbellifer *Thapsia gymnesica* Rosselló & Pujadas, *Ruta* species, *Coris monspeliensis*, the pinkish form of *Centaurium maritimum*, *Ajuga iva*, *Teucrium chamaedrys*, *Teucrium botrys*, *Micromeria filiformis*, *Arctotheca calendula*, and in the autumn, *Urginea maritima*.

In open areas in the higher parts of the mountains a high proportion of the plants are endemic to the Balearic islands or to Mallorca. *Hypericum balearicum*, *Phlomis italica* and the 'hedgehog plants' *Teucrium balearicum* (Pau) Castroviejo and *Astragalus balearicus* (hedgehog-sized lower down but up to 1m nearer the peaks) may be dominant over large areas, with other shrubby species locally, such as *Rhamnus lycioides*, *Buxus balearica*, *Acer granatense*, *Santolina chamaecyparissus* and occasional *Sorbus aria*, Yew and Holly. Herbaceous plants here include *Helleborus lividus* and *foetidus*, *Linaria aeruginea* subspecies *pruinosa*, *Pastinaca lucida*, *Arenaria grandiflora*, *Vincetoxicum hirundinaria* and later in the year *Merendera filifolia* and *Crocus cambessedesii*.

Roadsides and fields

One of Mallorca's main attractions (and one I have never seen mentioned in tour operators' brochures) is the country lanes, winding between orchards of almond, fig, carob or olive carpeted with *Calendula arvensis* or *Bellis annua* and crops with *Allium nigrum*, *Anchusa azurea* and *Gladiolus illyricus* sticking out above them and *Adonis annua* and *Nigella damascena* hiding beneath them. On either side are walls covered in *Clematis cirrhosa* and *Rosa sempervirens* or hedgerows of sloe, blackberry and wild olive as a backing to a herbaceous border of poppies, *Kundmannia sicula*, *Echium plantagineum*, *Urospermum dalechampii*, *Allium roseum* and later fennel and *Dittrichia viscosa*. A walk along such a lane is full of surprises — including people picking the tender shoots of *Asparagus acutifolius* to eat à la beurre.

Where the walls are of the traditional stone (many now, alas, are made of concrete blocks) they may support *Polypodium cambricum* L., *Sedum dasyphyllum*, *stellatum*, *rubens*, *sediforme*, *Umbilicus rupestris* and *horizontalis*, *Saxifraga tridactylites*, *Anagallis arvensis*, *Centranthus calcitrapae*, several species of *Valerianella*, *Campanula erinus*, *Muscari neglectum*, *Ophrys speculum* among many others.

Quercus woods

These are often too dense to be hospitable to other plants. In the most shaded parts there may be parasitic plants not dependent on chlorophyll, such as the yellow bird's nest, *Monotropa hypopitys*, and orchids *Neottia nidus-avis*, *Epipactis microphylla*, and *Limodorum abortivum*. Where a little less shaded *Cephalanthera damasonium* and *longifolia* may occur. *Cistus monspeliensis* is the only *Cistus* growing in moderately heavy shade; other plants which may survive here precariously include the almost ubiquitous *Pistacia lentiscus*, with bracken and *Ruscus aculeatus*.

Selaginella denticulata, *Asplenium trichomanes*, *Asplenium ceterach* L., *Polypodium cambricum* L., *Sibthorpia africana*, *Erodium reichardii* and *Arenaria balearica* are all common on moist overhung surfaces of walls and rocks.

Sandy habitats, including coastal dunes and higher parts of sandy shores

Larger shrubs in sandy coastal areas not covered by pines are *Pistacia lentiscus*, *Juniperus oxycedrus*, and *Juniperus phoenicea*. Locally *Halimium halimifolium*, *Solanum sodomeum*, *Myrtus communis*, *Phillyrea angustifolia* or *Cistus clusii* may also be found. Where not overexposed to trampling there may be an almost continuous cover between these of smaller shrubs, including small prostrate plants of *Cistus salvifolius*, with *Teucrium dunense* Sennen, *Helichrysum stoechas*, *Fumana thymifolia*, *Limonium echioides*, *Scrophularia ramosissima* and *Crucianella maritima*.

Herbaceous plants here include *Rumex bucephalophorus*, *Medicago littoralis*, *Lotus cytisoides*, *Centaurium tenuiflorum*, many species and hybrids of *Limonium*, *Erodium cicutarium*, *Frankenia* species,

13

Euphorbia terracina, Eryngium maritimum, Ononis reclinata, Convolvulus cantabrica, Orchis coriophora, Ophrys speculum, tenthredinifera, apifera and *bombyliflora,* and more locally *Asteriscus maritimus, Matthiola sinuata, Medicago marina, Thesium humile, Petrorhagia nanteuilii, Ajuga iva* and *Tuberaria guttata.*

Saltmarshes

Some of these have disappeared under coastal development, though saltmarsh species survive in the areas behind the hotels at Can Pastilla and S'Arenal. Small areas remain in several places, including Port de Pollença, the Albufereta and Port d'Andratx. All these have their own peculiar plants with a limited distribution elsewhere, including *Gynandiris sisyrhinchium, Cressa cretica, Salsola soda,* and *Sphenopus divaricatus.*

The main areas are the Albufera (including areas outside the nature reserve) and the Salines of Campos. The Albufera has areas of dune (see above) as well as saltmarsh, though parts of the dunes outside the nature reserve are being bulldozed away to make artificial beaches. Large areas of the marsh are dominated by *Phragmites australis, Cladium mariscus, Scirpus maritimus, Arundo donax, Juncus maritimus, Juncus subulatus, Inula crithmoides, Sarcocornia fruticosa* (L.) Schott and *Arthrocnemum machrostachyum* (Moric.) Moris.

Other species in the wetter parts of the marsh include *Aster tripolium, Euphorbia hirsuta* L., *Pulicaria odora, Sonchus maritimus, Typha domingensis* and *Orchis laxiflora.* In the drier parts there are *Melilotus messanensis, Lotus glaber* Miller, *Dittrichia graveolens, Ranunculus trilobus, Juncus acutus* and *bufonius, Apium graveolens, Daucus carota, Plantago coronopus, Plantago crassifolia, Polypogon monspeliensis, Spergularia media, Ranunculus trilobus, Trifolium squamosum* and *Atriplex* species.

Many other habitats will be recognised, not least the urban areas explored by botanists after the evening meal and in breaks from longer excursions. I hope there will not be too many specimens to sort, and perhaps by making identification in the field easier, this book will help to achieve this.

The serious student of botany will find specimens of most of the Mallorcan flora already in herbaria somewhere, and for those whose interest in plants is more aesthetic than botanical a photograph beats a herbarium specimen every time. For the competitive plant hunter ('I found 70 species, how many did you find?') a careful list is as good as anything, and the sport becomes as innocuous as cricket if it involves minimal collecting. The lists will bring back happy memories for years.

Wild plants everywhere have many factors stacked against their survival. These include trampling, urban development, use of weedkillers and changes of climate. In the mountain areas of Mallorca very heavy grazing by goats is taking its toll. Collecting is making an impact too, and while careful collection of small specimens of common plants may seem to be harmless, I suspect that this is partly because our own little collection makes no obvious difference *at the time we make it.* Incrementally the effect may be enormous, and far worse the criminal theft of whole colonies of wild orchids, usually destined to perish, as has recently occurred in some parts of Mallorca.

Many of the rarer plants in this book were painted from close-up photographs taken in the field, though I did collect some specimens too. I regret in particular *Chaenorrhinum origanifolium* subsp. *serrae.* In 1984 I collected a small specimen from what was then a substantial patch. I didn't know what it was, nor that its only known station was on waste ground adjacent to a tourist centre. It is now probably extinct. A lot of botanists, amateur and professional, visit Mallorca, and many of us may have taken from the same patch.

Fostering an interest in plants encourages people to care for them, and to this extent a little judicious collecting may be defensible. But the notion that the only purpose of the natural world is to supply the needs of mankind is losing ground. If we leave plants where we find them they may incidentally delight people yet to come. More important, they will continue to multiply and evolve to enrich the diversity of species in this lovely but beleaguered planet.

ACKNOWLEDGEMENTS

I am much indebted to the authors and publishers of sources listed in the Bibliography, especially those mentioned in the Preface, and to Mr Anthony Bonner, whose *Plants of the Balearic Islands* (Palma de Mallorca 1982) with its excellent bibliography put me on the right track for many plants and nearly all the sources of information. He also gave a lot of assistance to sort out problems arising from my linguistic deficiencies.

Others who have helped include first and foremost Dr Stephen Jury, Curator of the Herbarium of Reading University and Dr Humphrey Bowen, until recently unofficial doyen of the same department. Their patience and willingness seemed unending.

Next I would like to thank the Botanical Society of the British Isles, particularly the Hon. General Secretary, Mrs Mary Briggs, but for whose encouragement in the early stages I might have given up. An advertisement in *BSBI News* produced many species I had failed to find, and I am indebted to the following people for photographs and specimens: Mr Rodney Burton, Mr Chris Burkinshaw (who produced *on the spot* a live plant of *Damasonium alisma* at a BSBI meeting in the British Museum of Natural History), Mrs A.A. Butcher, Mr Eric J.Clement, Dr Susan Eden (many photographs, specimens and general encouragement), Mr John Hooper, Mr David Nicolle, Mr John Ounsted (who gave me growing plants of *Veronica verna* and *Trifolium filiforme* L.), Mr Alan Outen, Mr R.M. Payne, Mr Mervyn Southam, Mrs R. Strickland, Mr W.F. Taylor, Mr Mark Thompson, Dr R.M. Veall and Mr J.J. Zawadski.

In the later stages Professor Lleonard Llorens of the Universitat de les Illes Balears went through the text and suggested some alterations, particularly to do with distribution of plants in Mallorca and recent changes in nomenclature. He also let me have a copy of his new list of Balearic plants before publication. Dr Juan Rita of the same department helped with specimens of some of the plants I had failed to find, and a new endemic species he had discovered himself. Dr Irene Ridge and Mr Fred Rumsey came to Mallorca with me, adding their professional skills to my inexpertise. Mrs Pat Bishop of the RSPB in Mallorca encouraged with her characteristic kindness, and she and her husband Mr. Dennis Bishop introduced me to other naturalists who shared their warm hospitality, including Professor Palmer Newbould, Mrs Jo Newbould and Mrs Dinah McLennan, all working for Earthwatch in the Albufera, who helped find several missing species.

Dr S.M. Walters kindly allowed me to take live specimens from the Cambridge University Botanic Garden. These include most of the species I have noted 'from garden specimen', though a few were from photographs taken at the Royal Botanic Gardens at Kew and the Oxford University Botanic Garden, and some from my own garden, grown from commercial sources. Mr Alan Cook's enthusiastic help in finding live specimens of some of the grasses at the Royal Botanic Gardens was particularly appreciated. Mr A.R. Vickery, the Keeper, kindly loaned some specimens from the British Museum Herbarium.

Others I thank for expert opinions on difficult species: Mr John Akeroyd, Dr B.R. Baum, Mr P.M. Benoit, Dr P.F. Cannon, Prof. C.D.K. Cook, Dr Matthias Erben, Dr Alfred Hansen, Dr A. C. Jermy, Prof. D.M. Moore, Dr J.R. Press, Dr Juan Rita, Dr T.C.G. Rich, Mr Fred Rumsey, M/s Fatima Sales, Mme Odette and M. André Sotiaux, Prof. Clive A. Stace, Mr P.D. Sell, Dr P.J.O. Trist, Dr Sara Webster, Dr Frank White and Mr Jeffrey Wood.

My thanks too to Señor Francesc Moll, the publisher, for his friendly cooperation and for bringing the whole endeavour to fruition. His personal knowledge of the plants of Mallorca and the out-of-the-way places where they grow was an added bonus.

Finally family and friends, many of whom came to Mallorca with me and helped in the search, an the people of Mallorca whose hospitality so adds to the many pleasures to be experienced in their beautiful island.

BIBLIOGRAPHY

GENERAL

ALOMAR, G., RITA, J. , ROSSELLÓ, J.A.: *Notas Florísticas de las Islas Baleares* (III) Boll. Soc. Hist. Nat. Balears 30 (1986) 145-154.

BARCELÓ Y COMBIS, D.F.: *Flora de las Islas Baleares*. Palma (1879-1881).

BONAFÈ, F.: *Flora de Mallorca*. 4 vols. Editorial Moll. Palma (1977-1980).

BONNER, A.: *Plants of the Balearic Islands*. Editorial Moll. Palma (1982).

DUVIGNEAUD, J.: *Catalogue Provisoire de la Flore des Baléares*. Second edition. Liège (1979) (Supplement to Fascicule no 17 of Société pour l'Échange des Plantes Vasculaires de l'Europe Occidentale et du Bassin Méditerranéen).

GREUTER, W., BURDET H.M., and LONG G.: *Med-Checklist* Vols 1, 3 and 4. Secretariat Med-Checklist, Conservatoire et Jardin Botanique de la Ville de Genève (1985-1989).

HANSEN, A.:. *Additions and Corrections to J. Duvigneaud: Catalogue Provisoire de la Flore des Baléares. 2nd Edition* (1985). Unpublished circulated list.

HUTCHINSON, J.: *The Families of Flowering Plants*. Oxford (1959).

LLORENS Ll. et al.: (list of plants occurring in the Balearic Islands (1991) in course of publication).

KNOCHE, H.: *Flora Balearica*. Montpellier (1921-1923).

MARTIN, W.K.: *The Concise British Flora in Colour*. London (1965).

RITA, J., BIBILONI, G., LLORENS, Ll.: *Notas Florísticas de las Islas Baleares* (I). Boll. Soc. Hist. Nat. Balears, 29 (1985) 129-133. Palma de Mallorca.

SMYTHIES, B.E.: *Flora of Spain and the Balearic Islands*. Englera 3 (1-3). Berlin (1984-1986).

TUTIN, T.G., HEYWOOD, V.H., BURGES, N.A., VALENTINE, D.H., WALTERS, S.M., WEBB, D.A.: *Flora Europaea*. Cambridge (1964-1980).

FOR PARTICULAR PLANTS OR OTHER ISLANDS

EUPHORBIA MYRSINITES: COLOM, G.: *Biogeografía de las Baleares*. (Palma 1957).

FILAGO PETRO-IANII: DITTRICH, M. and RITA J. in KIT TAN (Ed.): *Plant Taxonomy, Phytogeography and Related Subjects*. The Davis and Hedge Festschrift. (Edinburgh University Press. 1989)

IBIZA: KUHBIER, H.: Veröff. Überseemuseum Bremen 5: 6-37 (1978)

JUNCUS: COPE, T.A. and STACE, C.A.: Watsonia 12: 113-128 (1980) (Differences between J. bufonius and J. hybridus).

LIMONIUM: ERBEN, M.: *Bemerkungen zur Taxonomie der Gattung LIMONIUM I*. Mitt. Bot. Staatssamml. München 16: 547-563 (1980)

Bemerkungen zur Taxonomie der Gattung LIMONIUM II. Mitt. Bot. Staatssamml. München 17: 485-510 (1981)

Bemerkungen zur Taxonomie der Gattung LIMONIUM III. Mitt. Bot. Staatssamml. München 22: 203-220 (1986)

Bemerkungen zur Taxonomie der Gattung LIMONIUM IV. Mitt. Bot. Staatssamml. München 27: 381-406 (1988)

Bemerkungen zur Taxonomie der Gattung LIMONIUM V. Mitt. Bot. Staatssamml. München 28: 313-417 (1989)

MINORCA: CARDONA, A. and RITA, J.: *Aportació al Coneixement de la Flora Balear*. Fol. Bot. Misc., 3: 35-42 (Barcelona 1982)

TAMARIX: BAUM, B.R.: *The Genus TAMARIX* (Jerusalem 1978).

THYMUS HERBA-BARONA: MAYOL, M. y ROSSELLÓ, J.A.: Anales Jardín Botánico de Madrid: 47(2): 516 (1990)

TORILIS: JURY, S.L.:. *A new species of the genus TORILIS Adanson*. Bot. J. Linn. Soc. (1987) 95: 293-299

GLOSSARY

(Numbers in round brackets refer to drawings)

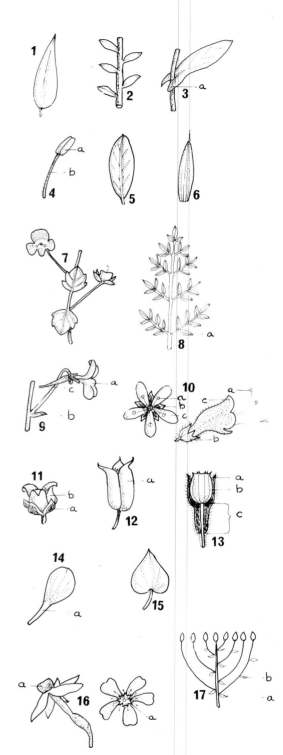

Acaulescent   without a stem (or with a very short one).

Achene   a dry one-seeded fruit (25c).

Acuminate   tapering to a point (1).

Alternate   (usually of leaves) strictly first on one side then the other of the stem in two rows (2). Used here (as often) to mean not in opposite pairs.

Amplexicaul   clasping the stem (3).

Anastomosing   (usually of veins) connecting by cross-branches.

Annual   a plant which goes through its complete life-cycle in one year (often recognised by absence of non-flowering shoots at flowering time).

Anther   the pollen-bearing organ of a flower (4a, 10a).

Apiculate   with a minute broad point at the apex (5).

Appressed   pressed against, e.g. of hairs against a stem, not sticking out from the stem (= spreading).

Arista   a bristly projection.

Aristate   with an arista (6).

Ascending   sloping or curved upwards.

Auricle   ear-like projection (usually at base of leaf, where it often clasps stem) (3a).

Awn   stiff, bristle-like projection (same as arista, but used in different contexts, especially flowers of grasses, 27e and f).

Axil   the angle between a leaf or bract and the stem from which it arises.

Axillary   arising in the axil (7 shows axillary flower and fruit).

Basal   at the base or lower end.

Berry   a fleshy fruit with one or more seeds in the pulp (seeds not enclosed in a stony or cartilaginous endocarp).

Biennial   a plant which germinates in the first year (usually producing a rosette of leaves), then flowers, produces fruit and dies in the second year.

Bifid   split into two parts.

Bipinnate   with the pinnae pinnate (8).

Bloom   a waxy coating (usually blue or whitish and on fruit).

Boss   a swelling or protuberance e.g. at the throat of the corolla tube in some Scrophulariaceae (9a).

Bract   a small scale or leaf-like structure (9b, 17a, 46d). In a spike or a raceme there may be a gradual transition up the stem from typical leaves to bracts.

Bracteole   a bract on a peduncle or pedicel, not on the main stem (20a, 46b, 17b).

Bristle   a stiff hair.

Bulbil   small bulb produced vegetatively and often above ground e.g. in some *Allium* species and in *Triglochin bulbosa*.

Caducous   falling soon after development.

Calyx   green or dull-coloured perianth-whorl, usually the outer whorl (10a, 28f), often persisting in fruit (11a, 13a). Sometimes the only whorl when this is dull-coloured.

Capitate   gathered into a head (of an inflorescence with many flowers).

Capsule   dry, usually thin-walled fruit formed from 2 or more fused carpels, usually splitting open when ripe (11b, 13b).

Carpel   a single unit of the gynoecium (12a)   there is often only one.

Carpophore   axis of flower between calyx attachment and base of ovary e.g. in *Silene* (13c).

Caruncle   a small fleshy appendage near the hilum of some seeds.

Ciliate   with regularly arranged projecting hairs.

Cladode   modified branch of stem which appears leaf-like (e.g. in *Ruscus* and *Asparagus)*.

Claw   narrowed inner end of petal (14).

Cleistogamous   fertilised without opening.

Connate   fused together.

Cordate   heart-shaped with the notch downwards (15).

Corolla   brightly coloured whorl of the perianth, composed of free or united petals. (10c).

Corona   whorl of free or united appendages attached to the inside of petals as in *Narcissus* and *Silene* (16a).

Corymb   a raceme in which the pedicels get progressively shorter towards the tip of the inflorescence, which is more or less flat-topped like an umbel (17).

18

Crenate wavy edged.

Cuneate wedge-shaped (base of leaf 18).

Cyathium cup-shaped structure in *Euphorbia* containing small groups of flowers with 4 or 5 glands at the top (19).

Cyme a branched inflorescence in which new growing points are continuously produced by division of the terminal parts of the inflorescence, so that the newer parts are at the periphery (20).

Deciduous falling off (a deciduous tree is one in which all the leaves fall in autumn).

Decumbent lying on the ground with growing tips turned upwards.

Decurrent running down,e.g. of edges of sessile leaf running down stem to form wings (21).

Deflexed turned downwards.

Dehiscent breaking open when ripe (of fruit see 11).

Dentate toothed (22) strictly different from serrate (q.v.), but often used interchangeably.

Denticulate with little teeth.

Dichasial cyme a cyme which divides repeatedly into two more or less equal branches, often with a flower at the point of each division (20).

Dichotomous dividing into two equal branches (dichasial cyme is repeatedly dichotomous).

Dioecious with male and female flowers on separate plants.

Drupe a fleshy fruit containing one or more seeds, each surrounded by a stony endocarp (e.g. a plum).

Eglandular without glands.

Emarginate with shallow apical notch (16a).

Endemic a species native of only a small (given) area.

Entire not toothed, notched or cut (23).

Epicalyx a calyx-like structure outside the calyx (24a), e.g. in *Lavatera*.

Excurrent running beyond the edge (e.g. of a vein running beyond the end of a bract to form a point).

Exserted not enclosed, sticking out, e.g. of stamens from a tubular corolla (10, drawing on right).

Fastigiate in bundles arising more or less from the same point (e.g. of leaves on a shoot).

Fertile capable of producing viable seed or pollen.

Filament the stalk of an anther (4b).

Filiform thread-like.

Fimbriate fringed (with fimbriae).

Floret a small flower, usually part of a compound inflorescence (25a).

Glabrous without hairs.

Gland a small globular vesicle containing fluid, often oily or sticky, sometimes sweetly or unpleasantly scented.

Glandular hair a gland with a stalk (26a).

Glaucous bluish-green.

Glomerules globe-shaped cluster of small flowers (as in *Cuscuta*).

Glume a tough more or less scarious bract, e.g. bracts at the base of a spikelet in Gramineae (27a and b).

Gynoecium the female reproductive parts of a flower, consisting of carpel (28c) or carpels with the stigma (28a) and style (28b).

Hastate spear-shaped (29).

Head an inflorescence of many closely set small flowers, especially in Compositae (25).

Hedgehog-plant a plant like a hedgehog, rounded and densely prickly.

Herb a plant without woody parts.

Hermaphrodite with male and female fertile parts.

Hispid with rough bristles.

Imbricate overlapping like tiles on a roof (30).

Indehiscent not breaking open (of a capsule).

Indusium membranous piece of tissue covering the sporangium in ferns (31a).

Inferior ovary an ovary with the perianth inserted at the outer end (32 receptacle is fused with ovary compare 28, which has superior ovary).

Inflorescence the flowering part of a plant, with branches, flowers and often bracts.

Internode interval between nodes.

Involucre calyx-like structure surrounding a flower head.

Involucral bracts sepal-like bracts forming the involucre (25e).

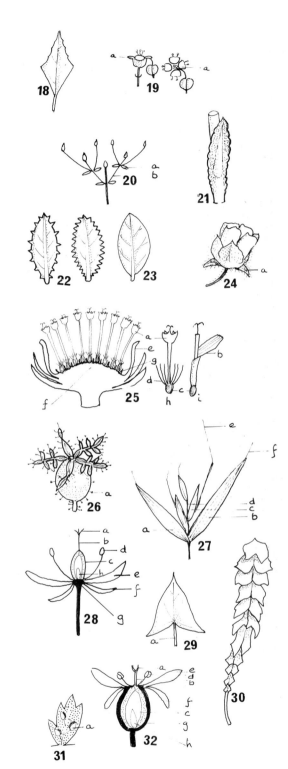

Keel   the sharp edge where two surfaces meet, like the keel of a boat, as in a keeled grass leaf (33a). Sometimes includes the surfaces too, as in the flower of most Leguminosae, where the keel is the boat-like structure formed by the fusion of the two lower petals (33b, 55c).

Lamina   the soft blade of a leaf (excluding the stalk and the central vein).

Lanceolate   lance-shaped (34).

Latex   juice, often milky, especially of *Euphorbia* and some Compositae.

Leaflet   leaf-like segment of a compound leaf (8a, 41a).

Lemma   outer bract of a single floret in a flower spike (27c).

Ligulate   with a ligule, as in the ligulate floret (25i).

Ligule   a tongue-like process, e.g. the membranous or hairy structure at the junction of the blade of a grass leaf with the sheath, or the elongated fused perianth segments of a floret in Compositae (25b).

Linear   long and narrow with more or less parallel sides (35).

Lobed   deeply indented, e.g. in a leaf, with the lamina continuous. If the lamina is divided to the rhachis the leaf is compound (36).

Monoecious   with male and female parts in separate flowers on the same plant.

Mucro   a short point.

Mucronate   with a mucro.

Nectar-pit   the nectar-secreting depression at the base of 'petals' in *Ranunculus* ('petals' here are strictly 'honey-leaves') (37a).

Node   a thickening in the stem where one or more leaves arise (38a).

Nut, nutlet   one-seeded indehiscent fruit with hard outer covering.

Ob-   a prefix meaning upside-down, as in oblanceolate, obcordate.

Obtuse   blunt.

Ochrea   a membranous sheath or partial sheath formed from fused stipules, as in *Polygonum* (39).

Opposite   in pairs on opposite sides of the stem (40).

Ovary   the part of the flower containing the ovules (composed of one or more carpels (28c, 32c, 42c)).

Ovate   egg-shaped.

Ovule   the female gamete before fertilisation (when it becomes a seed).

Palmate   with more than 3 leaflets arising from the same point (41).

Panicle   branched inflorescence.

Papilla   a small fleshy projection (adj. papillose, covered in papillae).

Pappus   hairs or scales representing the calyx in florets of Compositae (25d).

Paripinnate   pinnate with an even number of leaflets, without a terminal leaflet (43b).

Pectinate   comb-like.

Pedicel   the stalk of a single flower in an inflorescence (17b, 46a).

Peduncle   the stalk of an inflorescence or partial inflorescence (20b).

Perennial   a plant that continues to flower and set seed seasonally for more than one year (usually recognised by the presence of non-flowering shoots at flowering-time).

Perianth   the calyx or corolla. Both may be present, in which case there are two perianth whorls, or there may be one only.

Pericarp   wall of ripened ovary.

Perigynous zone   the part of the receptacle of a flower between the base of the ovary and the insertion of the perianth, sometimes distinct, sometimes very small or absent. (42i, compare 28 and 32).

Persistent   not caducous.

Petal   segment of the corolla (10a).

Petaloid   like a petal (brightly coloured).

Petiole   the stalk of a leaf (29a).

Pinna   a leaflet of a pinnate leaf.

Pinnate   (of a compound leaf), with separate leaflets arranged like the branches of a feather in rows on opposite sides of the rhachis (43).

Pinnatifid   with lobes of the leaf arranged like a feather, but not divided to the rhachis (and so not separate leaflets) (44).

Pinnatisect   as pinnatifid, but with some of the divisions to the midrib.

Pinnule   the 'pinna' of a pinna in a bipinnate leaf (8a).

Procumbent   lying loosely along the surface of the ground.

Prostrate   lying closely appressed to the ground.

Puberulent   softly covered with short downy hairs.

Pubescent   as puberulent.

Raceme   an unbranched inflorescence in which the pedicellate flowers are arranged along a central axis (45a).

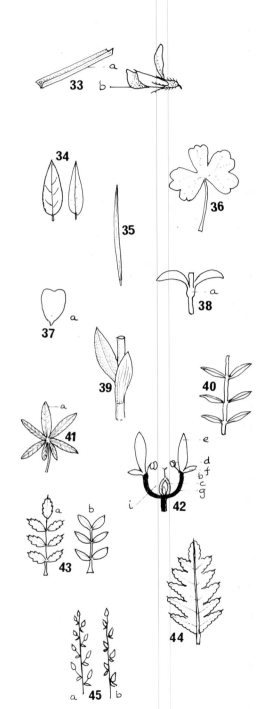

Ray   one of the peduncles of an umbellate inflorescence (46c).

Ray-leaf   a leaf at the base of a ray in Euphorbiaceae (comparable with bract in Umbelliferae).

Raylet   the stalk of a further division of an umbellate inflorescence, where the divisions of the umbel are further umbellately divided (46a).

Receptacle   the upper part of a stem from which the parts of a simple flower arise   also the part to which the separate florets are attached in the heads of Compositae and some other families (25f).

Receptacular scales   small scales on the receptacle between the florets in some Compositae (25g).

Reticulate   forming a fine network.

Rhachis   the central axis (e.g. of a compound leaf, or of a spike or spikelet in grasses (27d).

Rhizome   an underground root-like perennial stem (adj. rhizomatous).

Ruderal   growing around stone rubbish (including road-chippings, ruins of buildings and waste places in towns).

Rugos e   wrinkled or with ridges.

Sagittate   arrow-shaped (47).

Scarious   stiff and scale-like, not green.

Secund   all pointing towards one side, usually of a spike or a raceme (48).

Sepal   dull-coloured perianth segment, segment of the calyx (10b).

Sepaloid   like a sepal (as opposed to petaloid).

Septum   wall dividing a compartment (e.g. between the two parts of a silicula or siliqua).

Serrate   saw-toothed (49).

Serrulate   finely saw-toothed.

Sessile   unstalked.

Shrub   a perennial with several branched woody stems from at or near ground-level.

Silicula   bivalved pod less than 3 x as long as wide, with an internal septum dividing it into two compartments (50).

Siliqua   as silicula, but more than 3 x as long as wide (51).

Simple   not compound (e.g. of a leaf not divided into leaflets).

Sorus   a group of Sporangia.

Spadix   the thickened axis of a spike, as in Araceae (52a).

Spathe   a surrounding sheath, of the spadix in Araceae (52b), or the flower buds in, e.g. *Allium* (53a).

Spathulate   spoon-shaped (54).

Spike   an unbranched inflorescence with sessile flowers arranged along an elongated axis (45b). Spikelet   a group of florets arranged along an axis, especially in Gramineae (27).

Sporangium   spore-producing bodies of Pteridophyta (e.g. fruiting bodies on the underside of the blade of a fern).

Spore   a small asexual, usually unicellular, reproductive body.

Spur   sac-like projection (9c).

Stamen   the male reproductive part of a flower, the anther with or without a filament (4).

Standard   the upper petal of the flower in Leguminosae (55a).

Stellate   star-shaped (or, of hairs, with rays arising from a single point).

Stem   the main axis of a plant, bearing leaves and inflorescence.

Stigma   the part of the gynoecium which collects the pollen (28a, 32a, 42a).

Stipule   a bract at the base of a leaf, sometimes partly fused with the petiole (56b).

Stolon   a creeping stem (normally above ground) from a plant which is otherwise upright   hence stoloniferous, bearing stolons.

Sub-   prefix meaning almost (as suborbicular   almost round).

Sulcate   grooved.

Superior ovary   an ovary lying above the point of attachment of the perianth (28c).

Tendril   specialised part of plant (usually derived from a leaflet) adapted for clinging on to surrounding plants (56a).

Terete   smooth, without projections (of a stem, smoothly rounded).

Ternate   (of a compound leaf) with three parts meeting at a point (57).

Tomentose   densely covered in cottony hairs.

Tricuspidate   with three points, e.g. of stamens in some *Allium* species, which have three points with an anther on the central point) (58).

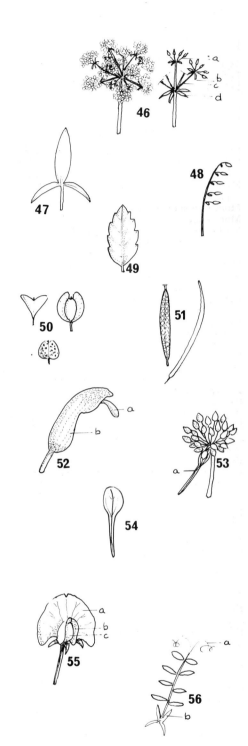

21

Trifoliate (of a compound leaf) used here to mean with three leaflets. (Trifoliolate is more correct but rarely used). This includes ternate leaves (57) and pinnately trifoliate (59).

Truncated cut straight across, not (or hardly) pointed or shaped at end (60, base of leaf).

Tuberculate with tubercles.

Tubercle small swelling (often very small, as on surface of seeds).

Tubular floret: in Compositae is one without a ligule, usually with 5 short equal teeth (25h). Ligulate florets, though tubular at the base, are not called tubular florets. In other families the base of the calyx or corolla segments are commonly fused to form a tube (61).

Umbel umbrella-like inflorescence with a whorl of 'spokes' arising from top of stem. The 'spokes' may be pedicels, but are more often peduncles supporting further umbels, when the inflorescence is said to be biumbellate (46).

Undulate wavy.

Valve the separate flaps by which a fruit opens.

Vesicle a small vessel containing fluid.

Wing either a thin extension of an organ, or the lateral petals (as in Leguminosae (55b).

INDEX TO PLATES

With a few minor exceptions genera are in the same order as in the Flora Europaea. Brackets in the heading indicate plants probably occurring in Mallorca but not illustrated.

PLATE
NUMBER

1 SELLAGINELLACEAE to ADIANTACEAE

2 PTERIDACEAE to MARSILIACEAE

3 PINACEAE to EPHEDRACEAE

4 FAGACEAE to URTICACEAE

5 SANTALACEAE: ARISTOLOCHiACEAE: RAFFLESIACEAE

6 POLYGONACEAE

7 CHENOPODIACEAE(1): *Atriplex* and *Chenopodium*

8 CHENOPODIACEAE(2): all others

9 AMARANTHACEAE: AIZOACEAE

10 CARYOPHYLLACEAE(1): *Arenaria* to *Cerastium*

11 CARYOPHYLLACEAE(2): *Sagina* to *Petrorhagia* (except *Silene*)

12 CARYOPHYLLACEAE(3): *Silene*

13 CERATOPHYLLACEAE: RANUNCULACEAE(1): All except *Ranunculus*

14 RANUNCULACEAE(2): *Ranunculus* part 1

15 RANUNCULACEAE(3): *Ranunculus* part 2: PAEONIACEAE

16 PAPAVERACEAE(1): all except *Fumaria*

17 PAPAVERACEAE(2): *Fumaria*: CRUCIFERAE(1): *Sisymbrium*

18 CRUCIFERAE(2): *Maresia* to *Clypeola*

19 CRUCIFERAE(3): *Erophila* to *Coronopus*

20 CRUCIFERAE(4): *Conringia* to *Hirschfeldia*

21 CRUCIFERAE(5): *Carrichtera* to *Raphanus*: RESEDACEAE

22 CRASSULACEAE: SAXIFRAGACEAE

23 PLATANACEAE: ROSACEAE (1): *Rubus, Rosa*

24 ROSACEAE (2): all others

25 LEGUMINOSAE (1): *Ceratonia* to *Psoralea*

26 LEGUMINOSAE (2): *Cicer, Vicia, Lens*

27 LEGUMINOSAE (3): *Lathyrus*

28 LEGUMINOSAE (4): *Ononis, Melilotus*

29 LEGUMINOSAE (5): *Trigonella, Medicago*

30 LEGUMINOSAE (6): *Trifolium*

31 LEGUMINOSAE (7): *Dorycnium, Lotus, Tetragonolobus*

32 LEGUMINOSAE (8): *Anthyllis* to *Hedysarum*

33 GERANIACEAE

34 OXALIDACEAE: LINACEAE

35 EUPHORBIACEAE (1): *Chrozophora, Mercurialis, Ricinus, Euphorbia* part 1

36 EUPHORBIACEAE (2): *Euphorbia* part 2: RUTACEAE

37 CNEORACEAE: ANACARDIACEAE: RHAMNACEAE

38 MALVACEAE

39 THYMELAEACEAE: GUTTIFERAE: VIOLACEAE

40 CISTACEAE

41 TAMARICACEAE: FRANKENIACEAE

42 CUCURBITACEAE: CACTACEAE: LYTHRACEAE: TRAPACEAE: MYRTACEAE: PUNICACEAE

43 ONAGRACEAE: HALORAGACEAE: THELIGONACEAE: ARALIACEAE: UMBELLIFERAE (1): *Bowlesia* to *Echinophora*

44 UMBELLIFERAE (2): *Scandix* to *Foeniculum*

45 UMBELLIFERAE (3): *Kundmannia* to *Ammi*

46 UMBELLIFERAE (4): *Ligusticum* to *Pseudorlaya*

47 PYROLACEAE: ERICACEAE: PRIMULACEAE

48 LIMONIACEAE

49 OLEACEAE: GENTIANACEAE

50 ASCLEPIADACEAE: RUBIACEAE (1): *Sherardia* to *Asperula*

51 RUBIACEAE: (2) *Galium, Valantia, Rubia*

52 CONVOLVULACEAE: BORAGINACEAE (1): *Heliotropium*

53 BORAGINACEAE (2): all others

54 VERBENACEAE: CALLITRICHACEAE: LABIATAE (1): *Teucrium*

55 LABIATAE (2): *Ajuga* to *Ballota*

56 LABIATAE (3): *Stachys* to *Salvia*

57 SOLANACEAE

58 SCROPHULARIACEAE (1): *Verbascum* to *Chaenorrhinum*

59 SCROPHULARIACEAE (2): *Linaria, Cymbalaria, Kickxia*

60 SCROPHULARIACEAE (3): *Digitalis* to *Bellardia*

61 GLOBULARIACEAE: OROBANCHACEAE

62 PLANTAGINACEAE: CAPRIFOLIACEAE

63 VALERIANACEAE: DIPSACACEAE: CAMPANULACEAE

64 COMPOSITAE (1): *Eupatorium* to *Logfia*

65 COMPOSITAE (2): *Evax* to *Phagnalon*

66 COMPOSITAE (3): *Inula* to *Xanthium*

67 COMPOSITAE (4): *Santolina* to *Artemisia*

68 COMPOSITAE (5): *Senecio* to *Staehelina*

69 COMPOSITAE (6): *Carduus* to *Onopordum*

70 COMPOSITAE (7): *Cynara* to *Carthamnus*

71 COMPOSITAE (8): *Carduncellus* to *Rhagadiolus*

72 COMPOSITAE (9): *Urospermum* to *Scorzonera*

73 COMPOSITAE (10): *Reichardia* to *Lactuca*

74 COMPOSITAE (11): *Taraxacum* to *Hieracium*

75 ALISMATACEAE: POTAMOGETONACEAE

76 RUPPIACEAE: POSIDONIACEAE: ZANNICHELLIACEAE: NAJADACEAE

77 LILIACEAE (1): *Asphodelus* to *Urginea*

78 LILIACEAE (2): *Scilla* to *Smilax* except *Allium*

79 LILIACEAE (3): *Allium*

80 AMARYLLIDACEAE: IRIDACEAE (1): *Iris, Gynandiris, Crocus*

81 IRIDACEAE (2): *Romulea, Gladiolus:* JUNCACEAE

82 GRAMINEAE (1): *Festuca* to *Cutandia*

83 GRAMINEAE (2): *Sphenopus* to *Briza*

84 GRAMINEAE (3): *Sesleria, Melica, Bromus*

85 GRAMINEAE (4): *Brachypodium* to *Triticum*

86 GRAMINEAE (5): *Hordeum* to *Aira*

87 GRAMINEAE (6): *Anthoxanthum* to *Alopecurus*

88 GRAMINEAE (7): *Parapholis, Hainardia, Phalaris, Piptatherum*

89 GRAMINEAE (8): *Stipa* to *Eragrostis*

90 GRAMINEAE (9): *Sporobolus* to *Heteropogon*

91 ARACEAE: SPARGANIACEAE: TYPHACEAE

92   CYPERACEAE (1): *Scirpus, Eleocharis, Cyperus, Cladium*

93   CYPERACEAE (2): *Carex*

94   ORCHIDACEAE (1): *Epipactis* to *Neotinea*

95   ORCHIDACEAE (2): *Orchis, Aceras, Barlia*

96   ORCHIDACEAE (3): *Anacamptis, Serapias, Ophrys*

THE PLATES

Plate 1

SELAGINELLACEAE: ISOETACEAE: EQUISETACEAE: OPHIOGLOSSACEAE: SINOPTERIDACEAE: ADIANTACEAE.

SELAGINELLACEAE: *SELAGINELLA*

1. *Selaginella denticulata* Toothed Clubmoss. Creeping perennial. Leaves in 4 ranks, often denticulate. Inner 2 ranks usually smaller than outer, but in older parts of plant all 4 ranks are often similar and closely imbricate. Common in shady moist places in mountain areas. **K D (Ma,** Mi, I) FE I **5**

ISOETACEAE: *ISOETES*

2. *Isoetes hystrix* Quillwort. Sporangia embedded in base of leaf. Near torrent, where flooded in winter, rare. (Recorded previously as *I. durieui*, but recently identified at the University of the Balearic Islands as *I. hystrix*). **D** (**Ma,** Mi) FE I 6

EQUISETACEAE: *EQUISETUM*

3. *Equisetum ramosissimum* Stems greyish-green, all alike. Branching irregular and variable. Teeth of sheaths apiculate. Common in damp places, including higher parts of sea-shore. **K D (Ma,** Mi, I) FE I 7
4. *E. arvense* Common Horsetail. Fertile and sterile stems distinct. Sterile stems green with 6-19 grooves. Fertile stems brownish with 4-6 sheaths. Sheaths with 6-12 teeth. Rare. (From British specimen). **D** (Ma) FE I 8
5. *E. telmateia* Great horsetail. Fertile and sterile stems distinct. Sterile stems broad and whitish with at least 20 shallow grooves. Fertile stems brownish with numerous sheaths. Sheaths with 20-40 teeth. Rare in damp places. (From British specimen × about 1/2. Small part of sterile stem shown with branches reduced). K **D** (Ma, Mi) FE I 8

OPHIOGLOSSACEAE: *OPHIOGLOSSUM*

6. *Ophioglossum lusitanicum* Adder's Tongue. Dec. - Mar. Damp places, including higher parts of saltmarsh. Rare and easily overlooked. K **D** (Ma, Mi, I) FE I 8

SINOPTERIDACEAE: *CHEILANTHES*

7. *Cheilanthes pteridioides* (Reichard) C. Chr., (*C. fragrans, C. acrostica* (Balbis) Tod.) Small coumarin-scented fern. Sori covered by deflexed leaf margin which has scarious fimbriate border. Occasional in shady places in mountains. (× 2, detail further enlarged). **K D (Ma,** I) FE I 10)
8. *C. vellea* (Aiton) F. Mueller, (*C. catanensis, Cosentinea vellea* (Aiton) Tod.) Like 7, but leaves with dense hairlike scales on both sides. Rare. (Specimen from Spanish mainland). K lists for Ibiza only. D Ll (Ma, Mi, I) FE I 10

ADIANTACEAE: *ADIANTUM*

9. *Adiantum capillus-veneris* Maidenhair fern. Rhizomatous fern with 23-pinnate leaves. Common in damp places. (Terminal part of 20cm leaf × 1). **K D (Ma,** Mi, I) FE I 10

In other islands:
Isoetes velata Minorca FE I 6
I. durieui Minorca FE I 6
Equisetum fluviatile ?Ibiza. Not Bl in FE I 7

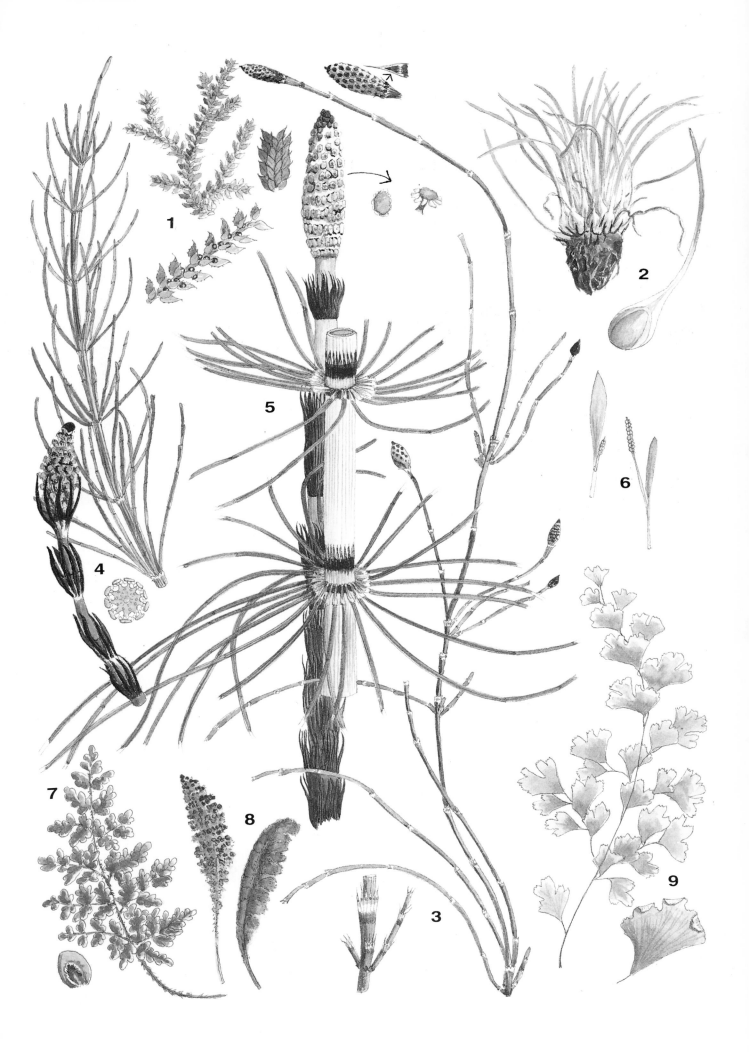

Plate 2

PTERIDACEAE: GYMNOGRAMMACEAE: HYPOLEPIDACEAE: ASPLENIACEAE: ATHYRIACEAE: ASPIDIACEAE: POLYPODIACEAE.

PTERIDACEAE: *PTERIS*

1. *Pteris vittata* Tufted rhizomatous fern. Leaf up to 60cm, pinnate with simple pinnae. Rare. (Cretan specimen × about 1/2, detail of longest pinna × 1). D Ll (Ma) FE I 11

GYMNOGRAMMACEAE: *ANOGRAMMA*

2. *Anogramma leptophylla* Small fern. Fertile leaves typically longer than sterile, with narrower pinnules (in this specimen there were many sori on the short leaves with broad segments as well as on longer narrow leaves). Local in damp shady wall and rock crevices. K D (**Ma**, Mi, I) FE I 11

HYPOLEPIDACEAE: *PTERIDIUM*

3. *Pteridium aquilinum* Bracken. Rhizomatous fern. Height usually less than 1m here. Common in hilly areas. (Illustration much reduced). **K D** (**Ma**, Mi) FE I 12

ASPLENIACEAE
ASPLENIUM

4. *Asplenium marinum* Sea spleenwort. Leaves 1-pinnate. Rhachis with green wings. Rare. (From small British specimen). **K** D Ll (Ma, Mi) FE I 15

5. *A. petrarchae* Leaves 1-pinnte. Petiole and rhachis densely covered in glandular hairs. Occasional in mountain areas. **K D** (**Ma**, Mi, I) FE I 15

6. *A. trichomanes* Common spleenwort. Leaves 1-pinnate, segments entire or dentate. Common in crevices of rocks and walls. **K D** (**Ma**, Mi, I) FE I 15

7. *A. adiantum-nigrum* Black spleenwort. Leaves 2-pinnate, basal pinnae longest. Indusium elongated, white. Occasional. Recorded by K and D, but Ll omits. (From Mallorcan specimen, but could have been misidentified). (**Ma**, Mi) Bl in Atlas FE, not in FE I 16 (nor in Med-Checklist)

8. *A. onopteris* Resembles 7, but darker and more shining, with long 'tails' at apex and apices of longer pinnae. Often larger than 7. (Small specimen). Fairly common in mountains. **K D** (**Ma**, Mi, I) FE I 16

9. *A. ruta-muraria* Wall Rue. Stalk green except at very base. Leaves very variable, with veins arranged fan-wise. Occasional in rock fissures. **K D** (**Ma**, Mi, I) FE I 16

10. *Asplenium ceterach* L. (*Ceterach officinarum*) Rusty-back. Common on walls and rocks. **K D** (**Ma**, Mi, I) FE I 17

11. *Asplenium scolopendrium* L. (*Phyllitis scolpendrium*) Hart's Tongue. Rare. (From British specimen × 1/2). **K D** (Ma) FE I 17

12. *A. sagittatum* L. (*Phyllitis sagittata*) Resembles 11, but with auricles at the base, very variable, often misshapen. Occasional on damp shady rocks. **K D** (**Ma**, Mi, I) FE I 17

ATHYRIACEAE
ATHYRIUM

13. *Athyrium filix-femina* Lady fern. Rhizomatous perennial. Rare. (Specimen from Spanish mainland × 0.5). Not K or D, but listed by H and Ll (Ma) Bl excluded in FE I 18

CYSTOPTERIS

14. *Cystopteris fragilis* Brittle bladder-fern. White, pointed-ovate indusium. Rare. (British specimen, × 1/2, details enlarged). K quotes Hermann (1912) and Bianor (1910-1914). D Ll (Ma) FE I 18

ASPIDIACEAE
POLYSTICHUM

15. *Polystichum aculeatum* Hard Shield-fern. Petiole (only part here) about 1/3 length lamina, with pale brownish scales. Leaves pinnate or bipinnate, with bristle-tipped segments. Pinnules sessile or subsessile, decurrent. Innermost pinnule on upper side of each pinna has almost straight inner edge, meets lower margin at acute angle (see detail). Indusium circular with central boss. Rare. (Specimen from Spanish mainland). ?K (possibly included in *P. aculeatum* Swartz with next species). D Ll (Ma) Not Bl in FE I 20

16. *P. setiferum* Soft shield-fern. Rather like 15. Lower part of lamina often paler than upper part. Pinnules distinctly stalked, not decurrent, with obtuse angle where margins of innermost pinnule on each pinna meets stalk. Rare in higher parts of mountains. (From small British specimen × 1/2, detail ×4). ?K (as above), D B Ll (Ma) FE I 20

DRYOPTERIS

17. *Dryopteris pallida* (Bory) Chr. subsp. *balearica* (Litard.) Fraser-Jenkins Leaves tufted, glandular-hairy. Indusium kidney-shaped. Rock crevices in mountains, occasional. **K** D (**Ma** endemic subsp.) FE I 21 (cf. *Dryopteris villarii* subsp. *pallida*)

POLYPODIACEAE: *POLYPODIUM*

18. *Polypodium cambricum* L. subsp. *serrulatum* (Sch. ex Archangeli) Pic Polypody. Variable in size and colour, often yellowish. Pinnae dentate, basal pair projecting forwards. Walls and rocks, common. (Small specimen). **K D** (**Ma**, Mi, I) FE I 23 (cf. *P. australe*)

MARSILIACEAE: *MARSILEA*

19. *Marsilea strigosa* Rhizomatous semi-aquatic fern. Leaves with 4 leaflets, coiled in bud. Spores are produced in hairy brown 3-5mm sporocarps in the axils of the leaves. FE:'Habitats subject to periodic shallow inundation'. Very rare. (After Bonafè's black and white photo and live garden specimen of related species). D Ll (Ma, Mi) Not Bl in FE I 24

The following are also recorded from Mallorca, but not illustrated:
Asplenium azomanes Rosselló & Cubas. Ll lists as endemic (Ma, I). (Not described in FE)
A. fontanum K (quotes Bianor, 1917). D Ll FE I 15
?*A. billotii* D lists but Ll omits. (?Ma, ?Mi) Not Bl in FE I 16
A. majoricum **K D** Ll (endemic Ma) FE I 15
Dryopteris tyrrhena Fraser-Jenkins & Reichst (1975) Ll lists. Not described in FE
There are also many hybrids, especially in the Sóller area.

Minorca only:
Asplenium obovatum FE I 16
A. balearicum Shivas (1969: not in FE)
Pilularia minuta FE I 24

Plate 3

PINACEAE: CUPRESSACEAE: TAXACEAE: EPHEDRACEAE

Illustrations of shrubs and trees are much reduced. Details about × 1 except where stated otherwise.

PINACEAE: *PINUS*

1. *Pinus halepensis* Aleppo pine. Branching low. Unexpanded cone conical. Apr. Common, coast and hills. **K D** (**Ma**, Mi, I) FE I 35

2. *P. halepensis* var. *ceciliae A.* et Ll. Llorens. Fastigiate form of 1. Status uncertain, not described in FE. (After Bonafè's black and white photo and description). **D** (**Ma**, Mi, I, endemic var.)

3. *P. pinea* Stone or Umbrella pine. Regular, erect tree, branching from upper part trunk. Unexpanded cone globular. Apr. Occasional. **K D** (Introduced **Ma**, Mi, native I) FE I 35

CUPRESSACEAE
CUPRESSUS

4. *Cupressus sempervirens* Cypress. Leaves scale-like in mature plants, May. Introduced here in fastigiate and natural bushy forms. (Male cone × 2). K lists as cultivated plant. **D** (**Ma**, introduced) FE I 37

JUNIPERUS

5. *Juniperus oxycedrus* Prickly Juniper. Shrub or small tree, leaves very prickly. May. Dry hilly places (subsp. oxycedrus, with ripe cone 8-10mm, shining) and maritime sands (subsp. *macrocarpa*, with ripe cone 12-15mm, pruinose). (Details only. Habit of subsp. *microcarpa* usually resembles illustration of J. phoenicea (below). subsp. *oxycedrus* more erect or a small tree). **K D** (**Ma**, Mi, I)) FE I 38

6. *J. phoenicea* Phoenician Juniper. Similar to 5, but adult leaves scale-like, overlapping, not prickly. May. Mainly coastal. (Detail of scale-like leaves × 3). **K D** (**Ma**, Mi, I) FE I 39

TAXACEAE: *TAXUS*

7. *Taxus baccata* Yew. Small tree with reddish-brown scaling bark. June. Occasional on mountain tops, as small trees (these near peak of Massanella), or small shrubs in rock crevices. Local name, Teix, is given to one of the mountains where this species occurs. **K D** (**Ma**) FE I 39

EPHEDRACEAE: *EPHEDRA*

8. *Ephedra fragilis* Joint pine. Straggling shrub, often growing through and more or less supported by other shrubs. Leaves reduced to minute scales. Fruit fleshy, with bluish bloom. May. Local in hilly areas and on coast. (Right hand detail × 3). **K D** (**Ma**, Mi, I) FE I 40

Plate 4

FAGACEAE: (SALICACEAE): ULMACEAE: MORACEAE: URTICACEAE: (JUGLANDACEAE).

FAGACEAE: *QUERCUS*

1. *Quercus coccifera* Kermes Oak. Usually a shrub here. Front of mature leaves shining, with easily visible veins, back woolly with obscure veins. Apr. - May. Local. **K D (Ma, I)** FE I 62

2. *Q. ilex* Holm oak. Substantial tree. Leaves leathery, grey-felted beneath, stipules thick and hairy. Acorns are bitter. Dominant over much of hillier part of Mallorca. (Very variable: this specimen is somewhat atypical. Mature leaves are often rather like those of *Q. coccifera*, but with the veins on the back clearly visible). Apr. - May. **K D (Ma, Mi)** FE I 63

Q. rotundifolia (Lam.) Morais (treated as doubtful taxon in Med Checklist) (= *Q. ilex* subsp. *ballota* (Desf.) Samp.), very like 2, but with membranous stipules and sweet acorns, occurs occasionally. It is probably not native here, though possibly so in Minorca (Llorens). (Not illustrated). ?**D** (Ma, Mi, I) Not Bl in FE I 63

3. *Q. faginea* Lusitanian Oak. Semi-evergreen tree. Known in Mallorca, in one area where the trees might be wild or introduced. (Leaf only). **D (Ma)** Bl in FE I 64

ULMACEAE:
ULMUS

4. *Ulmus minor* Smooth-leaved Elm. Bush or small tree. Bark fissured. Anthers purplish-red. Fruit dry, winged. Mar. - Apr. (Young twig and mature leaf slightly reduced). **K D (Ma, Mi, I)** FE I 65

CELTIS

5. *Celtis australis* Nettle Tree. Tree with long pointed, simply serrate leaves. Fruit a fleshy berry, eventually blackish. Widely planted for ornament and seeding itself freely. Locally common - there is a full-grown specimen at Lluch on the north side of the monastery. (Single leaf and fruit only). **D (Ma, I)** Not Bl in FE I 66

MORACEAE: *FICUS*

6. *Ficus carica* Fig tree. Spreading shrub or small tree, with large aromatic leaves. Cultivated, often apparently wild in rocky places. Native in parts of S. Europe. (× 1/3). **K D (Ma, Mi, I)** FE I 67

URTICACEAE
URTICA (Illustrations all somewhat reduced).

7. *Urtica atrovirens* Perennial stinging-nettle with male and female flowers in the same raceme. Conical bases of 9-13 stinging hairs on surface are very large. Endemic subsp. here, subsp. *bianorii* (Knoche) Font Quer et Garcias Font) differs from FE description in the deeply incised leaves and racemes shorter than adjacent petiole. May - June. Very local in mountains. (× 1/2). **K D (Ma)** FE I 68

8. *U. urens* Annual stinging-nettle with male and female flowers in the same raceme, which rarely exceeds 2cm. Petiole about 2/3 lamina; May - Oct. Common, especially round human habitation. **K D (Ma, Mi, I)** FE I 68

9. *U. dubia* (= *U. membranacea* Poiret) Like 8, but lower racemes female, upper male and exceeding 2cm, with flowers on one side of raceme only. 2 stipules at each node other species here have 4. May - June. Common, often with 8. (Male spikes and leaf only). **K D (Ma, Mi, I)** FE I 68

10. *U. pilulifera* Roman Nettle. Annual. Female flowers with inflated perianth in globular heads, male in erect branched clusters. May - June. Fairly common in waste places. **K D (Ma, Mi, I)** FE I 68

PARIETARIA

11. *Parietaria judaica* L. Pellitory-of-the-wall. Perennial. Bracts shorter than fruiting perianth, connate at base. May - Sept. Common on walls and rocks. (Two very dissimilar specimens × 2/3, detail of fruiting perianth and bracts enlarged). K D **(Ma, Mi, I)** FE I 69 (cf. *P. diffusa*)

12. *P. lusitanica* Annual. Bracts equalling or exceeding fruiting perianth. May. Locally common. (Details show fruiting perianth and enlarged bracts). K D **(Ma, Mi)** FE I 69

SOLEIROLIA

13. *Soleirolia soleirolii* Helxine, Mother-of-thousands. Perennial. Like small *Parietaria* but creeping, rooting at nodes. Apr. - May. (Main illustration from Mallorcan specimen, details from garden specimen). Native only in Mallorca, Italy, Sardinia and Corsica. K D **(Ma)** FE I 69

Other species which may occur in Mallorca:
Salix and *Populus* species are widely planted.
Juglans regia Walnut. Probably always associated with present or previous habitation. Also recorded from Minorca. Not Bl in FE I 56
Quercus lusitanica Lam. (*Q. humilis* Miller). Ll lists (Ma) Not Bl in FE I 64 (cf. *Q. fruticosa*)

In other islands:
Salix species, planted.
Q. pubescens Minorca. Not Bl in FE I 64
Parietaria mauritanica Formentera. Not Bl in FE I 69

Plate 5

SANTALACEAE: (LORANTHACEAE): ARISTOLOCHIACEAE: RAFFLESIACEAE: (BALANOPHORACEAE)

SANTALACEAE

OSYRIS

1. *Osyris alba* Small parasitic shrub with slender more or less vertical branches. Described in FE and by Bonafè as dioecious, but plants here seem to have either solitary hermaphrodite flowers (slightly enlarged in illustration) or short racemes of male flowers. May - June. Locally common. **K D** (**Ma,** Mi) FE I 70

THESIUM

2. *Thesium divaricatum* Leafy parasitic perennial up to 25cm, with much branched stems. Inflorescence pyramidal. Nut reticulately veined. (Specimen from Spanish mainland). Possibly extinct. K (quotes Barceló (1867-1877) but found a specimen in Bianor's herbarium). D ?Ll (Ma) FE I 72
3. *T. humile* Fleshy parasitic annual. Nut longitudinally veined. Occasional in sandy fields. K **D** Ll (**Ma,** Mi, I) FE I 72

ARISTOLOCHIACEAE: *ARISTOLOCHIA*

4. *Aristolochia clematitis* Birthwort. Creeping perennial up to 1m. Flowers 2-8 together in leaf-axils, 2-3cm. May - July. (From garden specimen). K quotes Barceló (1867-1877) D Ll (Ma, Mi) FE I 74
5. *A. paucinervis* Pomel Flowers solitary, 3-6cm. Apr. - May. Rather rare. (Illustrations × 1). K **D** (**Ma,** Mi, I) FE I 74 (cf. *A. longa*)
6. *A. bianorii* Glabrous perennial. Flowers solitary, 1-3cm, rather variable in colour, usually shades of green, brown and purple. May - July. Rather local in rocky places. (Main illustration × 2, details ×1). **K D** (**Ma,** Mi, endemic) FE I 74

RAFFLESIACEAE: *CYTINUS*

7. *Cytinus hypocistis* Perennial without chlorophyll, parasitic on roots of white-flowered *Cistus* species. May - June. Occasional. **K D** (**Ma,** Mi, I) FE I 75
8. *C. ruber* is parasitic on pink-flowered *Cistus* species. May - June. Not common. **K D** (**Ma,** I) FE I 75

Other recorded for Mallorca:
Viscum album (Loranthaceae) K (quotes Barceló 1867-1877). ?B (probably extinct). Ll omits. Bl not excluded in FE I 72

Asarum europaeum Not listed by K or Ll. D quotes FE. Very dubious. Bl in FE I 73
In Ibiza:
Osyris quadripartita FE I 70
Cynomorium coccineum (Balanophoraceae) Not Bl in FE I 75

Plate 6

POLYGONACEAE *POLYGONUM, FALLOPIA, RUMEX, EMEX*

POLYGONUM

1. *Polygonum maritimum* Woody, more or less procumbent perennial. Apr. - May. Common on sea shores and sandy places near the sea. **K D** (**Ma,** Mi, I) FE I 77
2. *P. aviculare* Knotgrass. Annual or short-lived perennial. Flowers with broad, overlapping petals. Nut dull. Apr. - May. Common. **K D** (**Ma,** Mi, I) FE I 78
3. *P. salicifolium* Perennial, with rooting procumbent or decumbent stems, 30-70cm. Ochreae long-ciliate. April. Very local in and beside fresh water. **D** (**Ma,** Mi) FE I 79

FALLOPIA

4. *Fallopia convolvulus* (L.) Löve (*Bilderdykia convolvulus*) Black bindweed. Twining or prostrate annual. Occasional. K D Ll (**Ma,** Mi) FE I 81

RUMEX

All species may turn red in fruit: colour not significant for identification.

5. *Rumex intermedius* Perennial. Leaves sagittate with narrow lobes. May. Widespread in rocky places. (Stem reduced). **K D** (**Ma,** Mi, I) FE I 85
6. *R. crispus* Curled dock. Perennial. Basal leaves usually wedge-shaped at base. Margins of leaves undulate. Pedicels jointed below middle, longer than valves, which are more or less entire, with narrow tubercles. May. Very common, ruderal and in damp places. **K D** (**Ma,** Mi, I) FE I 87
7. *R. conglomeratus* Sharp dock. Perennial. Valves entire, elongated egg-shaped, tubercles large, often almost covering valve. May. Common in moist and waste places. **K D** (**Ma,** Mi, I) FE I 87
8. *R. pulcher* Fiddle dock. (Subsp. *divaricatus* illustrated: subsp.*pulcher* with 4 teeth each side of valve also recorded). Perennial. Panicle open, with spreading, often curved branches. Valves toothed, with thick veins. Pedicels jointed near middle. May. Common, usually ruderal. **K D** (**Ma,** Mi, I) FE I 87

9. *R. obtusifolius* subsp. *obtusifolius* Broad-leaved Dock. Perennial. Basal leaves large. Valves toothed, only one with a prominent tubercle. May. Local. (From British specimen, slightly reduced). **K D** (**Ma,** I) FE I 87
10. *R. bucephalophorus* Annual, often with partly or entirely red inflorescence, sometimes red leaves and stem too. Apr. - May. Common in sandy places near the sea. **K D** (**Ma,** Mi, I) FE I 88

EMEX

11. *Emex spinosa* Annual. Male flowers in upper part of stem, female below. Perianth segments 6, connate in female flowers, the outer 3 becoming hard and spiny in fruit. Mar. - May. Common in waste places. **K D** (**Ma,** Mi, I) FE I 89

Other species recorded for Mallorca:
Polygonum equisetiforme Ll lists for (Ma) Not Bl in FE I 77
P. romanum Woody based procumbent perennial. Flowers in short dense axillary spikes. Rare. **K** and D. Ll lists as endemic subsp. *balearicum* Rafaelli & Villar. (Ma) FE I 77 (subsp. not described)
P. patulum or related species. Annual, erect and much branched. Nut glossy. K D lists 'Polygonum cf. *patulum*'. Not Ll. (Ma) FE I 78
P. oxyspermum B records finding in 1963. D and Ll omit. (?Ma) Not Bl in FE I 78
P. rurivagum Bor. ?D ?Ll (?Ma, ?I) FE I 78
P. bellardii All. Ll lists. (Ma, I) (FE index equates with *P. rurivagum*)
P. arenastrum Ll lists. (Ma, Mi, I) FE I 79
P. persicaria Annual. Leaves broad lanceolate, often with a blackish blotch. Ochreae shortly ciliate. Flowers pink, in dense cylindrical spikes. Apr. - June. Rare. **K** D Ll (Ma, Mi) FE I 79
P. lapathifoilum Annual. Leaves ovate to linear-lanceolate, sometimes with blackish spot. Ochreae entire or very shortly ciliate. Flowers white or grenish in cylindrical spikes, usually dense. Apr. - June. Rare. K (quotes Barceló 1867-1877) D Ll FE I 79
Rumex acetosella subsp. *angiocarpus* ?K Ll lists. D omits. (Ma, Mi) 'Throughout Europe' in FE I 83

Plate 7

CHENOPODIACEAE (1) *CHENOPODIUM, ATRIPLEX*

(for *BETA* see Plate 8)

CHENOPODIUM

1. *Chenopodium ambrosioides* Pubescent aromatic annual, with many sessile glands. Flowers in small clusters in leaf-axils. Jul. - Oct. Not common. (From garden specimen). Native of tropical America, formerly cultivated as vermifuge. K **D** (Ma, Mi, I) FE I 93
2. *C. bonus-henricus* Good King Henry. Perennial. Leaves triangular hastate, subentire except for basal lobes. Sept. (From British specimen). **K.** Ll treats as alien. (Ma) Bl excluded in FE I 93
3. *C. glaucum* Annual. Leaves densely mealy beneath. Apr.-May. Occasional. **D** Ll (**Ma**) Bl excluded in FE I 93
4. *C. vulvaria* Stinking Goosefoot. Foul-smelling grey annual, more or less mealy, especially beneath leaves. Leaf shape variable, more or less rhombic, often with an acute angle on margin at broadest part. May - Sept. Fairly common. **K D** (**Ma**, Mi) FE I 94
5. *C. murale* Nettle-leaved Goosefoot. Very robust, much-branched annual, with shining, coarsely toothed dark green leaves, often turning yellow or red. Seeds black with acute margin and closely adherent testa. Mar.- Sept. Common, waste places. **K D** (**Ma**, Mi, I) FE I 94
6. *C. opulifolium* Annual, leaves broader than long, mealy at least below. Rare here. Flower resembles flower of 7, but sepals usually more strongly keeled. Seeds with obtuse margins. (From Italian specimen). K lists only from small island off coast of Minorca. B D Ll (Ma, Mi, I) FE I 94
7. *C. album* Fat Hen. Green to greyish mealy annual, leaves longer than wide, more or less diamond-shaped, toothed or not. Seeds with obtuse margins, testa easily rubbed off. Apr.- Sept. Common. **K D** (**Ma**, Mi, I) FE I 94
8. *C. suecicum* Like 7, but leaves thin and translucent with acute, forward-pointing teeth. Cymes lax. Testa with deep radial furrows. (Possibly not previously recorded: F. Rumsey, May 1990, from Gorg Blau). (Probably casual). (**Ma**) Not Bl in FE I 95

ATRIPLEX

9. *Atriplex halimus* Small to medium shrub. Aug.- Sept. Local, near sea. K **D** (**Ma**, Mi, I) FE I 95
10. *A. rosea* Procumbent whitish annual. Cymes axillary. Bracteole up to 12mm, rhombic, dentate, becoming hard in lower half. K **D** (**Ma**, Mi, I) FE I 96
11. *A. patula* Common orache. Mealy annual. Upper leaves lanceolate, lower more or less diamond shaped. Apr. - Sept. Common near the sea. **K D** (**Ma**, Mi, I) FE I 96
12. *A. prostrata* Boucher. Green-leaved annual, inflorescence often red. Lower leaves hastate. (Ma, Mi, I) (cf. *Atriplex hastata* FE I 97)

Also recorded from Mallorca:
Chenopodium ficifolium Bonafè quotes Garcias (1905-1968), but adds 'A verificar'. **D** Not Ll. (?**Ma**, Mi) Not Bl in FE I 96
A. tornabenei Tineo ex Guss. Cymes in terminal leafless panicles. **D** (Ma, Mi) (cf. *Atriplex tatarica*, not Bl in FE I 96)

40

Plate 8

CHENOPODIACEAE (2) All except *ATRIPLEX* and
CHENOPODIUM

BETA

1. *Beta vulgaris* subsp. *maritima* Sea Beet. Perennial or occasionally annual. Variable, usually procumbent, sometimes erect. Up to about 1.5m diameter. Short (commonly 1 or 2-flowered) cymes arranged in spike-like inflorescence, dense, often interrupted towards base. Bracts absent or very small at apex of inflorescence. Receptacle bowl shaped with incurved segments up to 3mm in fruit. Fruits connate in groups by swollen bases. Saline habitats. Common. (Single cauline leaf, and basal part fruiting spike × 2). **K D (Ma,** Mi, I) FE I 91

2. *B. macrocarpa* Resembles 1, but annual with inflorescence lax and clearly bracteate to apex. Segments of fruiting perianth up to 5mm, erect, often incurved at apex. Rare. (× 2, specimen from Spanish mainland). **D.** Ll queries except for Ibiza. (?Ma, ?Mi, I). Not Bl in FE I 92

HALIMIONE

3. *Halimione portulacoides* Sea Purslane. Small silvery shrub usually up to about 80cm. Salt marshes. Common. **K D (Ma,** Mi, I) FE I 97

BASSIA

4. *Bassia hyssopifolia* Erect hairy annual, up to 1m with numerous strict branches. Saltmarshes. (From garden specimen). **D** Ll treats as alien. (**Ma,** introduced) Not Bl in FE I 98

SARCOCORNIA

5. *Sarcocornia perennis* (Miller) Scott (*Arthrocnemum perenne*) Shrubby Glasswort. Shrubby perennial with creeping underground stems and green erect stems, becoming red or brownish. usually about 1m. Segments generally longer than wide. Flowers immersed in cymes, falling to leave tripartite hollow in segment. Seeds covered with curved or hooked hairs. Very rare. (Fragment of dried specimen from Spanish mainland with seed × 10 and septate hollows after fruit has fallen × 4). **K D (Ma,** Mi) FE I 101

6. *S. fruticosa* (L.) Scott. As 5, but glaucous and not mat-forming. Seeds covered in conical hairs. Fairly common in saltmarshes. (Non-flowering shoot × 1, seed from specimen from Spanish mainland × 10: this one had a few curved hairs at one end, though most of the hairs were tuberculate). **K D (Ma,** Mi, I) FE I 101 (*Arthrocnemum fruricosum)*

ARTHROCNEMUM

7. *A. machrostachyum* (Moric.) Moris (*A. glaucum*) Erect bluish shrub, becoming yellowish-green or reddish. Segments generally broader than long. Flowers of each segment protruding, free, falling to leave undivided hollow. Seeds black, covered in very small tubercles. Common in saltmarshes. (Flowering branch × 1, detail enlarged: small sterile branch × 1: seed × 10). K **D (Ma,** Mi, I) FE I 101

SALICORNIA

8. *Salicornia ramosissima* Woods Glasswort. Annual, up to 20cm, sometimes becoming prostrate. Local in saltmarshes. (Centre small plant × 1/3: upper left detail × 6 from dried specimen to show scarious margin: on right from top of plant × 2)). **D** Ll **(Ma,** Mi, I) Not Bl in FE I 101.

SUAEDA

9. *Suaeda vera* Shrubby seablite. Small green shrub, usually up to 1m. Leaves semicylindrical, often glaucous. Common in saltmarshes. **K D (Ma,** Mi, I) FE I 103

10. *S. maritima* (? = *S. spicata* Willd. Moq.) Annual seablite. Like 9, but annual. Common in saltmarshes. **K D (Ma,** Mi, I) FE I 103

SALSOLA

11. *Salsola soda* Erect annual, ca 15cm here. Lower leaves opposite, upper alternate with short mucro. Rare, saltmarshes. K D (**Ma,** Mi) FE I 105

12. *S. kali* Saltwort. Erect or spreading annual. Bracteoles with long spiny apex. Common in sandy places. **K D (Ma,** Mi, I) FE I 105

13. *S. vermiculata* Pubescent shrub, ca 1m. Leaves semicylindrical to filiform. Local in dry soils. (× 1: details to show shoot with small axillary branches and single leaf enlarged). K **D (Ma,** Mi) FE I 106

Also recorded for Mallorca:
Beta patellaris Moq. (*Patella patellaris* (Moq.) Scott) Procumbent annual. Perianth segments 1-1.5mm in fruit, incurved or erect. Rare. **D** Ll (Ma) Not Bl in FE I 92
Kochia scoparia **D** Ll (Ma, I) (Ornamental Asian species, sometimes escaping from cultivation). Not Bl in FE I 98
Suaeda splendens Annual. Leaves acuminate or mucronate. Fruiting perianth much inflated. Rare. **D** Ll (Ma) Not Bl in FE I 104

In Formentera:
Salsola oppositifolia Desf. (*Salsola verticillata*) B. Not Bl in FE I 106

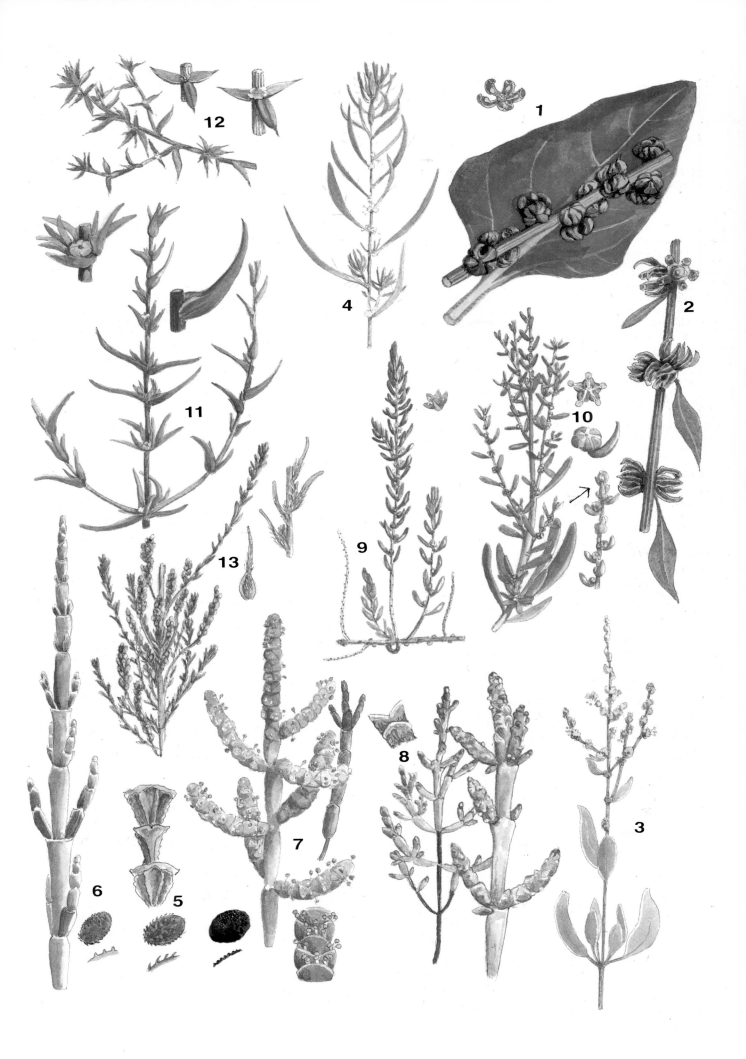

Plate 9

AMARANTHACEAE: PHYTOLACCACEAE: AIZOACEAE:
(TETRAGONIACEAE): PORTULACACEAE

AMARANTHACEAE: *AMARANTHUS*

These are weedy introduced plants of dry waste places and roadsides. They are all annuals except nos 3 and 6. Most are natives of N. and S. America, flowering from June to September. The nomenclature is quite confusing, and as my specimens were identified from the FE key I have generally preferred FE names, even though more recent research has regrouped many of the species given here.

1. *Amaranthus hypochondriacus* L. Resembles 2, but terminal inflorescence long-spicate, interrupted at base where there are a few long branches. Bracteole twice length acute perianth segments, usually recurved when dry. (Detail flower and bracteole only, × 1 1/2). Occasional. K (as cultivated plant). **D** Ll (**Ma**, Mi, I) Not Bl in FE 1 109 (*A. hybridus* pro parte)
2. *A. cruentus* Terminal inflorescence usually dense, uninterrupted at base and with many short branches. Bracteoles about 1 1/2 × acute perianth segments. Common: easily confused with *A. retroflexus*. *A. hybridus* is also rather similar. (× 1, detail enlarged). **D** (**Ma**, Mi, I) Not Bl in FE I 109
3. *A. muricatus* Decumbent perennial. Leaves linear to narrow ovate lanceolate. Fruit indehiscent, muricate. Fairly common. (× 1, detail enlarged). **D** (**Ma**, Mi, I) Not Bl in FE I 109
4. *A. blitoides* Erect or decumbent. Leaves with distinct membranous margin. Fruit transversely dehiscent. Occasional. (Slightly reduced, details × 2). **D** (**Ma**, I) Not Bl in FE I 110
5. *A. albus* Usually erect. Leave slightly notched, mucronate. Bracteoles curved with spiny tip. Capsule dehiscing transversely. Common. (Slightly reduced, detail × 4). K **D** (**Ma**, Mi, I) FE I 110
6. *A. deflexus* Procumbent perennial. Densely puberulent in upper part of flowering stems (often less so when in fruit). Fruit pear shaped, inflated, not dehiscent. Occasional. (× 1, detail ×2). K **D** (**Ma**, Mi, I) FE I 110
7. *A. blitum* L. (*A. lividus*) Leaves often emarginate. Fruit rugose. Occasional. (× 1, detail × 3). **D** (**Ma**) Not Bl in FE I 110

PHYTOLACCACEAE: *PHYTOLACCA*

8. *Phytolacca americana* Pokeweed. Tall fleshy perennial. Flowers green or pink. Formerly cultivated for the red dye obtained from the fruit. June - Aug. Locally common around habitation. (× 1/2, ripe fruit × 1). K D Ll Introduced from N. America. (**Ma**, Mi, I) FE I 112

AIZOACEAE

AIZOON

9. *Aizoon hispanicum* Fleshy papillose annual with greenish-white sepaloid perianth segments and 10 stamens. Very rare here, probably only one station, where plant is very small. (From Greek specimen). **D** Ll (Ma, Mi, I) ?Bl in FE I 112

CARPOBROTUS

10. *Carpobrotus acinaciformis* Leaves glaucous, widest at or above the middle. Apr.- Aug. Native of S. Africa, very widely naturalized, especially on sandy beaches. (× 1/3). **D** (**Ma**, I) Not Bl in FE I 112
11. *C. edulis* Hottentot Fig. Leaves green, broadest below. Flowers yellow or purplish, not bright carmine like 10. Apr. Aug. Native of S. Africa, less common here than 10. (× 1/2). **D** (**Ma**, I) Not Bl in FE I 112

LAMPRANTHUS

12. *Lampranthus multiradiatus* (*L. glaucus*) Raised ring surrounding 5 prominent stigmas is characteristic of this genus. Apr. - May. (× 1) Introduced from S. Africa. **D** (**Ma**) Not Bl in FE I 113
13. *L. roseus* (Willd.) Schwantes Apr.- May. (× 1). Ll Native S. Africa. (**Ma**, I) (Not in FE).

MESEMBRYANTHEMUM

14. *Mesembryanthemum nodiflorum* Gasoul. Apr.- July. Maritime, local. K D Ll (**Ma**, Mi, I) FE I 113
15. *M. crystallinum* Ice plant. May - June. Native, widespread in waste places between Ca'n Pastilla and Palma. (× 1). K lists for Minorca only. D Ll (**Ma**, Mi, I) FE I 113

PORTULACACEAE: *PORTULACA*

16. *Portulaca oleracea* Procumbent annual. May - Oct. Native range unknown. Occasional in dry places near the sea, including beaches. (× 3/4, including single leaf from near base of plant. Details of flower × 2). K D (**Ma**, Mi, I) FE I 114

Others for Mallorca (all introduced plants more or less naturalized):
Amaranthus retroflexus Pigweed. Very like *A. cruentus*, but perianth segments more or less spathulate, obtuse or truncate. Common. K D (**Ma**, Mi) FE I 109
A. graecizans Resembles *A. albus*, but bracteoles not spinescent. Occasional. **K** D (**Ma**, Mi, I) FE I 110
A. viridis L. Ll (Ma, Mi) Possibly not in FE under any name.
Mirabilis jalapa (Nyctaginaceae) Erect perennial with yellow or red tubular flowers. Introduced from tropical America. Common garden escape. (**Ma**, I)Not Bl in FE I 111
Aptenia cordifolia Procumbent perennial resembling *Mesembryanthemum* but with 4 stigmas. Flowers purple. **D** From South Africa. (Ma, Mi, I) Not Bl in FE I 113
Disphyma crassifolium Also in Minorca. From S. Africa. Not Bl in FE I 113
Drosanthemum hispidum (L.) Schwantes **D** From S. Africa. (**Ma**) (Not in FE).
Tetragonia tetragonioides (Tetragoniaceae) New Zealand Spinach. Occasionally naturalized (Bonafè). (**Ma**) Not Bl in FE I 114

In other islands (all introduced):
Amaranthus caudatus. Ibiza. Bl not excluded in FE I 109
Phytolacca dioica Ibiza. Not Bl in FE I 112
Carpobrotus chilensis Minorca and Ibiza. Not Bl in FE I 113

Plate 10

CARYOPHYLLACEAE (1) *ARENARIA, MOEHRINGIA, MINUARTIA, RHODALSINE, STELLARIA, CERASTIUM*

ARENARIA

1. *Arenaria grandiflora* Perennial. Somewhat variable, and two subsp. are described here, both endemic. May. Dry rocky places in mountains. Occasional. **K D (Ma)** FE I 119
2. *A. balearica* Perennial. May. Widespread in shady moist places in mountains. (Upper illustration × 1). **K D (Ma)** FE I 119
3. *A. serpyllifolia* Thyme-leaved Sandwort. Annual, ascending or erect. Length capsule less than twice width. Capsule distinctly swollen at base. Mar.- Apr. Local in dry sandy places and on walls. **K D (Ma, Mi)** FE I 121
4. *A. leptoclados* Very like 2, but plant more delicate, often prostrate. Capsule length more than twice width, equalling or shorter than sepals, not or hardly swollen at base. Common. ?K (possibly included with 3 in K371). **D (Ma, Mi)** FE I 121

MOEHRINGIA

5. *Moehringia pentandra* Ascending annual. Petals absent or rudimentary. Pedicels elongated and deflexed in fruit, swollen above. Apr. - May. Shady places in mountain. **K D (Ma, Mi)** FE I 124

MINUARTIA

6. *Minuartia hybrida* Fine-leaved Sandwort. Annual. Leaves narrow lanceolate. Capsule teeth 3, obtuse, everted when ripe. Apr.- May. Dry places in mountain areas. **K D (Ma, Mi, I)** FE I 127

RHODALSINE

7. *R. geniculata* (Poiret) Williams (*Minuartia geniculata*) Glandular pubescent perennial, easily taken for *Spergularia* species, but without stipules. Apr.-May. Common in dry places near the sea. **K D (Ma)** FE I 132

STELLARIA

8. *Stellaria media* Chickweed. Annual. Lower leaves long-petiolate, upper usually sessile. Pedicels erect or patent in fruit. Petals usually present. Seeds reddish-brown, usually with rounded tubercles. Common. **K D (Ma, Mi, I)** FE I 134
9. *S. pallida* Lesser Chickweed. Like 8 only usually more slender. Leaves usually all petiolate, petals absent or minute. Seeds pale yellowish-brown with rounded or conical tubercles. Common. ?**K** (possibly included with 8 in K365). **D (Ma, I)** FE I 134
10. ?*S. media* subspecies. Like 8, but more robust. This from specimens and photos from near Lluc monastery, resembles *S. neglecta* in the robust habit with broad stems and pedicels reflexed in fruit, also in the reddish-brown seeds with conical tubercles. It keys out in FE key as *S. media*, and has other features described for this species. (Petals shorter than sepals, stamens 5). This might prove to be a new endemic species. *S. neglecta:* ?**K. D** records having found it. Ll omits. Not Bl in FE I 134

CERASTIUM

11. *Cerastium brachypetalum* Annual, with long eglandular hairs protruding beyond apex of sepals. Glandular hairs present or not. Pedicels longer than sepals, deflexed below apex in larger buds and in fruit. Petals longer or shorter than sepals, bifid up to half length. Capsule curved, slightly exceeding sepals. Mar. - May. Common in mountain areas. **K D (Ma)** FE I 143
12. *C. glomeratum* Hairy annual, with glandular and eglandular hairs, eglandular hairs protruding beyond apex of sepals. Flowers in compact clusters, pedicels shorter than sepals. Petals equalling or exceeding sepals, bifid up to 1/4 length. Capsule curved, up to twice length sepals. Mar.- May. Common. **K D (Ma, Mi, I)** FE I 144
13. *C.* cf. *semidecandrum* Specimens used here keyed out as *C. pumilum* in FE key, but looked more like *C. semidecandrum*. They resembled specimens of *C. semidecandrum* var *sennenii* in herbarium of University of the Balearic Islands. Stem and sepals with eglandular and dense glandular hairs. Sepals about 3.5mm. Pedicels about equalling sepals. Upper bracts with short scarious tips (typically bracts in *C. semidecandrum* are 1/3 to entirely scarious. Mar.- Apr. Occasional. (Details from above down: flower × 4, capsule × 3, upper bract ×6 and stem-leaf × 3). K D (Ma, Mi) FE I 144
    Llorens et al. (1991) list 2 subsp., including 3 varieties of subsp. *semidecandrum* in the area. This genus is very confusing here, and the illustrations of 13 and 14 are not reliably identified.
14. *C. diffusum* subsp. ?*diffusum*. Annual. Upper bracts completely herbaceous, or with just perceptible scarious tip. Pedicels longer than 4-9mm sepals with narrow scarious margin. Petals shorter than sepals, about 1/5 bifid. Apr. - May. Occasional. (Details all x 1.5: flower, capsule, upper bract). K D (Ma) Not Bl in FE I 145

Also recorded for Mallorca:
Minuartia mediterranea Resembles 6, but pedicels not longer than sepals, and cymes crowded. K and D do not list for Ma. Ll does. (Ma, Mi) FE I 127
Cerastium fontanum Mouse-ear Chickweed. Perennial. K's record ambiguous. D lists. Ll omits. (?Ma, ?Mi) Bl not excluded in FE I 142
C. pumilum Bracts only marginally scarious. Pedicel longer than very slightly curved capsule. **K D** (Ma) FE I 14
C. siculum Annual. Flowers clustered, with pedicels shorter than sepals. K lists for Ibiza only. **D (Ma, Mi)** Not Bl in FE I 145

Plate 11

CARYOPHYLLACEAE (2) *SAGINA, (SCLERANTHUS), (CORRIGIOLA), PARONYCHIA, HERNIARIA, POLYCARPON, SPERGULARIA, AGROSTEMMA, (GYPSOPHILA), SAPONARIA, (VACCARIA), PETRORHAGIA, (DIANTHUS)*

SAGINA

1. *Sagina apetala* Annual Pearlwort. Usually slightly hairy. Distinguished from 2 by aristate leaves. Ripe capsule equalling or exceeding patent (susp. *erecta*) or appressed (subsp. *apetala*) sepals. Apr. - May. Occasional, streets and dry places. K D (**Ma,** I) FE I 147
2. *S. maritima* Sea Pearlwort. Rather like 1, but usually glabrous, and often much denser, with a great many stems. Leaves slightly fleshy with mucronate tip. Ripe capsule equalling or shorter than obliquely spreading sepals. Apr. - May. Common, usually near the sea. K D (**Ma**, Mi, I) FE I 148

PARONYCHIA

3. *Paronychia argentea* Procumbent perennial. Flowers small, in axillary clusters with conspicuous, large silvery bracts. Mar. - May. Common in dry places. **K D** (**Ma**, Mi, I) FE I 150
4. *P. capitata* Tufted perennial up to 15cm. Flower clusters terminal. Calyx lobes very unequal. Mar. - May. Not common. K D (**Ma**, Mi, I) FE I 150

HERNIARIA

5. *Herniaria hirsuta* (including *H. cinerea* DC.) Rupture Wort. Hairy prostrate annual. Small flowers in dense leaf-opposed clusters. Apr. - June. Fairly common in dry places. K D (**Ma**, Mi, I) FE I 152

POLYCARPON

6. *Polycarpon tetraphyllum* All-seed. Annual to perennial. Leaves mostly in whorls of 4. Stipules conspicuous, silvery. Flowers small in lax spreading inflorescence. Sepals mostly less than 2mm. Apr. - June. Common, usually inland. **K D** (**Ma**, Mi, I) FE I 153
7. *P. alsinifolium* Very like 6, but inflorescence very condensed, and sepals usually more than 2mm. Apr. - June. Common, usually coastal. D (**Ma**, Mi, I) FE I 153
8. *P. polycarpoides* subsp. *colomense* (Porta) Pedrol Perennial, with ovate fleshy, suborbicular leaves, generally in pairs. Stipules small, greyish. Apr. - June. Uncommon. Coastal rocks. (From Minorcan specimen, slightly enlarged). K **D** (Ma, Mi) FE I 153

SPERGULARIA

Knoche lumps here: 'À mon avis tous les *Spergularia* des Baléares ne sont que des formes de cette espèce' (i.e. *S. rubra*).

9. *Spergularia media* Greater Sea Spurrey. Robust perennial, glabrous throughout or glandular-hairy above. Stipules broadly triangular. Petals white or pink, about 5mm, at least equalling sepals. Capsule much exceeding calyx. Seeds, dark brown, usually winged. Apr. - June. Common, saltmarshes, saline sand. ?**K D** (**Ma**, Mi, I) FE I 155
10. *S. marina* Sea Spurrey. Usually annual, often glandular above. Petals pink, white towards base, not exceeding sepals. Capsule usually exceeding calyx. Seeds light brown, some unwinged. Apr.- May. Less common than 9. ?**K D** (**Ma**, Mi, I) FE I 155

11. *S. rubra* Sand Spurrey. Usually annual and glandular above. Leaves fasciculate. Bracts in inflorescence almost as large as leaves. Petals uniformly pink. Capsule about equalling calyx. Seeds dark brown, unwinged, minutely tuberculate. Apr. - May. Common in dry sandy places, often inland. ?**K D** (**Ma**, Mi, I) FE I 155

AGROSTEMMA

12. *Agrostemma githago* Corn Cockle. May. Rare. (From garden specimen). (Ma, introduced from Eastern Mediterranean). **K** D FE I 157

SAPONARIA

13. *Saponaria officinalis* Soapwort. Perennial, up to 90cm. June - Sept. (From garden specimen). K D Ll (Ma, probably only as garden escape). FE I 185

PETRORHAGIA

14. *Petrorhagia nanteuilii* Inflorescence capitate, with broad scarious bracts enclosing calyx and capsule. Seeds less than 2mm, tuberculate, compressed. May - June. Local in sandy places. **K D** (**Ma**, Mi) ?Bl in FE I 188

Other species recorded for Mallorca:
Sagina procumbens Probably does not occur here. D quotes FE. Ll omits. (?Ma) Bl not excluded in FE I 147
Scleranthus verticillatus Tausch (*S. annuus*) B records. D and Ll omit. (?Ma) All except Bl in FE I 149
Corrigiola telephiifolia Ll lists. (D for Mi only). ?Bl in FE I 149
Herniaria incana Very unlikely. K (quotes Weyler 1854) and adds 'A vérifier'. ?D. Ll omits. ?Bl in FE I 152
Spergularia diandra, with short triangular stipules and slender, much branched inflorescence lacking upper bracts. Ll (Ma, Mi, I) FE I 155
S. nicaeensis D ?Ll (?Ma) FE I 155
S. bocconei Rather like 11, but leaves not fasciculate and bracts much reduced in inflorescence. Seeds grey-brown, tuberculate, less than 0.5mm. Common in south of Mallorca (Prof. Llorens). ?**K** D Ll (Ma, I) Not Bl in FE I 156
S. heldreichii Also rather like 11, but always annual. Stipules heart shaped with short point. Seeds metallic black, smooth. **D** Ll (Ma) Not Bl in FE I 156
Gypsophila pilosa Probably extinct. K (quotes Barceló 1867-1877) Ll omits. (?Ma) ?Bl in FE I 184
Vaccaria hispanica (Miller) Rausch. (*V. pyramidata*) K Ll (Ma, Mi) Not Bl in FE I 186
Petrorhagia dubia (Rafin) López & Romo. Ll lists (Ma, Mi) Not described in FE or listed in Med-Checklist: possibly included in, or related to. *P. velutina* B records this and not *P. nanteuilii*. ?Bl in FE I 188
Dianthus rupicola A *Dianthus* species has been recorded from time to time. Barceló records *Dianthus cariophyllus* L. only as a cultivated plant. Knoche records that Rodríguez was unable to identify a specimen from another collector, and a similar specimen was found later in a different place. Bonafè lists *D. rupicola* with a good photo, and D and Ll also list this species. (Ma) FE I 201.

In other islands:
Paronychia echinulata Minorca. FE I 150
Loeflingia hispanica Ibiza. Not Bl in FE I 153
Spergularia fimbriata Ibiza. Not Bl in FE I 155

48

Plate 12

CARYOPHYLLACEAE (3) *SILENE*

Small illustrations of calyx in flower and (where different) in fruit are approximately × 1. Main illustration ×2/3 - 1.

1. *Silene mollissima* Softly pubescent robust woody perennial. Flowers always whitish. May - June. Local in northern mountain areas. **K D** (**Ma,** Mi endemic subsp.) Ibiza only according to FE I 163

2. *S. vulgaris* Very variable perennial with inflated, glabrous calyx. Flowers usually white, sometimes pink. Jan. - Oct. Common. **K D** (**Ma,** Mi, I) FE I 168

3. *S. pseudatocion* Viscid, pubescent annual, with large (ca 1cm), entire pink petals. Apr. - June. Confined to one locality, but common there. African species probably with only Europaean station here - also one unconfirmed record from Spanish mainland. **K D** (**Ma**) FE I 175

4. *S. rubella* Pubescent annual. May - June. Occasional field weed, often among broad beans or lucerne. **K D** (**Ma,** Mi, I) FE I 175

5. *S. sedoides* Small, much-branched viscid annual. May. Local, in dry places near the sea. K lists for Minorca only. D lists. Ll omits. (From Mallorcan specimen and photographs). (**Ma,** Mi) FE I 176

6. *S. nicaeensis* Viscid annual, with pink or whitish flowers. May. (From herbarium and garden specimens). K (quotes Garcia 1905) and D list. ?Ll (adds query). (?**Ma**) FE I 178

7. *S. colorata* Pubescent annual. Flowers solitary, terminal. May. Local on sandy ground in the SE, mainly coastal. Ll. (**Ma**) Not Bl in FE I 180

8. *S. nocturna* Annual. Flowers very small, whitish, sometimes included in calyx. Veins of calyx conspicuously anastomosing. Apr. - June. Fairly common casual. **K D** (**Ma,** Mi, I) FE I 179

9. *S. gallica* Annual, sticky above. Petals pink or white, usually entire. Apr. - June. Widespread, especially near the sea. **K D** (**Ma,** Mi, I) FE I 179

10. *S. bellidifolia* Softly hairy annual, with elegant raceme-like cymes of numerous flowers with deeply bifid pink petals. May - June. Locally common. **K D** (**Ma,** Mi) FE I 179

11. *S. cerastioides* Somewhat like 9, but with conspicuously anastomosing veins on the fruiting calyx, which is more contracted above, and with smaller, bifid petals. Flowers with white petals are common, and the plants seem usually more robust than those with pink petalled flowers. Apr.-June. ?Widespread. The photographs and specimens from which this is illustrated were both from a common plant, but could possibly have been misidentified. K and **D** both record finding this species. Ll omits under this name. (**Ma,** Mi, I) FE I 179

12. *S. disticha* Hispid annual with subcapitate inflorescence. Petal limb almost included in calyx. May. Rare. (From Corsican specimen). K (quotes Marès and Vigineix 1880). D Ll (Ma, Mi, I) FE I 180

13. *S. secundiflora* Annual. Leaves almost glabrous. Calyx pubescent, much enlarged in fruit, with conspicuously anastomosing veins. Seeds with back narrowly grooved between 2 undulate wings. Apr.-June. Locally common near the sea and in mountains. **D** (**Ma,** Mi, I) FE I 180

14. *S. apetala* (includes *S. decipiens* Barc.) Pubescent annual. Calyx 7-10mm, petals small or (often) absent. Seeds dark brown, back deeply grooved between undulate wings - this and 13 the only 2 species with winged seeds here. Feb.- Mar. Rare (or overlooked because early and inconspicuous). (Specimen from Spanish mainland). **K D** (Ma, I) FE I 180

Also recorded from Mallorca:
Silene muscipula **K.** D omits. ?Ll (?Ma, ?I) Not Bl in FE I 176
S. almolae Ll lists (Ma) FE I 178
S. sclerocarpa Léon Dufour (Not in FE: possibly related to or included in no 11 above). Ll lists for (Ma, Mi, ?I)

In Ibiza:
Silene hifacensis FE I 163
S. cambessedesii Boiss & Reuter Endemic. (cf. *S. littorea* FE I 178)
S. tridentata FE I 180

Plate 13

(NYMPHAEACEAE): CERATOPHYLLACEAE:
RANUNCULACEAE (1) - all except *Ranunculus*

CERATOPHYLLACEAE: *CERATOPHYLLUM*

1. *Ceratophyllum demersum* Submerged aquatic perennial. Leaves in dense whorls, flowers tiny, axillary, unisexual. Common in fresh water. D (**Ma,** Mi) Not Bl in FE I 206

RANUNCULACEAE (1: all except *Ranunculus*)

HELLEBORUS

2. *Helleborus foetidus* Stinking Hellebore. Robust branched perennial.Leaves divided into 7-9 narrow segments. Feb. - May. Local in mountains. (Slightly reduced). **K D** (**Ma**) FE I 207
3. *H. lividus* subsp. *lividus* Leaves trifoliate. Feb. - Mar. Local, shady places in the mountains.(× 0.5) **K** D (**Ma,** endemic subsp.) FE I 207

NIGELLA

4. *Nigella damascena* Love-in-a-mist. Annual. Mar. - May. Common in cultivated ground. **K D** (**Ma,** Mi, I) FE I 210

DELPHINIUM

5. *Delphinium staphisagria* Licebane. May - June. Local, stony places in the mountains. (Plant × about 1/5: details × 1, including large seed. Leaf here is from middle stem). Local in mountains. **K D** (**Ma,** Mi, I) FE I 216
6. *D. pictum* Flowers whitish. Outer perianth segments turn deep blue on drying. May - June. Local, mainly in mountain areas. (Details of flowers × 1: middle stem-leaf with more or less linear, shining segments usually rather larger than shown). **K D** (**Ma**) FE I 216

ANEMONE

7. *Anemone coronaria* Corolla red or blue. Feb. - Mar. Not common. (From garden specimen). **K** D (**Ma,** Mi) FE I 219

CLEMATIS

8. *Clematis flammula* Maiden's Bower. Leaves are irregularly bipinnate, flowers clusters creamish-white. May - Oct. Fairly common on fences and in rocky places. **K D** (**Ma,** Mi, I) FE I 221
9. *C. vitalba* Old Man's Beard. Leaves irregularly pinnate, flowers in axillary clusters, petals greenish. June - Aug. Rare. (From British specimen). **D** Ll (Ma) Not Bl in FE I 221
10. *C. cirrhosa* Flowers solitary, nodding. Jan. - Apr. Common on walls and rocks.(× 1) **K D** (**Ma,** Mi, I) FE I 221

ADONIS

11. *Adonis annua* Pheasant's Eye. Corolla red. Inner margin of achene straight. Mar. - July. Fairly common field weed. K **D** (**Ma,** Mi) FE I 222
12. *A. microcarpa* Resembles 11, but corolla usually yellow. Inner margin of achene with a projection near the beak. Mar. - July. Occasional field weed. (Detail from Greek specimen). **K D** (Ma, Mi, I) FE I 223

MYOSURUS

13. *Myosurus minimus* Mouse tail. Mar. - May. Very rare here. (From British specimen, slightly reduced). **D** Ll (Not K). (Ma) FE I 238

Other species recorded for Mallorca:
Nymphaea alba (Nymphaeceae) Probably extinct here as a wild plant. (Bonafè). FE I 204
Ceratophyllum submersum Resembles *C. demersum*, but nut has no basal spine. Recorded by several botanists recently. Not Bl in FE I 206.
Consolida ambigua Larkspur. Occasional escape from cultivation. (**Ma,** Mi) FE I 217
Adonis estivalis Ll lists. Not Bl in FE I 223

In other islands:
Nigella gallica Minorca. Not Bl in FE I 209
Delphinium halteratum Ibiza. Not Bl in FE I 215
Consolida regalis Ibiza. Bl excluded in FE I 217

Plate 14

RANUNCULACEAE (2) *RANUNCULUS* part 1.

1. *Ranunculus repens* Creeping Buttercup. Stoloniferous perennial, rooting at nodes. Basal leaves with 3 leaflets, the central one stalked. Achenes 3mm, compressed, bordered, with curved beak. Apr. - June. Not common. (From British specimen). K **D** Ll (Ma) Bl excluded in FE I 227

2. *R. macrophyllus* Robust hairy perennial. Basal leaves up to 12 cm or more across. Achenes 4mm, compressed, bordered, minutely pitted or hairy. Mar. - June. Common in damp ditches. **K D** (**Ma**, Mi, I) FE I 229

3. *R. bulbosus* Bulbous Buttercup. Bulbous-based perennial. Hairs appressed below, spreading above. Upper leaves deeply cut into more or less linear segments. Sepals reflexed in mature flower. Achenes 2-4mm, beak short, hooked, with twisted tip. Mar. - June. Local. **K D** (**Ma**) FE I 229

4. *R. sardous* Hairy Buttercup. Annual, resembling 3 but without bulbous-based stem. Hairs spreadng throughout plant. Leaves often shining and slightly fleshy. Leaves in middle part of inflorescence sessile, broad and much lobed, opposite pairs often overlapping to form a sort of 'ruff' round the stem. Achenes about 3mm, with blunt tubercles near margin, centre of face smooth. Mar. - June. Widespread. **K D** Ll (**Ma**, ?Mi, ?I) FE I 230

5. *R. trilobus* Annual, almost hairless. Lowest leaves simple, others three-lobed. Flowers 10-15mm diameter. Achenes 2mm, with low rounded tubercles and a short beak. Mar. - May. Common in marshy places. K **D** (**Ma**, Mi, I) FE I 230

6. *R. muricatus* Annual, almost hairless. Leaves shallowly lobed. Achenes 7-8mm, with spiny face and a smooth margin. Mar. - May. Occasional. **K D** (**Ma**, Mi, I) FE I 230

7. *R. arvensis* Corn Buttercup. Annual. Upper leaves divided into linear segments. Achenes large (6-8mm), few, with long curved spines from border, and shorter ones from ridges on face. Mar. - June. Widespread in cultivated areas. **K D** (**Ma**, Mi) FE I 230

(8 and 9: FE gives *R. parviflorus* for Bl, not *R. chius*, in this following Knoche. Duvigneaud gives *R. parviflorus* for Ma, Mi, and *R. chius* for Ma (not collected by him personally.) In fact the common plant of the mountains corresponds to the FE description of *R. chius*, particularly in regard to the achenes, but looks more like *R. parviflorus* specimens. The pedicels are much less thickened than usual in *R. chius*. Hansen records *R. parviflorus* here as 'most likely = *R. chius* DC'.

8. *R. parviflorus* (or ?*chius*; see above). Decumbent annual. Pedicels slightly thickened, recurved when ripe. Achenes 3mm with long beak and some of the tubercles pointed or slightly hooked. Apr. - June. Common throughout mountains and hills of Mallorca. **K D** (**Ma**, Mi, I) FE I 230

9. *R. chius* Spreading annual. Leaves all trilobed. Fruiting pedicels greatly thickened and often recurved. Flowers 3-6mm diameter. Beak at least half length 3mm achene. (From Greek specimen). D (Ma) FE I 230

10. *R. monspeliacus* Tuberous woolly or waxy perennial. Flowers 25mm diameter. Head of achenes cylindrical. Achenes sparsely pubescent, with curved beak 1/2 length achene. Rare if at all. (Specimen from Spanish mainland). K (quotes Barceló 1867-1877, and Rodríguez (d. 1905) opinion that this species might be doubtful here). Fruiting head rather like that of *R. paludosus*. D ?Ll (?Ma) Not Bl in FE I 230

54

Plate 15

RANUNCULACEAE (3): *RANUNCULUS* continued.
PAEONIACAE
LAURACEAE

RANUNCULACEAE: *RANUNCULUS* part 2.

1. *R. paludosus* Fan-leaved Buttercup. Stoloniferous perennial with fibrous roots and fleshy tubers. Flowers large, up to 3cm. Receptacle much elongated in fruit. Mar. - Apr. **K D (Ma,** I) FE 231

2. *R. sceleratus* Celery-leaved Crowfoot. Glabrous annual. Basal leaves large, kidney-shaped. Sepals deflexed. Receptacle much elongated in fruit. Occasional in wet places. K D (**Ma,** Mi) FE 1 233

3. *R. ficaria* Lesser Celandine. Perennial, with fibrous and tuberous roots. Mar. - Apr. K D (**Ma,** Mi) FE I 233

4. *R. weyleri* Tufted perennial. Basal leaves orbicular, 3-lobed, up to 1cm. Cauline leaves small and few. Very rare. (From garden specimen: achene × 3). **K** D (Ma, endemic) FE I 235

5. *R. ophiglossifolius* Snakestongue Crowfoot. Annual, up to 40cm. Basal leaves long-stalked, ovate and cordate. Apr. - May. Local in wet places. **K D (Ma,** Mi) FE I 235

There seems to be some doubt about which white aquatic species occur here. They are often difficult to identify.

6. *R. peltatus* subsp. *saniculifolius* (Viv.) Cook. Annual or perennial with laminate or capillary leaves, or both. **K** D lists with ?. (Ma, Mi) FE I 237 does not exclude Bl (and does not describe this subsp.).

7. *R. trichophyllus* Annual or perennial, with capillary leaves only. These rarely exceed 4cm. Petals rarely exceeding 5mm, half moon shaped. Local in fresh water. Probably K (some uncertainty about which species his synonyms represent). **D (Ma)** Bl excluded in FE I 237

PAEONIACEAE: *PAEONIA*

8. *Paeonia cambessedesii* March. Perennial. Local in the mountains, nowhere abundant. **K D (Ma,** Mi endemic) FE I 244

LAURACEAE: *LAURUS*

9. *Laurus nobilis* Sweet Bay. Evergreen shrub. Leaves entire. Flowers subsessile, cream coloured. Very local except in cultivation. (From garden specimen). **K** D (Ma, Mi) FE I 246

Other species possibly occurring in Mallorca:
R. barceloi Grau (treated as doubtful taxon in Med-Checklist under *R. paludosus).* Ll (Ma endemic). Not described in FE.
Ranunculus bullatus Perennial. Leaves all basal, simple, crenate and bullate. Pedicels up to 20cm with 1 or 2 flowers. Oct. K (his one location is now very trampled). D Ll (?Ma) Bl in FE I 234
R. peltatus Scrank subsp. *baudotii* (Godron) Cook. Annual or perennial with laminate or capillary leaves or both. Laminate leaves with 3 deep, cuneate, distant entire or crenate segments. Pedicel in fruit strongly recurved. Petals 5.5-10.5mm.Achenes numerous, distinctly winged. ?D ?Ll (?Ma) Bl in FE I 237 (*R. baudotii)*
R. peltatus Schrank subsp. *peltatus* ?D ?Ll (?Ma, ?Mi)
R. aquatilis K's records very confusing here. D (quotes FE). Ll omits. Bl not excluded Bl in FE I 237
R. penicillatus (Dumort) Bab. (*R. pseudofluitans).* Not K or D. Ll. Not Bl in FE 1 237

Plate 16

PAPAVERACEAE (1) - all except *FUMARIA*
Main illustrations × 2/3 - 1: details enlarged.

PAPAVER

1. *Papaver somniferum* subsp. *setigerum* Opium poppy. Glaucous annual. Mar. - June. Common. **K D** (**Ma**, Mi, I) FE I 247
2. *P. rhoeas* Field poppy. Annual. Hairs spreading on upper part flower stem. Capsule not or hardly elongated. Mar. - June. Common, especially along roadsides and as agricultural weed. **K D** (**Ma**, Mi, I) FE I 248
3. *P. dubium* Long headed poppy. Very like 2, but flower usually a more orange red. Anthers violet. Capsule at least twice as long as wide. Mar. - June. Fairly common as an agricultural weed. **K D** (**Ma**, Mi) FE I 248
4. *P. pinnatifidum* Rather like 3. Anthers yellow. Less common than either 2 or 3, but widespread. K lists for Minorca only. **D** (**Ma,** Mi, I) FE I 248
5. *P. argemone* Bristly annual with elongated bristly capsule. Not common here. (From British specimen). ?K ('selon mes notes', which seems to mean 'no specimen'). D Ll (Ma, I) FE I 248
6. *P. hybridum* Another hispid annual, often with a blue tinge to the pink or reddish colour. Variable (both illustrations from Mallorcan specimens), but globose and bristly capsule and white anthers are distinctive. Fairly common as agricultural weed. **K D** (**Ma,** Mi, I) FE I 249

ROEMERIA

7. *Roemeria hybrida* Like a small lavender-violet poppy. Capsule narrow, elongated, 5-10cm. Not common. (From garden specimen). K **D** (Ma, I) FE I 251

GLAUCIUM

8. *Glaucium flavum* Yellow horned Poppy. Distinctive usually much branched biennial or perennial, with yellow petals up to 3cm and a much elongated capsule (up to 30cm long) covered in yellowish tubercles. Apr. - Sept. Common near sea. **K D** (**Ma,** Mi, I) FE I 251
9. *G. corniculatum* Bristly annual. Capsule up to 10cm. Mar. Sept. Rare. (From garden specimen). **K D** (Ma) FE I 251

CHELIDONIUM

10. *Chelidonium majus* Greater celandine. Branched, slightly woody perennial. Flowers (petals up to 1cm) and fruit much like those of 8, but smaller. Rare. (From British specimen). K (quotes Bianor 1910-1914) D Ll (Introduced Ma, Mi, I) FE I 251

HYPECOUM

11. *Hypecoum imberbe* Glabrous annual, with 2 outer petals much larger than inner 2. Not common. **D** Ll (**Ma,** Mi) FE I 252

Also possibly occurring in Mallorca:
Eschscholzia californica Naturalized in Bl according to FE I 251
Hypecoum procumbens Very rare (Prof. Llorens). K (quotes Barceló 1867-1877). D (quotes FE). Ll (Ma, I) FE I 252

In Minorca only:
Hypecoum pendulum Not Bl in FE I 252

Plate 17

PAPAVERACEAE (2): *FUMARIA (PLATYCAPNOS)*
CAPPARIDACEAE: *CAPPARIS*
CRUCIFERAE part 1: *SISYMBRIUM, (DESCURAINIA),*
(ARABIDOPSIS).

PAPAVERACEAE: *FUMARIA* Fumitory.

Weak-stemmed annuals. Corolla zygomorphic with 4 petals, the upper largest with a sac-like spur at base and wings at the tip. The two inner petals are dark-tipped, and the lower petal is narrow.

1. *Fumaria agraria* Mature leaves with broad flat segments. Raceme longer than peduncle, 15-22 flowered. Corolla 12-14mm. Wings of upper petal pale. Fruit keeled with notched beak, ridged when dry. Feb. - Mar. Rare. (Portuguese specimen). **K** D (**Ma**, Mi, I) FE I 256

2. *F. capreolata* subsp. *capreolata* Leaves with broad flat segments. Raceme shorter than peduncle, up to 20 flowers. Corolla 10-14mm, whitish, often becoming reddish. Pedicels usually become recurved. Fruit smooth, slightly keeled. Common. **K** D (**Ma**, Mi, I) FE I 256

3. *F. bicolor* Straggling plant. Raceme longer or shorter than peduncle, with 8-12 slender flowers. Corolla whitish, becoming pink. Wings of upper petal remain pale. May. Fairly common. B. D quotes FE. Ll records for Mi only. (From Mallorcan specimen, identification confirmed by Mr P.D. Sell) (**Ma**, Mi)

4. *F. bastardii* Not usually climbing. Leaf segments broad and flat. Raceme longer than peduncle, 15-25 flowered. Corolla 9-12mm, pink. Wings of upper petal dark or (more usually) pale. Fruit ovoid, slightly keeled, usually rugose when dry. Feb. - Apr. Fairly common. B H Ll (**Ma**, Mi, I) FE I 257

5. *F. densiflora* Resembles *F. officinalis* subsp. *officinalis* (see below), but flowers 6-7mm and peduncle very short or obsolete. Bracts normally exceeding fruiting pedicels. fruit rounded-obtuse at apex. (Detail only × 2, British specimen). K **D** Ll (Ma, I) FE I 257

6. *F. officinalis* Scrambling plant with fairly narrow leaves. Raceme longer than peduncle. Corolla 7-9mm, upper petal with narrow dark wings. Bracts shorter than fruiting pedicel. Fruit with truncate or emarginate apex, wrinkled when dry. 2 subspecies here: subsp. *wirtegenii* has 10-20 flowers and sepals less than 2mm: subsp. *officinalis* has more than 20 flowers and sepals 2.5-3.5mm. Both common. **K** D (**Ma**, Mi) FE I 257

7. *F. parviflora* Leaves glaucous, segments very narrow, channelled. Racemes very dense, more or less sessile. Corolla 5-6mm, usually white but often turning pink or pinkish. Wings of corolla pale. Apr. - May. Locally common. **K** D (**Ma**, Mi, I) FE I 258

CAPPARIDACEAE: *CAPPARIS*

8. *Capparis spinosa* Caper. Flowers 4-petalled, the two upper petals rather smaller than the lower. June - Oct. Common in cultivation and wild. **K D** (**Ma**, I) FE I 259

CRUCIFERAE: *SISYMBRIUM*

9. *Sisymbrium irio* London rocket. Lower leaves sinuate pinnatifid, usually deeply lobed and dissected: cauline lobed or entire and hastate, shortly petiolate. Petals 2.5-3.5mm. Pedicels up to 20mm in fruit, much thinner than torulose, erecto-patent 3-veined siliquae. Mar. - June. Common in waste places.(× 1/2). **K** D (**Ma**, Mi, I) FE I 264

10. *S. orientale* Eastern Rocket. Petals pale yellow, stem and leaves grey-pubescent, 8-10mm. Apr. - June. Occasional.(× 1/5). **K** D (**Ma**, I) FE I 265

11. *S. erysimoides* Petals 1-2.5mm. Pedicels up to 5mm in fruit, as thick as patent 3-veined siliqua. Mar. - May. Common.(× 1/2). **K** D (**Ma**, I) FE I 266

12. *S. officinale* Hedge Mustard. Petals 2-4mm. Siliqua conical, 10-20mm, held stiffly erect and appressed to stem. Mar. - Sept. Common. (Main illustration × 1/3). **K** D (**Ma**, Mi, I) FE I 266

Also recorded for Mallorca:
Fumaria vaillantii D lists for Ibiza only. ?Ll (?Ma) FE I 258
Sisymbrium polyceratium Inflorescence bracteate to apex. K D Ll (Ma, Mi) Not Bl in FE I 265
Sisymbrium runcinatum D (quotes FE). Ll lists. Bl in FE I 266
Descurainia sophia K (quotes Barceló 1867-1877). D Ll FE I 266
Arabidopsis thaliana Annual. Corolla white. Siliqua with one vein. Lower parts of plant with unbranched and bifid hairs. K (quotes Bianor, 1910-1914) D Ll (Ma, Mi) FE I 267

Species recorded from other islands, or record for Bl unspecified.
Fumaria barnolae Sennen & Pau *(Fumaria bella)* Ibiza. Not Bl in FE I 256
F. bracteosa Pomel. Formentera and Cabrera. Not described in FE.
F. gaillardotii Ibiza. Not Bl in FE I 256
F. flabellata Minorca. FE I 256
F. muralis Ibiza. Not Bl in FE I 257
F. sepium ?Minorca Not Bl in FE I 257
Platycapnos spicata Ibiza. Not Bl in FE I 258
Capparis ovata Bl in FE I 259
Erysimum grandiflorum Bl in FE I 271

Plate 18

CRUCIFERAE (2) *(MALCOLMIA), MARESIA, CHEIRANTHUS, MATTHIOLA, NASTURTIUM, CARDAMINE, ARABIS, LOBULARIA, CLYPEOLA*

MARESIA

1. *Maresia nana* Tiny branched annual, more or less densely covered in stellate hairs (often greyish). May be confused with *Malcolmia ramosissima*, but distinguished by presence of style (absent in *Malcolmia ramossissima*) and translucent septum of siliqua (opaque in *Malcolmia ramossissima*). May. Sandy places near sea.(× 2, details × 4). **D** (**Ma,** I) FE I 278

CHEIRANTHUS

2. *Cheiranthus cheirii* Wallflower. Perennial. Feb. - Apr. From garden specimen. K quotes Barceló (1867-1877). D (Introduced Ma, Mi, I) FE I 279

MATTHIOLA

3. *Matthiola incana* Stock, Gilliflower. Flowers may be white, violet or pink. Apr. - May. Occasional as garden escape. **K D** (Ma, Mi, I) FE I 280
4. *M. sinuata* Sea stock. Usually biennial, up to 60cm. Densely white tomentose. Apr. - June. Common on sand-dunes. **K D** (**Ma,** Mi, I) FE I 280
5. *M. tricuspidata*. Rare. Annual up to 40cm. Sepals 7-11mm, petals 15-22mm, purple. Siliqua with 2 horns. (From Greek specimen). K (quotes Bianor 1910-1914) D Ll (Ma, Mi) FE I 280

NASTURTIUM

6. *Nasturtium officinale* Watercress. Flowers throughout year. Common in running water. **K D** (**Ma,** Mi, I) FE I 284

CARDAMINE

7. *Cardamine hirsuta* Hairy Bittercress. Feb. - June. Widespread. **K D** (**Ma,** Mi, I) FE I 289

ARABIS

8. *Arabis hirsuta* (From Welsh specimen: but found subsequently in Mallorca in two sites, both high in mountains, with leaves less pointed and broader but otherwise similar). Leaves cordate or rounded at the base. May. **K** ?D Ll (**Ma**) FE I 292
9. *A. collina* subsp. *collina* Apr. - May. Rare in mountains. **D** Ll (**Ma,** Mi) Not Bl in FE I 292
10. *A. verna*. March - Apr. Fairly common in damp places in the mountains. **K D** (**Ma**) FE I 293

LOBULARIA

11. *Lobularia maritima* Sweet Alison. July - Sept. Common in sandy places near the sea. **K D** (**Ma,** Mi, I) FE I 307

CLYPEOLA

12. *Clypeola jonthlaspi* Apr. - June. Local, mountains. K D (**Ma,** I) FE I 307

Others recorded for Mallorca:
Malcolmia africana Annual up to 40cm. Siliqua patent, 25-65mm, more or less 4-angled, densely hispid. Ll lists. Not Bl in FE I 277
Matthiola parviflora Annual up to 20cm. Sepals 4-6mm, petals 6-10mm, purple or brownish-purple. D quotes FE. Ll lists. (Ma, I) FE I 280
Arabis sagittata Resembles 8, but cauline leaves sagittate at base. B lists. Ll omits. (?Ma) Not Bl in FE I 291
Arabis muralis I originally identified the specimen used for no 9 as this species, but distinction between this and *A. collina*, as suggested in FE, was not clear-cut. D records. Ll omits. ?Bl in FE I 292

In other islands:
Malcolmia ramosissima (Mi, I) FE I 277
M. maritima Minorca FE I 277
Matthiola fruticulosa Ibiza FE I 280

Plate 19

CRUCIFERAE (3) *EROPHILA, (CAMELINA), NESLIA, CAPSELLA, HYMENOLOBUS, HORNUNGIA, THLASPI, (IBERIS), BISCUTELLA, LEPIDIUM, CARDARIA, CORONOPUS*

EROPHILA

1. *Erophila verna* subsp. *praecox* Whitlow grass. Annual. Feb. Apr. Common. **K D (Ma)** FE I 312

NESLIA

2. *Neslia paniculata* subsp. *thracica* Ball mustard. Annual. Mar. - May. Uncommon casual. K **D (Ma, I)** FE I 315

CAPSELLA

3. *Capsella bursa-pastoris* Shepherd's Purse. Annual. Basal leaves very variable. Petals 2-3mm, white, longer than sepals. Lateral margins of silicula usually straight or convex. Most of year. Common. **K D (Ma, Mi, I)** FE I 316

4. *C. rubella* Pink Shepherd's Purse. Annual resembling 3, but with petals not exceeding sepals, either or both sometimes (but not usually) red-tipped. Lateral margins of silicula concave, apex usually more noticeably emarginate than in 3. Common. (Details × 4). ?K **D (Ma, Mi)** FE I 316

HYMENOLOBUS

5. *Hymenolobus procumbens* Annual, with scattered simple hairs, resembling 1, but with branched stems. Capsule reticulate-veined. Mar. - Apr. Common. K **D (Ma, Mi, I)** FE I 317

HORNUNGIA

6. *Hornungia petraea* Rock Hutchinsia. Annual, hairless or with a few stellate hairs. Apr. - May. Common in mountain areas in cracks of walls, rocks; often very small. **K D (Ma)** FE I 317

THLASPI

7. *Thlaspi arvense* Penny-cress. Annual. Fruit almost circular, 10-15mm. Apr. - Sept. Waste places, rare. (From British specimen x 0.5) **K** recorded once. D (Ma) FE I 319

8. *T. perfoliatum* Resembles 7, but fruit heart-shaped, 5-7mm. (Specimen from Spanish mainland) **K D** (Ma) FE I 319

BISCUTELLA

9. *Biscutella auriculata* Annual. Stems hispid at least below. Cauline leaves sessile, amplexicaul. Petals up to 15mm with long claw. Outer sepals strongly saccate. Silicula with thin wing which is excurrent with style up to 1cm. Rare. (Specimen from Spanish mainland: style in upper detail somewhat shortened). K (quotes Bianor 1910 1914) D Ll (Ma, I) FE I 329

LEPIDIUM

10. *Lepidium graminifolium* Perennial 1m or more, inflorescence much branched. Silicula unwinged, cauline leaves linear or pinnatisect with narrow lobes. Apr. - Sept. Fairly common in waste places and drier parts of saltmarshes. **K D (Ma, Mi)** FE I 333

CARDARIA

11. *Cardaria draba* Hoary Pepperwort. Mar. - June. Common wayside weed. (× 0.5) **K D (Ma, Mi, I)** FE I 333

CORONOPUS

12. *Coronopus squamatus* Swine-cress. Annual or biennial, often prostrate. Fruit kidney-shaped, with irregular ridges. Mar. - May. Widespread in trampled places. K **D (Ma)** Not Bl in FE I 333

13. *C. didymus* Lesser Swine-cress. Like 13, but smaller in all its parts, fruit notched, with pits and ridges which are less marked than those in 12. Mar. - May. Occasional. K lists for Minorca only. **D (Ma, Mi, I)** FE I 333

Also possibly occurring in Mallorca:

Camelina microcarpa Annual or biennial with densely hairy stem and leaves. Petals pale yellow. Fruiting racemes rigid and elongated. Fruit pear shaped, woody and inflated. Bonafè (quotes Barceló 1867-1877, adds 'A verificar'. Ll lists for Ma. FE I 315

Iberis pinnata K (quotes Barceló 1867-1877) ?extinct. Ll omits. FE I 325

Lepidium latifolium K (quotes Barceló 1867-1877). D omits. Llorens et al list only as alien. Bl excluded in FE I 332

In other islands or listed for Bl in FE:

Biscutella laevigata L. subsp. *montana* (Cav.) Maire var densiflora (Font Quer) Bolòs & Masclans Ibiza. Bl in FE I 328 (cf. *B. sempervirens*

B. frutescens ?Ibiza. Bl in FE I 327

Lepidium spinosum Minorca. FE I 331

L. ruderale Minorca. FE I 332 does not exclude for Bl

Plate 20

CRUCIFERAE (4) *(CONRINGIA), MORICANDIA, DIPLOTAXIS, BRASSICA, SINAPIS, ERUCA, HIRSCHFELDIA*

MORICANDIA

1. *Moricandia arvensis* Hairless, glaucous perennial, often much branched. Mar. - May. Occasional casual. K **D** (**Ma,** I) FE I 334

DIPLOTAXIS

2. *Diplotaxis ibicensis* (Pau) Gomez-Campo 1981. Shrubby perennial. Stems leafy, much branched at base. Leaves pinnatifid. Flowers pale yellow. Apr. - May. Rare here, on sandy shore. Hansen lists for Cabrera, Ibiza and Formentera only. Bonafè treats as variety of *D. catholica*. Ll lists. (**Ma,** I) Not described in FE

3. *D. erucoides* Annual. Petals white with pink or purple claw and veins. Siliqua compressed, with seeds in 2 rows: beak short, cylindrical. Feb. - Mar. Common field weed. **K D** (**Ma,** Mi, I) FE I 335

4. *D. viminea* Slender annual. Leaves in basal rosette. Petals not exceeding 4mm, pale yellow. Outer 2 stamens sterile, otherwise like annual forms of 5. Rare or overlooked. (From Mallorcan specimen collected by Bianor). Mar. - Apr. K **D** Ll (Ma, ?Mi, I) FE I 335

5. *D. muralis* Stinkweed. Annual, biennial or perennial. Leaves variable. usually confined to basal rosette. Petals bright sulphur yellow, 4.5mm or more. Stamens all fertile. Mar. - Sept. Fairly common. K **D** (**Ma,** Mi) FE I 335

BRASSICA

6. *Brassica balearica* Hairless small shrub. Leaves nearly all basal. Mar. - Apr. Rock crevices in mountains, rather local. **K D** (**Ma,** endemic) FE I 336

SINAPIS

7. *Sinapis arvensis* Charlock. Bristly annual weed. Spreading fruit at least 20mm, cone-shaped beak not or hardly flattened, more than half length valve when ripe, often with one seed. Mar. - June. Common. (× 1/2, immature pod and mature pods front and side view × 1). **K D** (**Ma,** Mi, I) FE I 339

8. *S. alba* White Mustard. Resembles 7, but beak of fruit strongly compressed, as long as valves or longer. Stalk of fruit nearly as long as fruit or longer. Mar. - June. (× 1/2; fruit, front and side view and in dehiscence, × 1: specimen from Spanish mainland). **K** D Ll (**Ma,** I) FE I 339

ERUCA

9. *Eruca sativa* Miller Slightly hispid annual. Flowers pale yellow or white with brown or purplish veins. Mar. - June. Common, cultivated as salad plant and wild. (Reduced, details × 1). K **D** (**Ma,** Mi, I) (cf. *Eruca vesicaria* FE I 340)

HIRSCHFELDIA

10. *Hirschfeldia incana* Hoary Mustard. Annual, biennial or perennial, resembling 7 and 8. Lower stem with dense downwardly directed white hairs, basal leaves hipid, upper part of plant almost glabrous. Flowers pale yellow. Siliquae erect, appressed, up to 17mm long: beak about half length valves, with swelling about the 0-2 seeds (usually 1). Apr. - May. Widespread. (Reduced, with fruits × 1 from Turkish specimen). **K** D (**Ma,** Mi, I) FE I 342

Also recorded from Mallorca:
Conringia orientalis Hare's ear Cabbage. Glabrous annual. Cauline leaves simple, cordate-amplexicaul. Flowers inconspicuous, yellowish green. Fruit up to 14cm, quadrangular in section. Rare. K (quotes Bianor 1910-1914) D Ll lists. Native of central and E. Europe. (Ma, Mi introduced) FE I 334
Brassica tournefortii Annual, stems up to 50cm. Upper cauline leaves sessile, not amplexicaul. Petals narrow, pale yellow, more or less violet at base, becoming whitish. Fruit 35-65mm, constricted at intervals, with beak 10-23mm. Ll lists. (Ma) Not Bl in FE I 338.

In other islands:
Diplotaxis tenuifolia Minorca FE I 335
Brassica rapa Minorca FE I 337
B. barrelieri ?Ibiza ?Bl in FE I 338
Erucastrum gallicum Ibiza. Not Bl in FE I 340

Plate 21

CRUCIFERAE (5) *CARRICHTERA, SUCCOWIA, CAKILE,*
RAPISTRUM, RAPHANUS
RESEDACEAE: *RESEDA*

CRUCIFERAE (5)

CARRICHTERA

1. *Carrichtera annua* Annual. Pedicels wrapped round thick main
   stem so that flowers or fruit appear to lie on the wrong side.
   Mar. - May. Fairly common. **K D (Ma,** Mi, I**)** FE I 342

SUCCOWIA

2. *Succowia balearica* Annual. Apr. - May. Uncommon in shady
   and rocky places. (From garden specimen, not differing
   significantly from plants found later in Mallorca). K **D (Ma,** Mi,
   I: not endemic) FE I 342

CAKILE

3. *Cakile maritima* subsp. *maritima* Sea Rocket. Succulent
   annual. Mar. - Sept. Sea shore and near sea. **K D (Ma,** Mi, I**)**
   FE I 343

RAPISTRUM

4. *Rapistrum rugosum* Bastard Cabbage. Annual, hispid below,
   often glabrous above. Basal leaves pinnate, stem leaves simple.
   Numerous stems arising from basal rosette. Inflorescence with
   long slender, spreading branches, many held horizontally. Apr.
   - June. Common wayside weed. ($\times$ 0.1, details $\times$ 1) **K D (Ma,**
   Mi, I**)** FE I 344

RAPHANUS

5. *Raphanus raphanistrum* Wild radish. Hispid annual. Petals
   white, pale yellow or violet, usually with dark violet veins. Mar.
   - Sept. Common weed of roadsides and cultivated places, also
   coastal. **K D (Ma,** Mi, I**)** FE I 346

RESEDACEAE: *RESEDA*

6. *Reseda luteola* Dyer's Rocket, Weld. Biennial, up to 1.5m,
   stiffly erect, usually unbranched until main stem has already
   finished flowering. Leaves entire. May - Oct. Waste ground,
   roadsides. **K D (Ma,** Mi, I**)** FE I 347
7. *R. alba* White mignonette. Feb. - Apr. Waste ground, common.
   K D (Ma, Mi, I**)** FE I 347
8. *R. phyteuma* Annual or biennial. Sepals 6. Leaves usually
   entire, spathulate, sometimes with 1 or 2 small lobes on each
   side at the base. Capsule at least 13mm long. Rare. (From
   garden specimen). Bonafè seems dubious about the records of
   at least some authors for this plant. **K D (**Ma, Mi, I**)** FE I 348
9. *R. lutea* Wild mignonette. Annual, biennial or perennial. Like
   6, but branching early and with leaves mostly pinnatifid. May
   - Sept. Common in dry waste places. **K D (Ma,** Mi, I**)** FE I 348

Other species recorded for Balearic Islands:
Reseda media Bl in FE I 348
R. odorata Bl in FE I 348

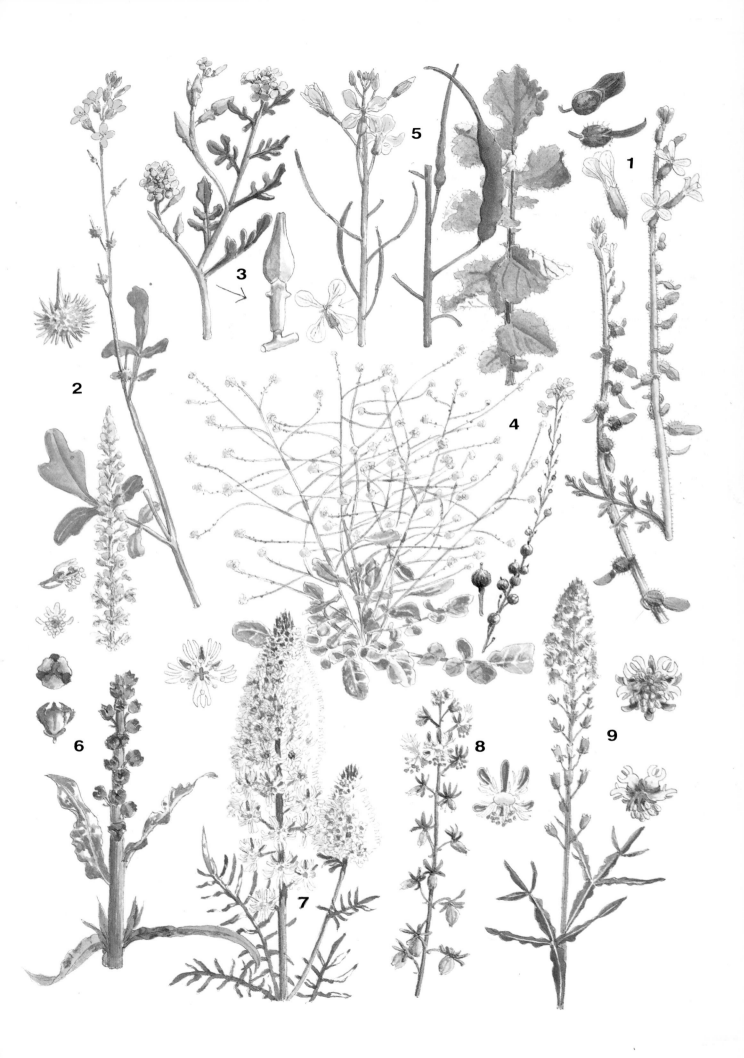

Plate 22

CRASSULACEAE: SAXIFRAGACEAE

CRASSULACEAE

CRASSULA

1. *Crassula tillaea* Minute, moss-like glabrous annual. Flowers sessile in leaf-axils. Fairly common. K **D** (**Ma,** Mi, I) FE I 351
2. *C. vaillantii* Annual, 2-6cm. Flowers pedicellate. (From Maltese specimen). Locally common. K lists for Minorca only. **D** Ll (Ma, Mi) FE I 351

UMBILICUS

3. *Umbilicus rupestris* Perennial. Raceme dense, occupying more than half the stem. Cauline leaves few. Pedicels 3-9mm, flowers usually pendent. Apr. - June. Common on walls and rocks. **K D** (**Ma,** Mi) FE I 352
4. *U. horizontalis* Perennial. Raceme occupying less than half stem, often with short branches. Cauline leaves very numerous. Apr. - June. Common on walls and rocks. **K D** (**Ma,** Mi, I) FE I 352
5. Intermediate forms between 3 and 4 are common here. This one resembles 4 in the long raceme and fewer cauline leaves, but has short-pedicelled horizontal flowers.

AEONIUM

6. *Aeonium arboreum* Somewhat woody perennial, up to 1m. Dec. - Apr. Common in waste places. (× about 1/2) **D** (Native of Morocco, introduced, Ma, I) FE I 356

SEDUM

7. *Sedum sediforme* Robust perennial, often glaucous. June - Aug. Widespread on walls and rocks. K **D** (**Ma,** Mi, I) FE I 358
8. *S. dasyphyllum* Perennial, glandular-pubescent at least in upper part. May - Aug. Common on walls and rocks. **K D** (**Ma,** Mi, I) FE I 361
9. *S. stellatum* Glabrous annual. May - June. Dry places, local. K **D** (**Ma**) FE I 362
10. *S. rubens* May - June. Rather variable glandular-pubescent annual with glaucous linear leaves, which are more or less semi-circular in outline.. Locally common, rock crevices, roadsides etc. (All × 1 except details of leaf, flower and follicle). **K D** (**Ma,** Mi, I) FE I 363

SAXIFRAGACEAE: *SAXIFRAGA*

11. *Saxifraga tridactylites* Annual, usually glandular hairy, often reddish. Common. Mar. - Apr. **K D** (**Ma,** Mi, I) FE I 370

Others recorded from Mallorca:

Sedum acre K (quotes Bianor 1910-1914). D and Ll omit. Bl excluded in FE I 359

S. caespitosum Resembles 10, but glabrous with broadly ovoid leaves. **D** Ll (Ma, Mi) Not Bl in FE I 363

In other islands:

Sedum album Ibiza FE I 360
Saxifraga corsica Ibiza FE I 376

Plate 23

PLATANACEAE
ROSACEAE (1) *RUBUS, ROSA*

PLATANACEAE: *PLATANUS*

(The following 2 species are listed by Duvigneaud as introduced here. Llorens et al. (1991) give *P. hispanica* Miller, *P. occidentalis* L. and *P. orientalis* L. The Med-Checklist gives only *P. orientalis*, possibly because only this species is truly naturalised in the area. All species are large trees with scaling bark).

1. *Platanus orientalis* Oriental Plane tree. Leaves lobed more than half way: fruiting heads 3-6. (From Cretan specimen, reduced). D (Introduced **Ma**) FE I 384
2. *P. hybrida* Hybrid Plane tree. Leaves lobed up to half way. Fruiting heads usually 2. (From British specimen, reduced). **D** (Introduced **?Ma**) FE I 384

ROSACEAE (1)

RUBUS

3. *Rubus ulmifolius* Blackberry: Bramble. Densely tangled shrub with arching branches. Apr. - May. Common. **D** (**Ma**, Mi, I) FE II 15
4. *R. caesius* Dewberry. Low straggling bush with procumbent rooting stems. Fruit generally with bluish bloom. Mar. - Apr. Local. (From British specimen). ?K (he possibly uses this name to include other species). **D** Ll (Ma, Mi, I) FE II 25

ROSA Rose.

5. *Rosa sempervirens* Leaves shining, leathery. Flowers white, petals often reflexed as soon as flower is mature. Styles connate into a column at least as long as the inner stamens. Apr. - June. Commonest rose in lowland parts of Mallorca, walls, hedgerows and bushy places. **K D** (**Ma**) FE II 27
6. *R. arvensis* This is the only other species here with connate styles. Leaves herbaceous, not evergreen. Petals white. Apr. June. Not common. (From British specimen). **D** Ll (Ma, Mi) FE II 27
7. *R. canina* Dog Rose. Styles free. Pedicels glabrous. Leaflets without glands or with few glands confined to margins and main veins beneath. Flowers pink or white. Not common. Apr.

- June. (Fruit from British specimen). D (quotes FE). Ll lists. (**Ma**) FE II 29

Other species of *Rosa:* Knoche's Rosa nos 554 and 555 seem to include many species. It is not possible to separate them or determine which he saw. Several species are given for Bl in FE which are not listed independantly by Bonafè or Duvigneaud. In some areas (e.g. round the Embalse de Cúber) there seem to be ?hybrids which can be keyed out to *R. rubiginosa* agg., but differ in some respects from the species described in the FE. Many of the white flowered plants here are close to *R. agrestis*, but have glandular sepals, while the pink-flowered plants with glandular pedicels seem nearer *R. rubiginosa* or *R. micrantha* (though leaflets cuneate at base).

One of my specimens collected at flowering time matched the description of *R. rubiginosa* in all respects, but fruit was not available. There is room for some research here.

8. ?*R. rubiginosa* Apple-scented bush. Leaflets rounded at base. Pedicels densely glandular hairy. Petals deep pink. Styles hairy. Apr. - June. ? or rare. (Main illustration from Mallorcan specimen, fruit from garden specimen). ?D (quotes FE). ?Ll (?**Ma**) Bl in FE II 31
9. *R.* cf. *agrestis* Apple-scented. Leaves usually narrow, wedge shaped at base. Pedicels glabrous or with sparse stalked glands. Petals white. Styles glabrous or slightly hairy. (Plant here, otherwise fitting FE description). Apr. - June. Common in mountains. **D** Ll (**Ma**, I) FE II 31
10. *R.* cf. *micrantha.* Resembles 9, but pedicels with stalked glands and sepals glandular. Flowers pink according to Bonafè (in FE to be presumed white as *R. agrestis*). In this specimen leaves were mostly cuneate at base: FE describes leaflets of *R. micrantha* as 'usually rounded at base'. Bonafè lists several records. D Ll FE II 32

Also recorded from Mallorca:

Rosa pouzinii Resembles 7, but has pedicels densely covered in stalked glands (sometimes base of fruit too). Apr. - June. Local. **D** Ll (**Ma**) FE II 29

R. corymbifera Resembles 7, but leaves pubescent at least on veins below, sometimes all over both surfaces. Pedicels glabrous. Not common. ?D (quotes FE). ?Ll (?**Ma**) Bl in FE II 30

R. scabriuscula Leaves resin-scented, pubescent on veins beneath. Doubtful. ?D (quotes FE). ?B ?Ll ?Bl in FE II 30

R. candicans ?D (quotes FE). Ll omits. (?**Ma**) Bl in FE II 16

Plate 24

ROSACEAE (2) *AGRIMONIA, SANGUISORBA, POTENTILLA, APHANES, SORBUS, AMELANCHIER, CRATAEGUS, PRUNUS*

AGRIMONIA

1. *Agrimonia eupatoria* Agrimony. Perennial. June - Sept. Occasional. **K D** (**Ma,** Mi) FE II 32

SANGUISORBA

2. *Sanguisorba minor* Salad Burnet. Perennial. May - Sept. Very common. **K D** (**Ma,** Mi, I) FE II 33

POTENTILLA

3. *Potentilla reptans* Creeping Cinquefoil. Perennial with creeping stems, rooting at the nodes. May - Sept. Common in damp places. **K D** (**Ma,** Mi, I) FE II 45
4. *P. caulescens* Shrubby cinquefoil. Apr. - May. Local in the NW mountains. (From Austrian specimen). **K D** (Ma) FE II 45

APHANES

5. *?Aphanes arvensis* Parsley Piert. Hairy procumbent slender annual. All leaves petiolate. Sepals erect in fruit (here) 1.9mm. (This fits *A. microcarpa* better). From Mallorcan specimen (from near a high peak), but possibly misidentified. K **D** list, but Ll omits. Bl not excluded in FE II 64
6. *A. floribunda* Erect robust annual with long white hairs. Upper leaves sessile. Fruit more than 2.5mm with slightly spreading sepals. Local. **D** Ll (**Ma**) FE II 64

SORBUS

7. *Sorbus domestica* Service Tree. Small white-flowered tree. May - June. Native in many parts of S. Europe, but here introduced for edible fruit, sometimes appearing wild. **K, D** and Ll list as introduced species) (**Ma,** I) Not Bl in FE II 68
8. *S. aria* Whitebeam. Small tree. May - June. Rare in higher parts of mountains. (From British specimen: Mallorcan plant seen later was very similar). **K D** (**Ma**) FE II 68

AMELANCHIER

9. *Amelanchier ovalis* Snowy Mespilus. Shrub. Apr. - May. Rare in higher mountains. (Specimen from mainland Spain). K (quotes Bianor 1910 1914). B gives 2 locations. D Ll both list. (Ma) FE II 71

CRATAEGUS

10. *Crataegus monogyna* subsp. *brevispina* Hawthorn, May. Flowers appear after leaves. Stone large, occupying most of fruit. Apr. - May. Widespread in hilly places. **K D** (**Ma,** Mi) FE II 75

PRUNUS

11. *Prunus spinosa* Blackthorn, Sloe. Flowers appear before the leaves. Mar. - Apr. Common. **K D** (**Ma,** Mi) FE II 78
12. *P. dulcis* Almond. Small tree with pink or white blossom. Feb. - Mar. Planted in the island (formerly the main crop), occasionally naturalised, and then usually rather spiny. **K D** (Ma) FE II 78

Also recorded for Mallorca:
Aphanes cornucopioides Ll lists. Not Bl in FE II 64

Plate 25

LEGUMINOSAE (1) *CERATONIA, ANAGYRIS, CALICOTOME, GENISTA, SPARTIUM, ARGYROLOBIUM, ASTRAGALUS, PSORALEA.*

CERATONIA

1 *Ceratonia siliqua* Carob, Locust bean. Large tree. Leaves leathery pinnate. Flowers in catkins, without petals and with 5 free stamens. Ripe fruit a black pod. Aug. - Oct. Cultivated, often appears to be wild. (**Ma**, Mi, I) FE II 83

ANAGYRIS

2. *Anagyris foetida* Bean Trefoil. Tall shrub or small tree. Corolla with very short standard, stamens 10, free. Feb. - Mar. Local,in dry hilly areas. **K D** (**Ma**, Mi, I) FE II 85

CALICOTOME

3. *Calicotome spinosa* Robust prickly gorse-like shrub. Leaves trifoliate, blackening when dried. Outer part of calyx is pushed off by opening buds. Mar. - May. Common, especially in northern part of mountain range. **K D** (**Ma**, Mi, I) FE II 86

GENISTA

4. *Genista majorica* Cantó & Sánchez (*G. cinerea* subsp. *leptoclada*). Small spineless shrub with many thin greenish-grey branches. Flowers mostly in pairs. Mar. - Apr. Mainly in central part of mountain range. **K D** (**Ma** endemic) FE II 96
5. *G. lucida* Prickly gorse-like shrub with simple leaves. Feb. - Mar. Common in hilly areas in the east and south-west, rarer elsewhere. **K D** (**Ma**, endemic) FE II 99
6. *G. balearica* Porta & Rigo (*G. acanthoclada* DC subsp. *fasciculata* (Knoche) Bolòs & Vigo). Resembles 5, but more robust and prickly, with few leaves. May. Two small patches only, one on beach, one in mountains. K **D** (**Ma**, endemic subsp.) cf. FE II 100

SPARTIUM

7. *Spartium junceum* Spanish Broom. Large shrub or small tree. Leaves few, silky-haired on young shoots only. Flower spikes showy, on rush-like stems. Mar. - July. Widely planted, sometimes naturalised. **K D** (**Ma** introduced, Mi native). FE II 101

ARGYROLOBIUM

8. *Argyrolobium zanonii* Procumbent small woody plant. Undersides of leaves, and stems and pods silvery hairy. Apr. - May. Stony places in lower hills of northern range. **K D** (**Ma**, I) FE II 106

ASTRAGALUS

9. *Astragalus boeticus* Robust erect annual. Leaves pinnate with 10-15 pairs leaflets. Flowers in terminal clusters on long peduncles. Pods short, broad and hairy. Mar. Sandy waste places. K **D** (**Ma**, Mi, I) FE II 111
10. *A. hamosus* Similar to *A. boeticus*, but smaller. Pods glabrous, long and curved. Mar. Waste places. **K D** (**Ma**, Mi, I) FE II 113
11. *A. balearicus* Hedgehog-like shrublet. Leaves with 3-5 pairs leaflets, the terminal leaflet usually replaced by a spine. Mar. - May. Common in hilly and mountain areas. (Plant much reduced, details × 1 or slightly enlarged). **K D** (**Ma**, Mi, endemic) FE II 119

PSORALEA

12. *Psoralea bituminosa* Pitch Trefoil. Large clover-like plant. Trifoliate leaves smelling of pitch when crushed. Flowers in terminal heads on rather rigid stalks. Apr. - Jun. Widespread, roadsides and waste places. **K D** (**Ma**, Mi, I) FE II 127

Also recorded for Mallorca:

Astragalus stella Annual, stems procumbent or ascending, up to 20cm. Leaves with 9 - 11 pairs leaflets and terminal leaflet. Racemes with 7-12 flowers. Calyx 5-6mm. Corolla yellowish, standard 9-11mm. Pods 10-15mm, densely hairy, erect or suberect, almost straight, laterally compressed, but scarcely dorsiventrally compressed at base. Ll lists. (See Alomar et al. 1986). Not Bl in FE II 113

A. epiglottis Annual with ascending stems up to 50cm. Leaves with 5 10 pairs leaflets and terminal leaflet. Calyx 2.5-3mm. Corolla yellow, standard 3mm. Pods 7-9mm, dorsiventrally flattened and cordate at base, densely hairy. (Ma, I) Not Bl in FE II 113

Species recorded for other islands only:
Calicotome infesta (Presl.) Guss. (*C. spinosa* (L.) Link subsp. *infesta* (Presl.) Burnat). Minorca. FE II 86 (where treated under *C. villosa)*
Chronanthus biflorus Ibiza FE II 93
Teline linifolia Minorca, cultivated in Mallorca. FE II 94
Genista hirsuta Ibiza FE II 98
G. dorycnifolia Endemic Ibiza FE II 99
Ulex parviflorus Ibiza FE II 102
Lupinus micranthus Minorca FE II 105
Robinia pseudacacia Naturalized Ibiza Not Bl in FE II 106
Astragalus sesameus Formentera. Not Bl in FE II 113
A. incanus ?Minorca ?Bl in FE II 122
Biserrula pelecinus Minorca FE II 127

Plate 26

LEGUMINOSAE (2): *CICER, VICIA, LENS*
Annuals unless stated otherwise.

CICER

1. *Cicer arietinum* Chick Pea. May - July. Cultivated, possibly escaping. **D** (**Ma,** introduced). Not Bl in FE II 128

VICIA

2. *Vicia villosa* Several subsp. have been recorded, differing in hairiness of stems and pod, number of flowers in raceme, and colour of corolla wings. Mar. - Aug. All are fairly rare. (subsp. *villosa* from garden specimen). **K D** (Ma, Mi) FE II 132

3. *V. benghalensis* Annual or perennial. Wings usually with blackish purple markings which extend as flower matures. May - July. Occasional, hedgerows, scrub. K D (**Ma,** Mi) FE II 132

4. *V. ervilia* Leaves without tendrils. Corolla 6-9mm, white, tinged with red or purple. Pod 10-30 × 4-6mm, torulose. May - July. Cultivated, sometimes escaping. **D** Ll (Ma, I) Not Bl in FE II 133

5. *V. leucantha* Flowers 6-10mm. Tip of keel dark blue. Mar. - Apr. Rare casual. K lists for Minorca only. **D** (**Ma**) Ll ?Bl in FE II 133

6. *V. hirsuta* Hairy Tare. Leaflets 4-10 pairs. Calyx teeth all equal. Corolla 2-4mm, dingy whitish-purple. Pod black and hairy, with 2 seeds. Locally common. (From British specimen). **K D** Ll (Ma, I) FE II 133

7. *V. parviflora* Cav. (*V. tenuissima, V. laxiflora* Brot.) Slender Tare. Leaflets 2-5 pairs, linear < 3mm wide. Racemes with 1-5 flowers, exceeding leaves. Calyx teeth unequal, shorter than tube. Corolla 6-9mm, pinkish-lilac, often bicoloured. Pod brown, seeds 4-6. Apr. - May. Common. **K D** (**Ma,** Mi, I) FE II 133

8. *V. tetrasperma* Leaflets − 3 mm wide. Racemes with 1 or 2 flowers, about equalling leaves. Calyx teeth unequal, shorter than tube. Corolla 4-8mm, pale purple. Pod brown. Seeds 3-5. Occasional. (From British specimen). **K** D Ll (Ma, Mi) FE II 133

9. *V. pubescens* Like 8, but sparsely pubescent and with leaflets elliptical to ovate-oblong, 3-5mm wide. Lower calyx teeth equalling tube or longer. Racemes with up to 6 flowers. Pod brown with 3-5 seeds. Apr. - May. Common. K **D** (**Ma,** Mi) FE II 133

10. *V. sativa* Stipules toothed, often with black spot. Peduncles very short or 0. Corolla usually more than 10mm. Apr. - May. Common, often cultivated. Several subspecies occur here. FE II 134

a) subsp. *nigra* Linear leaflets and narrow (3-6mm) black pod. Common in mountain areas. **K D** (**Ma,** I)

b) subsp. *macrocarpa* has broader leaflets and a reticulate veined dark brown pod 8-10mm wide. **K D** (**Ma**)

Main illustration and black pod subsp. *nigra*, details from other subspecies.

11. *V. lutea.* Yellow Vetch. Leaflets linear or oblong. Flowers in groups of 1-3 together. Standard glabrous. Pods with long bulbous-based hairs. Apr. - May. Occasional. K **D** (**Ma,** Mi) FE II 135

12. *V. bithynica* Bithynian Vetch. Leaflets 2-3 pairs, varying from almost linear to broadly elliptical. Corolla 16 - 20mm. Apr. - May. Common, waysides and in dry stony places. **K D** (**Ma,** Mi) FE II 135

13. *V. faba* Broad Bean. Robust plant. Leaves without tendril. Flowers white with black-blotched wings. Widely cultivated. FE II 135

LENS

14. *Lens culinaris* Lentil. Leaves with or without short tendril. Calyx-teeth up to 6 × tube. Pod strongly compressed. Seeds like biconvex lens (which derives name from plant). May - June. Cultivated, sometimes escaping. (Garden specimen). **D** (Ma) FE II 136

15. *Lens ervoides* Resembles *Vicia* Sect. *Ervum* (nos 4-9), but leaves without tendrils or upper leaves with short tendril. Calyx-teeth 2-4 × tube. May - Aug. Local in mountain areas. (Enlarged details specimen with broader leaflets). Not listed by K. **D** and Ll both list this species. (**Ma**) FE II 136

Other species recorded for Mallorca:
Vicia serinica Perennial. Smythies lists *V. argentea* Lapeyr. subsp. *serinica* for Bl. K D and Ll omit. Not Bl in FE II 131

V. monantha Corolla 10-20mm, pale purple. Stipules with 2 entire lobes. Not common. K quotes Bianor (1914-1917). **D** Ll (Ma, I) FE II 133

V. peregrina Leaflets emarginate, appearing 3-lobed. Stipules entire. Corolla 10-16mm. Not common. K D Ll (Ma, Mi, I) FE II 135

V. lathyroides B (quotes Marès and Vigineix, collecting 1880). D and Ll omit. Bl excluded in FE II 135

V. hybrida K (quotes Barceló 1867-1877). D Ll (Ma, Mi) Bl in FE II 135

V. narbonensis K doubts, but B gives one location. Ll treats as alien. Not Bl in FE II 135

Lens nigricans K (quotes Marès and Vigineix 1880) Ll (Ma, I) ?Bl in FE II 136

In Minorca:
V. disperma FE II 133

V. bifoliata (K also quotes Gandoger (1899) for Majorca, but adds 'A vérifier'. Ll only gives Mi. Mi endemic in FE II 133

Plate 27

LEGUMINOSAE (3) *LATHYRUS, PISUM*

1. *Lathyrus latifolius* Everlasting Pea. Perennial. Conspicuous, with 5-15 large (corolla 2-3cm) flowers on long peduncle. Apr. - May. Common. (× about 1/2, pod × 1). **K D (Ma)** FE II 141

2. *L. saxatilis* Small annual. Stem unwinged, leaves without a tendril. Leaflets of lowest leaves obcordate, with 3 teeth at apex. Flowers small, solitary bluish or yellowish. Mar. - May. Roadsides, local. K lists for Ibiza only. **D (Ma, I)** FE II 141

3. *L. sphaericus* Annual. Stem unwinged (FE) or commonly very narrowly winged. Flowers solitary, orange-red, peduncles aristate. Calyx teeth equalling or slightly longer than tube. Pod 30-70 × 4-7mm, with prominent longitudinal veins and 8-15 seeds. Mar. - May. Local in rocky places in mountains. (× about 2/3). **K D (Ma,** Mi) FE II 141

4. *L. cicera* Red Vetchling. Annual. Flowers solitary. Calyx teeth large, equal, longer than tube. Pod with 2 keels on dorsal suture. Mar. - May. Common. **K D (Ma,** Mi, I) FE II 142

5. *L. annuus* Annual. Stem winged. Racemes with 1-3 yellow flowers. Pod glandular when young. Apr. - June. Local in hedgerows and bushy places. (Immature pod here: mature pod straight, up to 30-80 × 7-12mm). **K D (Ma,** Mi) FE II 142

6. *L. clymenum* Annual. Stem winged. Lower leaves without leaflets, with rhachis broad and leaf-like: upper with leaflets. Standard notched, crimson; wings violet or lilac (rarely pale yellow). Style aristate. Pod with channelled dorsal suture. Apr. - June. Common, grassy and bushy places. **K D (Ma,** Mi) FE II 142

7. *L. articulatus* Annual, very like 6. Difference in leaflet width described in FE do not seem to be constant here. Colour of corolla wings is the most obvious difference in flower. The pods are more distinct: *L. articulatus* has torulose pods without a channel on the dorsal suture. Apr. - June. Locally common. **K D (Ma,** Mi) FE II 142

8. *L. ochrus* Annual. Petiole and rhachis of leaves very broadly winged, lower leaves with tendrils and no leaflets. Flowers usually solitary, sometimes 2, pale yellow. Pod with 2 wings on dorsal suture. Mar. - May. Common, grassy and bushy places. **K D (Ma,** Mi, I) FE II 142

9. *L. aphaca* Yellow vetchling. Leaves on mature plants without leaflets, but with tendril. Stipules large, arrow-shaped and leaf like. Flowers solitary, yellow. Mar. - May. Fairly common, dry places. **K D (Ma,** Mi, I) FE II 143

PISUM

10. *Pisum sativum* Pea. Stems smooth. Stipules large and leaf-like, ovate to elliptical, semi-cordate at base. Wings of corolla adnate to keel. Two subsp., one with white flowers and one with purple and lilac (flower and stipule only, slightly reduced). Mar. - May. Crop, and occasionally seen in hedges. Not Bl in FE II 143

Also in Mallorca:
Lathyrus inconspicuus K (quotes Hermann 1912). Ll omits. Dubious. (?Ma) ?Bl in FE II 142
L. setifolius. Annual, much like 3, but peduncles not aristate and pod broader, with 2-3 seeds. K D Ll (Ma) FE II 142
L. amphicarpos K and Ll omit. D (quotes FE). Dubious. (?Ma) Bl in FE II 142

Recorded for Ibiza only:
Lathyrus sativus Not Bl in FE II 142

Plate 28

LEGUMINOSAE (4) *ONONIS, MELILOTUS*

ONONIS

1. *Ononis natrix* Sticky shrublet, up to 60cm. Leaflets ovate to linear, margins not undulate. Pod 10-25mm. Subsp. *hispanica* has corolla usually 6-12mm and smooth greyish seeds; subsp. *natrix* has corolla 12-20mm and dark brown minutely tuberculate seeds. May - July. Both subsp. locally common. (Subsp. *hispanica* illustrated × 3/4, ripe pod × 1). **K D (Ma, Mi, I)** FE II 144

2. *O. crispa* Resembling 1, but leaflets round with undulate margins. Stipules and calyx lobes leaf-like, also more or less undulate margins. May - July. Not common. (Specimen from Spanish mainland). K **D (Ma, Mi)** FE II 145

3. *O. ornithopodioides* Sticky erect annual, to 30cm. Pod 12-20mm, torulose. Mar. - Apr. Occasional. (× 1/2, detail of pod × 1). K **D (Ma, I)** FE II 145

4. *O. reclinata* Sticky erect or procumbent annual up to 15cm, without spines. Pedicels deflexed after flowering. Mar. - Apr. Common. **K D (Ma, Mi, I)** FE II 145

5. *O. pubescens* Sticky annual, up to 35cm. Upper and lower leaves with 1 leaflet, middle wth 3. Branches of inflorescence awnless. Mar. - June. Not common. K lists for Minorca only. **D** Ll **(Ma, ?Mi)** ?Bl in FE II 145

6. *O. viscosa* subsp. *breviflora*. Sticky annual, to 80cm. Branches conspicuously aristate (arista here commonly 25-30mm). Apr. - June. Common by roadsides. **K D (Ma, Mi, I)** FE II 145

7. *O. minutissima* Shrublet, up to 30cm. Calyx teeth glabrous or with short glandular hairs, becoming more or less stellate in fruit. Pod 6-7mm, partly concealed by calyx. Apr. - Oct. Common in dry rocky places. **K D (Ma, Mi, I)** FE II 146

8. *O. spinosa* subsp. *antiquorum* Rather variable shrublet, to 1.5m. Usually spiny. Common. **K D (Ma, Mi, I)** FE II 147

9. *O. alopecuroides* L. subsp. *exalopecuroides* (*O. exalopecuroides* López), Robust annual. May. Possibly originating from bird seed. Roadside in Puerto Alcudia. (× 1/2). Possibly not previously recorded. Not K or D. **(Ma)** (treated as *O. baetica* in FE). Not Bl in FE II 148

MELILOTUS

Most of these grow up to about 60cm and are much branched, with small flowers in axillary racemes. They grow mainly by roadsides and in waste places. (Only small part of each plant illustrated × 1, with enlarged pods shown separately).

10. *Melilotus italica* Annual. Leaflets large, especially below, rounded at apex. Racemes lax, many-flowered. Stipules of middle leaves toothed. Corolla 6mm or more. Fruit 5-6mm, strongly reticulate veined. Feb. - May. Uncommon. (From Bianor's Mallorcan specimen). K D **(Ma, I)** FE II 149

11. *M. indica* Annual. Stipules of middle leaves entire or minutely denticulate. Racemes dense, usually with very many flowers. Corolla 2-3mm. Fruit 1.5-3mm, reticulate-veined. Mar. - May. Common. K D **(Ma, Mi, I)** FE II 149

12. *M. elegans* Annual. Flowers 4mm or more, keel longer than standard and wings. Racemes lax, with 15-30 flowers. Fruit transversely ridged. Feb. - May. Not common. **K D (Ma, Mi, I)** FE II 150

13. *M. sulcata* Annual. Corolla up to 4mm, standard shorter than keel. Racemes lax with 8-25 flowers, becoming longer than subtending leaf in fruit. Corolla 3-4mm. Pod globose, concentrically-striate, 3-4mm, sessile. Mar. - May. Common. **K D (Ma, Mi, I)** FE II 150

14. *M. segetalis* Annual. Corolla 4-8mm, standard shorter than keel. Racemes dense, 30-50 flowers. Pod 2.5-5.5mm, concentrically striate, narrowed to a stalk at calyx attachment. Apr. - May. Common. **K D (Ma)** FE II 150

15. *M. messanensis* Annual. Corolla 4-5mm, standard and keel similar length, longer than wings. Raceme shorter than subtending leaf, 3-10 flowered. Pod oblique-ovoid, concentrically-straite, with a point. Mar. - May. Marshy ground near coast, common. **K D (Ma, Mi, I)** FE II 150

Others recorded from Mallorca:

Ononis pusilla Small shrublet, to 25cm. Resembles 7, but leaves with eglandular hairs. calyx-teeth with long eglandular and glandular hairs. Apr. - May. Not recorded by K. D and Ll both list. (Ma, Mi, I) Not Bl in FE II 146

O. mitissima Knoche (quotes Hermann 1912). D Ll (Ma, Mi) FE II 147

Melilotus officinalis K D Ll (Ma, I) FE II 149

M. neapolitana K "A vérifier". Ll omits. D quotes FE. Dubious. FE II 149

M. infesta Corolla 6mm or more, wings longer than standard and keel. Racemes lax, with 15-50 flowers. Pod globose or obovoid, 4-5mm, concentric-striate, blackish-brown. B lists for Ma (very rare). Ll lists for (Mi only). (?Ma, Mi) FE II 150

Plate 29

LEGUMINOSAE (5) *TRIGONELLA, MEDICAGO*

TRIGONELLA

1. *Trigonella monspeliaca* Star-fruited Fenugreek. Mar. - May. Rare. (From Cretan specimen). **D** (Ma, I) FE II 152

MEDICAGO

Nos 3 and 7 perennial: others annual. Most flower from Apr. - June.

2. *Medicago lupulina* Black Medick. Racemes up to 50-flowered, dense. Pod kidney-shaped, black when ripe. Common. **K D** (**Ma,** Mi, I) FE II 154

3. *M. sativa* subsp. *sativa* Lucerne. Corolla blue. Pod in a loose spiral with a hole through the centre, without spines. Cultivated, sometimes escaping. **K** (**Ma,** Mi, I) FE II 154

4. *M. orbicularis* Disc Medick. Pod usually at least 10mm diameter, flattened, disc-like. Locally common. **K D** (**Ma,** Mi, I) FE II 155

5. *M. ciliaris* Pod large (12mm ore more), ovoid, with straight spines and dense glandular hairs. Grassy places, not common. K **D** (**Ma,** I) FE II 155

6. *M. scutellata* Pod glandular-pubescent and without spines, spirally coiled with the inner coils more or less enclosed by the outer. Occasional. **K D** (**Ma,** Mi, I) FE II 155

7. *M. marina* Sea Medick. Maritime sands. Whole plant densely white tomentose. Pod with a hole through the centre, with short conical spines. **K D** (**Ma,** Mi, I) FE II 156

8. *M. truncatula* Peduncle aristate. Pod cylindrical, sparsely villous. Spines curved, arising from marginal and submarginal veins. Length of spines variable (detail from specimen with longer spines. Fine detail rather like no 13, but this is a very tight spiral). Occasional. **K D** (**Ma,** Mi, I) FE II 156

9. *M. littoralis* Pod 4-6mm diameter. Spines if present arising only from submarginal vein which becomes confluent with marginal vein in ripe pod. Common in dry sandy places. **K D** (**Ma,** Mi, I) FE II 156

10. *M. doliata* Carmign. (*M. aculeata*) Pod 7-10mm, globose to ellipsoid with 5-7 turns, usually glandular-hairy with conical spines. (Specimen from Spanish mainland). **K** D Ll (Ma, Mi) FE II 156

11. *M. turbinata* Leaflets obovate. Pod glabrous, usually with short, broad, obtuse spines. Transverse veins ending in a wide veinless border (see 12). **K** D (**Ma,** Mi) FE II 156

12. *M. murex* Leaflets obcordate or triangular. Pod glabrous, usually spherical, with or without spines. Transverse veins ending in a wide veinless border. This specimen differs from FE description in being coiled in a left-handed spiral (which would make it *M. turbinata*, but leaf-shape and spines do not seem to fit this species). (Detail shows section of pod with wide veinless border). Local. **K** (**Ma,** Mi) FE II 156

13. *M. arabica* Spotted Medick. Leaves commonly with black spot. Pod glabrous, in lax barrel-shaped spiral. Margin with 3 conspicuous grooves - central one is sulcate marginal vein. Usually spiny. Occasional. K D (**Ma,** Mi) FE II 156

14. *M. polymorpha* Rather like 13, but leaflets without spot. Marginal vein not sulcate, so there are 3 keels separated by 2 grooves. Common and variable. Apr. - May. **K D** (**Ma,** Mi, I) FE II 156

15. *M. praecox* Peduncles much shorter than leaf. Pod slightly hairy. Feb. - Apr. Occasional. K D (**Ma,** Mi, I) FE II 157

16. *M. minima* Plant dark greyish, villous. Common, often on higher parts of beaches. **K D** (**Ma,** Mi, I) FE II 157

Also recorded from Mallorca:

Medicago secundiflora Seen by Bianor (1910-1914) on one peak. D and Ll list. FE II 154

M. rigidula Resembles *M. truncatula* but peduncle not aristate and pod usually glandular-pubescent. K B D Ll FE II 156

From other islands:

Medicago sativa subsp. *falcata* Minorca, Ibiza FE II 154

M. arborea subsp. *citrina* (Font Quer) Bolós & Vigo Ibiza, endemic subsp. FE II 155 (does not describe subsp.)

M. disciformis Formentera Not Bl in FE II 157

Plate 30

LEGUMINOSAE (6) *TRIFOLIUM*

1. *Trifolium repens* White Clover. Creeping almost glabrous perennial, rooting at the nodes. Leaflets often emarginate. Flowers pedicellate. Apr. - Sept. Cultivated areas. **K D (Ma,** I) FE II 162

2. *T. nigrescens* Rather like 1, but annual, not rooting at nodes. Leaflets usually pointed, with terminal tooth. Apr. - May. Field margins, waste places, locally common. (Detail beside *T. repens* for comparison, main illustration bottom right). **K D (Ma,** Mi) FE II 163

3. *T. glomeratum* Completely glabrous annual. May - June. Dry tracks, grassland, fairly widespread. Recorded by K and D for Minorca only. Bonafè records from Mallorca. **(Ma,** Mi) FE II 164

4. *T. suffocatum* Annual. Heads confluent, internodes usually less than 5mm. Mar. - Aug. Dry grassland, occasional. (From British specimen). K D Ll (Ma, Mi) FE II 164

5. *T. fragiferum* Strawberry Clover. Hairy perennial. May. - Aug. Damp places. Not common. **K** D **(Ma,** Mi, I) FE II 164

6. *T. resupinatum* Flowers characteristically inverted, keel uppermost. Fruiting peduncles recurved. Apr. - June. Widespread in cultivated areas, often an escape from cultivation. **K D (Ma,** Mi) FE II 165

7. *T. tomentosum* Rather like 6, but fruit woollier, peduncles not recurved. Apr. - June. Common in cultivated areas. **K D (Ma,** Mi, I) FE II 165

8. *T. campestre* Hop-trefoil. Small annual, easily mistaken for *Medicago* species in flower, but flowers here are persistent, recurved and brownish in fruiting head. Apr. - Oct. Common. **K D (Ma,** Mi, I) FE II 166

9. *T. filiforme* L. (*T. micranthum*) Small annual. Only 1-6 flowers in each head. Apr. - Oct. Grassy places, not common. (From British specimen). **K** D (Ma, Mi, I) FE II 166

10. *T. striatum* Hairy annual. Calyx conspicuously ribbed with short, bristle-pointed teeth. Very rare. Possibly only one record from Massanella. (From British specimen). D Ll (Ma, Mi) FE II 166

11. *T. scabrum* An annual with numerous sessile axillary heads, superficially rather like 3, but hairy. Common in dry places. Apr. - June **K D (Ma,** Mi, I) FE II 167

12. *T. stellatum* Star Clover. The calyx teeth spread in the fruit of several species of *Trifolium* to produce 'stars'. In this species the stars are large, and often conspicuous because of red colour, against whitish background of long hairs. Apr. - June. Common in dry places **K D (Ma,** Mi, I) FE II 168

13. *T. lappaceum* Bright green annual, heads conspicuously covered in purplish- black, long calyx teeth. Apr. - May. Local. K D **(Ma,** Mi) FE II 169

14. *T. cherleri* Similar to 16, but calyx teeth usually dark green. Heads with a broad involucre of enlarged stipules, below which fruiting head breaks off when ripe. Apr. - May. Locally common. **K D (Ma,** Mi) FE II 169

15. *T. angustifolium* Another annual, easily recognised by the very elongated heads and long, narrow leaflets. Apr. - July. Dry grassy places, common. K D **(Ma,** Mi) FE II 170

16. *T. squamosum* Easily recognised by the paired leaves below the head and the characteristic stipules. Fairly common, especially in damp places near the sea. May - June. **K D (Ma,** Mi) FE II 171

17. *T. subterraneum* This has usually only 2-5 elongated, fertile flowers. In fruit the long peduncle becomes deflexed to bury the pods in the soil, where they are anchored by numerous rigid sterile calyces which appear at this stage. Apr. - June. Dry places. (Main illustration from British specimen; detail below from very robust specimen found later in Mallorca). **K D (Ma,** Mi) FE II 172

Other species recorded for Mallorca:

Trifolium ornithopodioides Heads with 1-5 flowers. Peduncles up to 8mm. Pods 6-8mm, slightly curved and exserted. Ll (see Rita J. et al. 1985) (Ma, Mi) FE II 161

T. vesiculosum K (quotes Barcelò 1867-1877). D and Ll omit. Not Bl in FE II 164

T. bocconei Annual with densely pubescent stems. Leaves alternate. Heads dense, cylindrical or conical, terminal ones often paired but unequal. K (lists after Barcelò 1867-1877) D Ll (Ma, Mi) FE II 167

T. ligusticum Annual. Stems dark green with long spreading hairs. Heads ovoid, often paired with one axillary and long-pedunculate, one terminal and short-pedunculate. Corolla 3-4mm, much shorter than calyx. K (quotes Bianor 1910-1914). D Ll (Ma, Mi, I) FE II 167

T. diffusum Annual or biennial up to 40cm or more with much-branched hairy stems. Heads 15-25mm, globose to ovoid, sessile. Calyx-teeth filiform, 2 × tube. Corolla ca 12mm, reddish-purple, not or scarcely exceeding calyx. K (quotes Barcelò (1867-1877). D Ll (Ma, Mi) FE II 169

Recorded from Minorca:

Trifolium spumosum FE II 164

T. arvense FE II 167

T. squarrosum Not Bl in FE II 172

Plate 31

LEGUMINOSAE (7) *DORYCNIUM, LOTUS*

DORYCNIUM

1. *Dorycnium hirsutum* Scrambling, hairy shrublet. Flowers 10-20mm, in short-stalked axillary clusters of 4-10. Apr. - June. Dry bushy places. **K D (Ma,** Mi, I) FE II 172

2. *D. rectum* Similar to 1, but less hairy and with larger clusters of 20-40 smaller (4-6mm) flowers. May - June. By streams. **K D (Ma,** Mi, I) FE II 172

3. *D. pentaphyllum* subsp. *pentaphyllum* Smaller plant than 1 and 2. Leaves without rhachis, leaflets and stipules all arising from same point. Apr. - June. Dry places. K **D (Ma,** Mi, I) FE II 173

4. *D. fulgurans* (Porta) Lassen (*D.pentaphyllum* subsp. *fulgurans* (Porta) Cardona, Llorens et Sierra). Small 'hedgehog' plant, formerly considered *Anthyllis* species, (*Anthyllis fulgurans* Porta) but with typical white flowers and reddish-black keel of *Dorycnium*. Apr. - May. Very local. **K D (Ma,** Mi, endemic subsp.) Not in FE under any name.

LOTUS

5. *Lotus glaber* Miller (*L. tenuis).* Straggling perennial. Leaflets of upper leaves more than 3 × as long as wide. May - Sept. Wet places. K **D (Ma,** Mi, I) FE II 174

6. *L. corniculatus* Birds-foot trefoil. Similar to 4, but generally more compact. Upper leaves generally less than 3 × as long as wide. Common. May - June. **K D (Ma,** Mi, I) FE II 174

7. *L. angustissimus* Hairy annual. Very variable. Pod 4 -7 × length of calyx. Peduncle may be longer or shorter than sub-tending leaves. Beaked keel with angulated border characteristic. May - June. Dry grassy places. (Specimen from Spanish mainland). **K** D Ll (Ma, Mi) FE II 175

8. *L. edulis* Annual. Flower often twisted so that wings are above and below keel rather than on either side. Pod short and stout with dorsal groove. Mar. - Apr. Fairly common in waste places. **K D (Ma,** Mi, I) FE II 175

9. *L. cytisoides* L. (*L. creticus* L. subsp. *cytisoides* (L.) Ascherson & Graebner) Densely silvery-haired plant. Mar. - May. Coastal sands. **K D (Ma,** Mi, I) FE II 176

10. *L. ornithopodioides* Hairy annual. Flowers small, 2 to 5, exceeded by 3 broad, oval leaf-like bracts. Mar. - May. Common in waste places. **K D (Ma,** Mi, I) FE II 176

11. *L. tetraphyllus* Small neat perennial. Flowers nodding. May. Common in rocky places. **K D (Ma,** Mi endemic) FE II 176

12. *Lotus tetragonolobus* L. (*Tetragonolobus purpureus*) Asparagus pea. Pods winged on all 4 angles. Apr. - May. (From garden specimen). **K** D Ll (Ma, I) FE II 177

13. *L. conjugatus* L. subsp. *requienii* (Sanguinetti) Greuter (*Tetragonolobus requienii)* Pods winged on 2 adjacent angles. Apr. - May. (Main illustration from garden specimen. Detail of flower with stamen like marking from plant found later in Mallorca). K D Ll (**Ma**) FE II 177

Species in other islands not known to occur in Mallorca:
Dorycnium pentaphyllum subsp. *gracile* Minorca. FE II 173
Lotus preslii Minorca Bl in FE II 175
L. parviflorus Minorca and Ibiza FE II 175
L. subbiflorus Minorca FE II 175
L. halophilus Ibiza Not Bl in FE II 176

Plate 32

LEGUMINOSAE (8) *ANTHYLLIS, ORNITHOPUS, CORONILLA, HIPPOCREPIS, SCORPIURUS, HEDYSARUM*

ANTHYLLIS

1. *Anthyllis cytisoides* Small shrub. Leaves and stems white-felted. Leaves simple or trifoliate, lateral leaflets much smaller than terminal. Apr. - June. Rocky places, especially in SW (dominant in roadside vegetation of much of south-western part of C710 road) **K D** (**Ma,** Mi, I) FE II 178

2. *A. vulneraria* Kidney-Vetch. Two subspecies are recognised here (both with pink flowers), subsp. *font-queri* (Rothm.) Bolòs & Bolòs in the lower areas, and subsp. *balearica* (Coss. ex Marès & Vigineix) Bolòs & Vigo) in the mountains. These are not described in FE. Perennial herb. Flowers in terminal usually paired heads subtended by leafy bracts. Apr. - June. Widespread in dry sunny places. **K D** (**Ma,** Mi, I) FE II 179

3. *A. tetraphylla* Bladder Vetch. Creeping, softly hairy annual. May. - Aug. Common. **K D** (**Ma,** Mi, I) FE II 181

ORNITHOPUS

4. *Ornithopus compressus* Annual. Leaves with 7 - 18 pairs leaflets. Pods flattened. Mar. - May. (From garden specimen). K (quotes Barceló 1867-1877). D Ll (Ma, Mi) FE II 182

CORONILLA

5. *Coronilla valentina* subsp. *glauca* Scorpion-vetch. Glaucous, hairless shrub. Leaves with 2-6 pairs and terminal heart-shaped leaflets. (Smaller painting shows standard, keel and wings, about × 1). Apr. - June. Occasional, and sometimes planted. **K D** (**Ma,** Mi) FE II 183

6. *C. juncea* Thin shrub with rush-like stems. Leaves inconspicuous. Flowers in long stemmed clusters. May - June. Common in southern part of mountain range, where it is dominant on long stretches of roadside, like 1. **K D** (**Ma,** Mi) FE II 183

7. *C. scorpioides* Scorpion Senna. Hairless, glaucous annual. Leaves sessile, trifoliate, middle leaflet oval, much larger than more or less circular lateral leaflets. Flowers are small, 2-4 together on long axillary stem. Feb. - June. Weed of cultivated areas. **K D** (**Ma,** Mi, I) FE II 183

HIPPOCREPIS Horseshoe Vetch.

8. *Hippocrepis balearica* Showy perennial. Flowers up to 1.5cm in heads of 10 or more. Feb. - Mar. Exposed rocky places. **K D** (**Ma,** Mi, I, endemic) FE II 185

9. *H. ciliata* Peduncle about equalling leaves. Flowers 2 -6 together. Pod with long papillae, sinuses opening on concave edge of pod. Apr. - May. Not common. (Mallorcan specimen, plus mature pod from Spanish mainland). **K D** (**Ma,** Mi, I) FE II 185

10. *H. multisiliquosa* Peduncle equalling the leaves. Flowers 2-6 together. Pod with very small papillae or none, sinuses opening on convex edge of pod. Apr. - May. Rare.. (Specimen from Spanish mainland). K lists for Minorca only. **D** (Ma, Mi) FE II 185

11. *H. biflora* Sprengel (*H. unisiliquosa*) Prostrate annual. Peduncle very short. Flowers 1 or 2 together. Pod smooth. Mar. - June. Widespread, dry tracks. **K D** (**Ma,** Mi, I) FE II 185

SCORPIURUS

12. *Scorpiurus muricatus* (including (*S. subvillosus* L. and *S.sulcatus* L.) Spreading annual. Leaves entire. Flowers up to 6 together on long axillary peduncles. Pod irregularly coiled, spiny. Very variable. Apr. - June. Dry, often sandy places. **K D** (**Ma,** I) FE II 185

HEDYSARUM

13. *Hedysarum coronarium* French Honeysuckle. Spectacular bushy perennial, up to 1m or more. Flowers in large, clover-like heads. Detail here × 1, head × 0.5. Apr. - June. Casual in cultivated areas. **K D** (**Ma,** Mi) FE II 186

14. *H. spinosissimum* Annual. Flowers 4-10 together. Fruit distinctive, spiny. Apr. - May. Occasional in grassy places. **K D** (**Ma,** Mi, I) FE II 186

Other possible species for Mallorca:
Ornithopus pinnatus Recorded for Mi, Ll adds ?Ma (?Ma, Mi) FE II 182
Scorpiurus vermiculatus D lists ?Bl, Ll lists ?Ma. Not Bl in FE II 185

In Minorca only:
Anthyllis hystrix (Barc.) Cardona et al. (*A. hermanniae*) Mi endemic FE II 178
Coronilla repanda FE II 183

Plate 33

GERANIACEAE *GERANIUM, ERODIUM*

GERANIUM

All species annual here.

1. *Geranium rotundifolium* Leaves shallowly lobed, pubescent. Petal not or hardly notched, limb longer than claw. Sepals aristate. Apr. - June. Common. **K D** (**Ma**, Mi, I) FE II 198
2. *G. molle* Dove's-foot Cranesbill. Petal deeply notched, limb longer than claw. Mar. - June. Common. **K D** (**Ma**, Mi, I) FE II 198
3. *G. columbinum* Lower leaves deeply divided. Pedicels 2-6cm. Petals rounded, notched, or apiculate, limb longer than claw. Sepals aristate. Apr. - June. Locally common (often white-flowered). **K D** (**Ma**, Mi) FE II 198
4. *G. dissectum* Lower leaves deeply divided. Pedicels 0.5-1.5cm. Petals notched, limb longer than claw. Sepals aristate, glandular-hairy. 'Maypole' arrangement of dehiscing fruit characteristic of *Geranium* species. Mar. - June. Common. **K D** (**Ma**, Mi, I) FE II 198
5. *G. lucidum* Shining Cranesbill. Lower leaves 5 lobed, shining, sparsely hairy or glabrous. Petal limb shorter than claw. Mar. - June. Common. **K D** (**Ma**) FE II 198
6. *G. purpureum* Petals 6-9mm, anthers orange. Mar. - July. Common. **K D** (**Ma**, Mi, I) FE II 198

ERODIUM

7. *Erodium chium* Annual, biennial or perennial. Leaves rounded to pinnatifid, with not more than 1 pair distinct leaflets. Persistent spirally coiled carpel beak characteristic of *Erodium* species. Pit at apex of fruit without a furrow beneath it. Feb. - June. Locally common. **K D** (**Ma**, Mi, I) FE II 200

8. *E. malacoides* Much as 7, but pit at apex of fruit with deep furrow below it. Petals often more deeply coloured than other pinkish species (except *E. cicutarium*). Jan. - May. Common. **K D** (**Ma**, Mi, I) FE II 200
9. *E. reichardii* Small mat-forming perennial. Leaves 1cm, crenate. Flowers solitary, pale pink with darker veins. Most of year, especially May - June. Damp rocky places in the shade. **K D** (**Ma**, Mi, endemic) FE II 201
10. *E. ciconium* (L.) L'Hér. (including *E. senneni* Bianor) Annual or biennial. Leaves with small leaflets alternating with larger ones. Flowers bluish. Beak of fruit 6-10cm. Apr. - May. Very local. (This specimen from the area K gives for his 'forme sennenii') **D** (**Ma**) FE II 201
11. *E. cicutarium* Common Storksbill. Usually annual. Leaves pinnate, leaflets pinnatifid or more divided. Flowers often deeply coloured, 2 upper petals often smaller than other 3, with dark blotch at base. Dec. - July. Common. **K D** (**Ma**, Mi, I) FE II 202
12. *E. moschatum* Musk Storksbill. Annual or biennial musk-scented plant, with glandular hairs. Leaves pinnate, pinnae rarely reaching half way to midrib. Dec. - July. **K D** (**Ma**, Mi, I) FE II 203

Other species recorded for Mallorca:
Geranium robertianum Possibly recorded in place of 6. (K gives alternative names suggesting this). B records as dubious here. D includes. Ll omits. (?Ma) Bl in FE II 198
Erodium botrys Caulescent annual. At least upper leaves pinnatifid or pinnatisect with dentate or pinnatifid lobes. Beak of fruit 50-110mm, apex of fruit with deep eglandular pit with 2 basal furrows. K D Ll (Ma, Mi) FE II 201

In other islands:
Erodium laciniatum Cabrera. Not Bl in FE II 200
E. maritimum Dragonera. Not Bl in FE II 201
E. acaule ?Cabrera. Not Bl in FE II 203

Plate 34

OXALIDACEAE: *OXALIS*
TROPAEOLACEAE: *TROPAEOLUM*
ZYGOPHYLLACEAE: *FAGONIA, ZYGOPHYLLUM, TRIBULUS*
LINACEAE: *LINUM, (RADIOLA)*

OXALIDACEAE: *OXALIS*

1. *Oxalis corniculata* Small procumbent perennial. All year. Common, usually as a street weed. **K D** (**Ma,** Mi, I) FE II 192
2. *O. pes-caprae* Bermuda buttercup. Tufted perennial. Dec. - June. Common field and roadside weed, sometimes with double flower. Native of S. Africa. **K D** (**Ma,** Mi, I) FE II 193

TROPAEOLACEAE: *TROPAEOLUM*

3. *Tropaeolum majus* Nasturtium. Annual to perennial straggling plant. All year. Stream beds. Native of S. America. K lists as cultivated plant. **D** (**Ma**) FE II 204

ZYGOPHYLLACEAE

FAGONIA

4. *Fagonia cretica* Prostrate perennial. Stipules spiny. Apr. - May. Occasional. K **D** (**Ma,** I) FE II 205

ZYGOPHYLLUM

5. *Zygophyllum fabago* Syrian bean-caper. Erect, rather fleshy perennial. Leaves with two leaflets. June. Locally well established. Native of SE Europe. (**Ma**) FE II 205

TRIBULUS

6. *Tribulus terrestris* Caltrop. Procumbent hairy annual. Fruit very spiny. July - Sept. Common. **K D** (**Ma, Mi,** I) FE II 205

LINACEAE: *LINUM*

7. *Linum narbonense* Hairless perennial, to 50cm. Flowers large, always deep blue. Mar. (From garden specimen). K (quotes Chodat 1903). D Ll omits. Very dubious here. FE II 208
8. *L. bienne* Pale flax. Biennial or perennial to 60cm. Flowers smaller than in 7, always pale blue. Seeds without beak. Mar. - May. Widespread. **K D** (**Ma,** I) FE II 209
9. *L. maritimum* Sea Flax. Perennial to 80cm. June - Sept. Coastal sands; rare (but one site is much visited). **K D** (**Ma**) FE II 210
10. *L. trigynum* Annual to 30cm. Leaves entire. May - June. Common. **K D** (**Ma,** Mi, I) FE II 210
11. *L. strictum* Annual, to 45cm. Leaves minutely toothed (easily felt with thumb). May - June. Common. **K D** (**Ma,** Mi, I) FE II 210

Recorded for Minorca:
Radiola linoides FE II 211

Plate 35

EUPHORBIACEAE (1) *CHROZOPHORA, MERCURIALIS, RICINUS, EUPHORBIA* (1)

CHROZOPHORA

(Scale refers to main illustration except where stated).

1. *Chrozophora tinctoria* Turn-sole. Monoecious stellate-hairy annual. Flowers inracemes, with very short-stalked erect male flowers at tip, long-stalked drooping female flowers at base. Fruit 3-valved. Apr. - Oct. (Slightly reduced, details × 1). Common in waste places. **K D (Ma)** FE II 211

MERCURIALIS

2. *Mercurialis annua* L. (including *Mercurialis ambigua* L. fil.) Annual Mercury. Much-branched, glabrous plant up to 75cm. Monoecious or (here usually) dioecious. Male flowers in clusters on long axillary spikes, female sessile. Mar. - May. Common in waste places. (Branch from 60cm female plant × 1. Details of flowers and fruit enlarged). **K D (Ma, Mi, I)** See FE II 212

RICINUS

3. *Ricinus communis* Castor-Oil Plant. Very robust annual up to 4m. Leaves peltate, palmately divided. Flowers in panicules the male with numerous yellow stamens, the female smaller with a caducous perianth and 3 bilobed red styles. Fruit 10-20m, with long conical projections. Cultivated, mainly for ornament, and sometimes established in waste places. (× 1/5, fruit × 1). **D (Ma)** FE II 213

EUPHORBIA Spurge.

The appearance of *Euphorbia* species varies very much with maturity. Repeated dichotomous branching from beneath the cyathia leads to proliferation of new shoots, so that a mature plant is much more intricately branched than a young one. Most species lose the lower stem leaves when older. The general habit can help identification, but other features such as the number of rays, shape of raylet-leaves, and ornamentation of glands, capsule and seed are more important.

4. *Euphorbia nutans* Procumbent to ascending annual to 60cm. Capsules 1.8-2mm. Seeds 1.1mm, black, rugulose. Apr. - May. Local in disturbed ground. (Terminal part of stem and small section from near base stem showing single leaf and stipule, × 1. Capsule and seed enlarged). Native N. America. **D Ll (Ma)** Not Bl in FE II 215

5. *E. peplis* Procumbent fleshy, often greyish, annual. Leaves entire, asymmetrical. Glands reddish brown with small appendages. Seed smooth, greyish, egg-shaped, about 3mm. June - Sept. Sea-shores. Occasional. (Slightly reduced, details enlarged). **K D (Ma, Mi, I)** FE II 216

6. *E. chamaesyce* Procumbent glabrous or villous annual. Leaves usually 3-7 × 2.5-4.5mm, slightly asymmetrical at base, usually serrulate, often emarginate at apex. Glands with rounded white appendages. Seed 2mm, elongated quadrangular, with 4 sharp longitudinal angles and faint transverse ridges. June - Oct. Common. (× 1, details enlarged). **K D (Ma, Mi, I)** FE II 216

7. *E. dendroides* Tree Spurge. Shrub, dense and dome-shaped, up to 200cm. Leaves lanceolate, up to 90mm. Glands yellow to reddish, irregularly lobed. seeds (3mm) laterally compressed. Feb. - June. Locally common near the sea. (Shrub much reduced: part of inflorescence × 1, details enlarged). **K D (Ma, Mi, I)** FE II 216

8. *E. serrata* Hairless glaucous perennial to 50cm. Leaves sharply serrate. Ray and raylet-leaves usually bright yellow. (× 1/3, details enlarged). Mar. - July. Common. **K D (Ma, Mi, I)** FE II 216

9. *E. hirsuta* L. (*E. pubescens*) Hairy perennial to 1m. Stem usually with axillary rays. Terminal rays 5 or 6. Capsule 3-4mm, tuberculate. Seeds ca 2mm, almost globular, with dark tubercles and prominent comma shaped white caruncle. Jan. - Oct. Local in marshy places. (× 1/3, details enlarged). **K D (Ma, Mi, I)** FE II 220

10. *E. pterococca* Hairless annual, rather like 11, but generally less robust. Capsule winged (the wings more widely spaced than in *E. peplus* (Plate 36). Glands entire, rounded. Apr. - May. Locally common. (× 1, details enlarged) **K D (Ma, Mi)** FE II 221

11. *E. helioscopia* Sun Spurge. Annual. Leaves obovate, with rounded serrate apex. Rays 5, trichotomous then dichotomous. Axillary rays absent. Ray and raylet leaves similar but smaller, usually yellow. Fruit smooth, sulcate. Seeds 2mm, dark brown, ridged and reticulate. Dec. - May. Common. (× 1/3, details enlarged). **K D (Ma, Mi, I)** FE II 221

12. *E. fontqueriana* Greuter. Decumbent or ascending glaucous perennial. Glands with short blunt horns. Capsule 5mm, smooth. May - July. Very rare. (After illustration in Colom, Biogeografía de las Baleares. Palma 1957, details from Greek specimen of *E. myrsinites*). K B D Ll (Ma endemic) FE II 221 (cf. *E. myrsinites*)

13. *E. exigua* Dwarf Spurge. Hairless annual to 35cm, often very much smaller. Often glaucous. Rays 0-3. Capsule 1.6 - 2mm diameter, smooth or slightly tuberculate on keels. Mar.- May. Common. (× 1, details enlarged). K D (Ma, Mi, I) FE II 222

Others in Mallorca:

Euphorbia serpens Procumbent glabrous annual.Leaves entire. Stipules often connate. Seeds more or less quadrangular, 1mm or less. Native of S. America. Occasional. **D Ll (Ma)** Not Bl in FE II 216

E. prostrata Native of N. America. Bucknall claimed that Rodriguez' specimen of *E. chamaesyce*, was actually this species, though Knoche disagreed. H Ll (Ma) Not Bl in FE II 216

E. squamigera subsp. **D** Ll Not Bl in FE II 220

E. lathyris K (quotes Garcia, 1905.) D Ll (introduced) FE II 221

E. medicaginea Hairless annual. Jan.- May. Easily confused with *E. segetalis*. Capsule of this species is larger (2.5 × 2.5mm). Seeds white-rugose on a blackish ground. Common (Prof. Llorens: this one escaped me!). **K D (Ma, Mi, I)** FE II 221

E. dracunculoides subsp. *inconspicua* Ll (See G. Alomar, J. Rita, J.A.Rossello Notas Floristicas de las Islas Baleares (III) in Boll. Soc. Hist. Nat. Balears 30 (1986) 145-154) Not Bl in FE II 222

E. platyphyllos K lists only *E. platyphylla* subsp. *pubescens* (= *E. hirsuta* here). D (quotes FE) B gives 3 locations. Ll omits. Bl in FE I 220

In other islands:

Mercurialis elliptica ?Minorca. Not Bl in FE II 212

M. tomentosa Ibiza FE II 212

Euphorbia margalidiana Kuhbier & Lewejohann (1978) Endemic to Ses Margalides off the coast of Ibiza.

Plate 36

EUPHORBIACEAE (2): *EUPHORBIA* (2)
RUTACEAE: *RUTA*

EUPHORBIA (2) (Scale refers to main illustration except where stated).

1. *E. falcata* Glabrous annual to 40cm. Rays 4-5, up to 5 × dichotomous. Seeds pale grey or brown, transversely sulcate. May. - Sept. Common in fields and disturbed ground. (× ca 1/3, raylet leaves slightly enlarged, other details × 4). **K D (Ma, I)** FE II 222

2. *E. peplus* (including *E. peploides*) Petty Spurge. Hairless annual, with 2 or more basal branches and 3 rays, up to 5 × dichotomous. Leaves stalked. Seeds grey, longitudinally grooved on front, pitted dorsally. Dec. - Aug. Common. (Young specimen × 2/3, raylet leaves slightly enlarged, other details × 4). **K D (Ma, Mi, I)** FE II 222

3. *E. segetalis* L. Hairless annual or perennial, up to 50cm. Often no primary umbel, but umbel with 5 branches appears on each of several or many axillary branches. Branches of umbel up to 5 × dichotomous. Leaves linear, caducous. Glands with 2 or 4 horns, or hornless and notched. Seed ovoid, grey or reddish-brown, minutely pitted. All year. Common. (Mature specimen × 1/5, raylet leaves × 1, other details × 4). **K D (Ma, Mi, I)** FE II 222

4. *E. biumbellata* Whorled Spurge. Hairless perennial. Axillary rays present, some whorled below terminal umbel of 8-21 rays, up to 4 × dichotomous. Glands with club-shaped horns. Seeds grey, shallowly ridged. Mar. - Sept. Common. (Upper 2/3 mature plant × ca 1/3, raylet leaves slightly enlarged, other details × 2). **K D (Ma, I)** FE II 223

5. *E. maresii* Hairless, much branched perennial. Leaves variable. Glands truncate or with horns. May - July. Very rare in shady rock crevices. (from pressed specimen × 1, including details of leaves. Capsule and glands × 2). **K D (Ma, Mi endemic)** FE II 224

6. *E. pithyusa* Glaucous perennial to 55cm. Resembles 7, but whole plant minutely papillose (use lens), leaves and bracts serrulate. Lower leaves deflexed and imbricate. Rays 4-8, up to 4 × dichotomous. Seeds dark grey or whitish, sometimes ridged or tuberculate. All year. Common in mountains, main shoot often lost by grazing, basal shoots developing small umbels terminally. Subsp. *pithyusa* of rocky shores has < 40 non-flowering branches. Subsp. *cupanii* of rocky places inland has no non-flowering branches. There is a distinctive variety of subsp. *pithyusa* near Colonia de Sant Pere. (Specimen subsp. *pithyusa* x ca 1/3, leaf from middle stem × 1, glands, capsule and seeds × 2). Dec. - Aug. **K D (Ma, Mi, I)** FE II 225

7. *E. paralias* Sea Spurge. Glaucous, rather fleshy, tufted perennial to 70cm. Rays 3-6, up to 3 × dichotomous. Axillary rays up to 9. Glands notched or slightly horned. Seeds smooth, pale grey. May - Oct. Common on sandy shores. (Mature specimen × ca 1/3, leaf from middle stem × 1, other details × 2). Dec. - Aug. **K D (Ma, Mi, I)** FE II 225

8. *E. terracina* Variable hairless perennial to 70cm, with many ascending or erect branches from base. Rays 4-5, up to 5 × dichotomous. Glands with 2 long, slender horns. Seeds pale grey, smooth. Mar. - May. Common near sea. (Mature specimen × ca 1/3, raylet leaves slightly enlarged, other details × 2). **K D (Ma, Mi, I)** FE II 226

9. *E. characias* Mediterranean Spurge. Robust tufted tomentose perennial to 180cm. Leaves glaucous. Rays 10-20, up to 4 × dichotomous (usually only twice), with numerous axillary rays. Glands horned or notched. Fruit tomentose. Seeds silver-grey, smooth. Mar. - July. Common in mountains and dry hills. (Upper part of mature specimen × about 1/3, other details × 2). Dec. - Aug. **K D (Ma, Mi)** FE II 226

RUTACEAE: *RUTA* Rue.

10. *Ruta montana* Perennial, to 70cm. Leaf-segments linear. Inflorescence branches, pedicels, bracts and sepals densely glandular. Petals not ciliate. Capsule segments rounded at apex. June - July. Occasional. **K D (Ma)** FE II 227

11. *R. angustifolia* Resembles 12, but glandular-puberulent in the inflorescence. Bracts not or hardly broader than subtended branch. Petals fringed with long cilia. May - June. Common. **K D (Ma, Mi, I)** FE II 227

12. *R. chalepensis* Almost completely glabrous perennial, up to 60cm (sometimes a few minute glands in the inflorescence). Bracts wider than subtended branch. Petals shortly fringed. Capsule segments pointed. May - June. Common. **K D (Ma, Mi, I)** FE II 227

13. *R. graveolens* Glabrous prennial, often glaucous. Petals not fringed, often denticulate. Capsule rounded. Occasional escape from cultivation. May - June. **(Ma)** Bl in FE II 227

Other species recorded from Mallorca (some perhaps dubiously):
Euphorbia sulcata Annual, often much-branched from base. Leaves linear or narrow. Ray and raylet leaves similar but larger. Glands with 2 horns. Seeds pale grey, ovoid-hexagonal with furrow on each face, often darker in furrows. K (quotes Gandoger 1899). D Ll (Ma, I) FE II 222

E. pinea (*E. segetalis* L. subsp. *pinea* (L.) Hayek) D (quotes FE) Ll Bl in FE II 222

E. portlandica B (quotes Markworth 1958) D omits. ?Ll Not Bl in FE II 223

E. cyparissias K (quotes Barceló 1867-1877). D (quotes FE), H doubts, Ll omits. ?Bl in FE II 226

Recorded from Cabrera:
Euphorbia taurinensis D lists for Cabrera. Ll omits. Bl in FE II 222

Plate 37

CNEORACEAE: *CNEORUM*
POLYGALACEAE: *POLYGALA*
ANACARDIACEAE: *PISTACIA*
ACERACEAE: *ACER*
AQUIFOLIACEAE: *ILEX*
BUXACEAE: *BUXUS*
RHAMNACEAE: *RHAMNUS*

CNEORACEAE: *CNEORUM*

1. *Cneorum tricoccon* Evergreen shrub, to 1m. Mar. - June. Common in mountains. **K D** (**Ma,** Mi, I) FE II 230

POLYGALACEAE: *POLYGALA*

2. *Polygala rupestris* Perennial. Wings obovate, pointed, with 3 indistinct veins appearing as single broad midrib. Corolla pink. Racemes with up to 8 flowers, usually less. Mar. - Nov. Common in rock crevices. **K D** (**Ma,** Mi, I) FE II 232
3. *P. monspeliaca* Annual. Wings narrowly elliptical, pointed, with 3 main veins and many lateral branches, not anastomosing. Corolla small, whitish. Mar. - June. Occasional. **K D** (**Ma,** Mi) FE II 233
4. *P. vulgaris* Common Milkweed. Small perennial. Wings with 3 anastomosing veins. Flowers pink, white or blue. (From British specimen). June. Very local (Prof. Llorens). K **D** Ll (Ma) ?Bl in FE II 235

ANACARDIACEAE: *PISTACIA*

5. *Pistacia terebinthus* Turpentine tree. Dioecious shrub or small tree, up to 5m. Leaves with terminal leaflet, rhachis unwinged. Fruit obovoid, compressed, up to 7mm. March. Rare. (From Greek specimen). K **D** (Ma) FE II 237
6. *P. lentiscus* Gum mastic. Dioecious shrub, commonly up to 2m, rarely up to 10m. especially around SE coast. Leaves without a terminal leaflet, rhachis broadly winged. Mar. Common, stony scrub and shores. **K D** (**Ma,** Mi, I) FE II 237

ACERACEAE: *ACER*

7. *Acer opalus* Miller subsp. *granatense* (Boiss) Font Quer & Rothm. Small tree, rarely more than 3m here (one much larger is sheltered in the snow-pit near the peak of Massanella). May. Locally common in mountains, usually out of reach because of grazing. (Main illustration constructed from distant photo of mature fruiting tree and some immature leaves from a rock crevice. Single leaf from a mature branch found later). **K D** (**Ma**) FE II 239

AQUIFOLIACEAE: *ILEX*

8. *Ilex aquifolium* Holly. Small shrub here. Feb. - May. Rare in rock crevices of higher mountains. (From British specimen chosen for absence of spines - K says characteristic of Mallorcan plant). **K D** (Ma) FE II 241

BUXACEAE: *BUXUS*

9. *Buxus balearica* Balearic Box. Evergreen shrub up to 4m. ?Jan. - Feb. Local in mountain area. **K D** (**Ma**) FE II 243

RHAMNACEAE: *RHAMNUS* Buckthorn.

10. *Rhamnus alaternus* Evergreen shrub up to 5m. Spines absent. Leaves entire or slightly toothed. Dec. - May. Common, especially in mountain areas. **K D** (**Ma,** Mi, I) FE II 244
11. *R. ludovici-salvatoris* Evergreen shrub. Spines absent except for numerous small, close spiny teeth on leaves. Fairly common in mountain areas. Mar. - May. **K D** (**Ma,** Mi, I) FE II 244
12. *R. lycioides* Evergreen shrub to 1m, very spiny. Fruit compressed, with two stones. Apr. - May. Local, mainly in higher parts of mountains. **K D** (**Ma,** I) FE II 244

Also in Mallorca:
Vitis vinifera (Vitaceae) Vine. Much cultivated, occasionally escaping. Also other species introduced from America. FE II 246

In other islands:
Ailanthus altissima (Simaroubaceae). Ibiza. Not Bl in FE II 231
Polygala nicaeensis Formentera Not Bl in FE II 234
Coriaria myrtifolia (Coriariaceae). Ibiza. FE II 236

Plate 38

MALVACEAE: *MALVA, LAVATERA, ALTHAEA.*

MALVA

1. *Malva sylvestris* Common mallow. Erect, branching perennial. Flowers pinkish-purple (otherwise very like 4). Apr - Sept. Common, especially in damp places. **K D** (**Ma**, Mi, I) FE II 250
2. *M. nicaeensis* Annual. Flowers small (petals 10-12mm), pinkish-white in axillary clusters. Longest fruiting stalks generally more than 1cm. Apr. - June. Common in dry places. **K D** (**Ma**, Mi) FE II 251
3. *M. parviflora* Annual, usually prostrate. Petals 4-5mm. Fruiting pedicels usually less than 1cm. Apr. - May. Common in dry places. **K D** (**Ma**, Mi, I) FE II 251

LAVATERA

4. *Lavatera cretica* Branched, usually erect, perennial. Leaves often, but not always, greyish. Flowers pale pinkish with darker veins. Apr. - Sept. Very common. **K D** (**Ma**, Mi, I) FE II 251
5. *L. arborea* Tall, robust biennial. Stout stem with large velvety, stalked leaves. Spikes arise from upper part stem in second year. Dry places near the sea. Mar. - Apr. K **D** (**Ma**, Mi, I) FE II 252
6. *L. maritima* Low shrub. Feb. - Mar. Very local in dry rocky places. **K D** (**Ma**, Mi, I) FE II 252
7. *L. olbia* subsp. *hispida* Short-lived shrub. Leaves and stems covered in star-shaped hairs. Flowers in erect almost stalkless racemes. May - June. Rare. (Illustration from Mallorcan specimen growing in dry rocky area dominated by *Ampelodesmos).* K and D list for Minorca only, B (quotes Garcia, collecting 1905, who found it in same area). (**Ma**, Mi) FE II 252
8. *L. punctata* Annual. Upper leaves simple. June - July. (From specimen collected by Bianor from near Soller in 1910). **K D** B Ll (Ma, Mi) FE II 252
9. *L. trimestris* Tall annual. Flowers large, petals up to 5cm. Apr. - June. Local, in NW mountains. (From garden specimen: petals rather narrower in wild plant, found later). **K D** (Ma, Mi, I) FE II 252

ALTHAEA

10. *Althaea hirsuta* Small annual, generally prostrate. Epicalyx segments usually 6 or 7, narrow, hairy. May - June. Common in dry, rocky places. **K D** (**Ma**, Mi, I) FE II 253

Also recorded for Mallorca:
Malva pusilla K (quotes Maheu 1912). D and Ll omit. Not Bl in FE II 251
Althaea officinalis Marsh Mallow. D omits. **K** and Ll include. (Ma, Mi). Not Bl in FE II 253

In other islands:
Lavatera triloba subsp. *pallescens* Minorca: endemic subsp. FE II 252
Kosteletzkya pentacarpos Minorca and Cabrera. FE II 256

102

Plate 39

THYMELAEACEAE: *DAPHNE, THYMELAEA*
GUTTIFERAE: *HYPERICUM*
VIOLACEAE: *VIOLA*

THYMELAEACEAE

DAPHNE

1. *Daphne gnidium* Slightly glaucous evergreen shrub, 1m or more. Flowers fragrant. June - Sept. Widespread. **K D** (**Ma**, Mi, I) FE II 257

THYMELAEA

2. *Thymelaea hirsuta* Shrub, up to 1m. All year. Local, usually near the sea. **K D** (**Ma**, Mi, I) FE II 259
3. *T. myrtifolia* Shrub, up to 1m. Mar.- Apr. Local, mountains and maritime sands. **K D** (**Ma**, Mi, endemic) FE II 259
4. *T. passerina* D adds var pubescens Guss., probably = *Stellera pubescens* Guss., see FE under *T. passerina*). Pubescent annual. Greenish flowers in clusters along straight stems, subtended by tuft of white hairs and small lanceolate bracts. (Specimen from Spanish mainland × 1, cluster of flowers and fruit on right × 5). **D** records. K and Ll omit. (?Ma, ?Mi) Not Bl in FE II 260

GUTTIFERAE: *HYPERICUM*

5. *Hypericum hircinum* (including *H. cambessedesii* (Cosson ex Barc.) Ramos) Shrub, up to 1m. Leaves without marginal vesicles. Rather local in mountains. (From garden specimen). **K D** (**Ma**) FE II 263
6. *H. balearicum* Shrub, to 1m or more. Leaves with yellowish-white glandular vesicles at margins. All year, but chiefly May and June. Common in dry rocky places. **K D** (**Ma**, Mi, I, endemic) FE II 263
7. *H. tomentosum* Decumbent, tomentose perennial. June - Sept. Widespread where water stands in winter. **K D** (**Ma**, I) FE II 266
8. *H. perfoliatum* Perennial. Leaves usually amplexicaul. Sepals with dense marginal stalked glands and with irregular black streaks and dots. Petals with or without black streaks or dots towards the apex. May - June. Fairly widespread in damp or shady places. (Main illustration reduced). **K D** (**Ma**, Mi) FE II 266
9. *H. perforatum* Perennial, usually much branched. Black glands absent on sepals, black markings occasinaly present. Petals with a few black spots on margin. May - July. Fairly common, roadsides, waste places. (Main illustration reduced). **K D** (**Ma**, Mi, I) FE II 269

VIOLACEAE: *VIOLA*

10. *V. suavis* (including *V. barceloi* (L.) (Chod.) Rhizomatous perennial with short stout stolons. Stipules lanceolate with long, ciliate fimbriae. Leaves at flowering time 3-8 cm, cordate, hairy. Flowers fragrant, violet with a white or yellow throat. March. ?K. D and Ll list only for Ibiza. (My specimen was independantly identified for me). (**Ma**, I) Not Bl in FE II 272
11. *V. alba* subsp. *dehnhardtii*) Rhizomatous perennial, stolons often absent. Stipules as in 10. Leaves and capsules sparsely hairy to glabrous. Flowers dark or pale violet, lateral petals with white beard. Feb. - June. Common in mountains. **K D** (**Ma**) Not Bl in FE II 272
12. *V. jaubertiana* Like 11, but completely glabrous. Mar. - Apr. Rock fissures in Gorg Blau area. From specimen in Cambridge botanic garden. **K D** (**Ma** endemic) FE II 273
13. *V. arborescens* Woody plant. Leaves ovate to linear. Flowers pale pale violet, very variable in size (smaller flower below × 1, as is main illustration). Sept. - Oct. (and a few flowers at other times). Common in rock crevices. **K D** (**Ma**, Mi, I) FE II 281

Also recorded from Mallorca:
Thymelaea tartonraira subsp. *tartonraira* Ll lists for Ma. Not Bl in FE II 259
T. dioica K (quotes Willkomm 1873). Not D or Ll. Not Bl in FE II 260
Hypericum elodes K (quotes Barceló 1867-1877) Not D or Ll. Not Bl in FE II 266
Viola odorata Duvigneaud differentiates plants here as endemic
V. stolonifera Rodr., 'groupe de *V. odorata* L'Bonafè's description of this plant seems to differ from FE description of *V. odorata* in shape of the stipules (lanceolate acuminate rather than ovate) and sepals (oblong and subacute rather than ovate, obtuse). Feb. - Mar. ?K D Ll treats *V. odorata* as alien, omits *V. stolonifera* Rodr. FE specifically exclude *V. odorata* for Bl. See FE II 272
V. scotophylla Jordan is listed ?Ma by Ll. Not Bl in FE II 273 (See *V. alba* subsp. *scotophylla*
V. hirta L. ?Ll Not Bl in FE II 273

In other islands:
Daphne rodriguezii Endemic Minorca FE II 258
Hypericum australe Minorca FE II 268
H. triquetrifolium Minorca. FE II 269

Plate 40

CISTACEAE: *CISTUS, HALIMIUM, TUBERARIA, HELIANTHEMUM, FUMANA*

CISTUS

1. *Cistus albidus* Bush up to 100cm, leaves grey-tomentose, sessile. Apr. - June. Common. **K D** (**Ma**, Mi, I) FE II 283
2. *C. creticus* L. (*C. incanus*) Very like 1, but leaves stalked, often petiolate. Possibly extinct in Mallorca if it was ever there. (From garden specimen). K (quotes Gandoger 1899) 'à vérifier'. ?D B gives a Mallorcan location, but this has now largely been developed. Prof. Llorens doubts this species here, thinks it may have been a variety of *C. albidus*. It occurs in Minorca. (?Ma, Mi, ?I) FE II 283
3. *C. monspeliensis* Sticky bush. Leaves linear-lanceolate to linear. Sepals 5. Mar. - June. Common. **K D** (**Ma**, Mi, I) FE II 283
4. *C. salvifolius* Shrub, often procumbent. Leaves ovate or elliptical. Apr. - June. Common. **K D** (**Ma**, Mi, I) FE II 284
5. *C. clusii* Shrub, usually less than 40cm in Mallorca. Very similar to 3, but sepals 3, with long bristly white hairs. Local, near Palma, and coast in Campos area. **K D** (**Ma**, I) FE II 284

HALIMIUM

6. *Halimium halimifolium* Grey-blue erect shrub, up to 100cm. Stigma large, sessile, white. Leaves of non-flowering shoots diamond shaped. May - July. **K D** (**Ma**) FE II 285

TUBERARIA

7. *Tuberaria guttata* Spotted rockrose. Hairy annual, up to 30cm, usually less. Petals dark-spotted at base or plain yellow. May. - June. Local in sandy places. **K D** (**Ma**, Mi, I) FE II 286

HELIANTHEMUM

8. *Helianthemum caput-felis* Dwarf woolly shrublet, 10-30cm. Petals with orange blotch at base. Very local here. May - June. **K D** (**Ma**) FE II 287
9. *H. ?nummularium* Procumbent or ascending shrublet. Leaves oblong or lanceolate to ovate, stellate hairy; petioles shorter than the stipules. Inflorescence an elongated cyme with up to 12 flowers. Apr. - May. Rare if at all. (From own rather small specimen). D (quotes FE). Prof. Llorens doubts records. (?**Ma**). FE II 288

10. *H. appeninum* Small shrublet with (here) pink flowers. Rare. **K D** (Ma) FE II 288
11. *H. salicifolium* Annual, up to 30cm, usually much branched. Pedicels long, patent, usually upturned at the apex. Mar. - June. Uncommon. (From Greek specimen). **K D** (**Ma**) FE II 289
12. *H. origanifolium* subsp. *serrae* Dwarf procumbent to ascending shrub. Leaves dark green, ovate to cordate. Apr. - May. Very rare, possibly recently extinct. **K D** (**Ma**, I: endemic subsp.) FE II 290

FUMANA

13. *Fumana ericoides* Procumbent much branched shrublet. Leaves alternate, linear. Stipules absent. Flowers axillary or subterminal, pedicels exceeding adjacent leaves. May. Very occasional. **K D** (**Ma**, Mi, I) FE II 291
14. *F. thymifolia* Erect or ascending shrublet. Leaves opposite, more or less linear, with strongly revolute margins. Stipules linear, conspicuous, bristle-tipped. Mar. - June **K D** (**Ma**, Mi, I) FE II 292.
(Illustrations at 14a show detail of the flower with geniculate style, and detail of opposite mucronate leaves with 4 green long bristle-tipped stipules and axillary shoots, uncoloured so as not to conceal stipules). These are all characteristic of this rather variable species). Illustration 14b, in lower part of right margin, is from an erect substantial shrublet, usually over 30cm, which occurs locally under pine trees. Illustration 14c, with enlarged detail of bud, is the commonest form, an ascending bushy shrublet, usually less than 20cm, and less woody than 14b, with flowers more than 10cm across, and inset 14d is from a very glandular-hairy plant, under 10cm, with flowers up to 7mm across, locally common, especially in the southern part of the mountain range).
15. *F. laevipes* Shrublet, up to 30cm, stems slender, ascending. Leaves alternate, narrowly linear, often glaucous. Apr. - May. Very local. **K D** (**Ma**, Mi, I) FE II 292

Also recorded from Mallorca:
F. procumbens **K D** ?Ll (?Ma) FE II 291

In Minorca:
Tuberaria lignosa FE II 285

Plate 41

TAMARICACEAE: *TAMARIX*
FRANKENIACEAE: *FRANKENIA*
(ELATINACEAE: *ELATINE*)

TAMARICACEAE: *TAMARIX* Tamarisk.

Small trees with overlapping, scale-like leaves dotted with salt secreting glands. Flowers off-white or pink in spike-like racemes. The petals are often caducous, so sepals are much easier to count.

The species are quite similar in many respects. Bernard R. Baum *The Genus Tamarix* (Jerusalem 1978) is helpful. Note that the main illustrations 1 and 4, though differing in dimensions of the raceme, are probably both *T. boveana*, or possibly *Tamarix africana* × *boveana*.

1. *Tamarix* species. *T. africana*, with racemes 3-8cm × 5-9mm, and 5-merous flowers has been frequently recorded, sometimes at least in error for *T. boveana*. It would be interesting to know if specimens have been found which correspond exactly with *T. africana* as described by Baum (1978). Trees here all seem to have at least some 5-merous flowers on each raceme. (Main illustration and unlabelled details from Mallorcan specimen originally identified as *T. africana*, on account of the 5-merous flowers. a and b after illustration in Baum of *T. africana*). See Sotiaux & Sotiaux Bol. Soc. Hist. Nat. Balears (Palma de Mallorca). Ll gives distribution as ?Ma, Mi, I. FE II 293

2. *T. canariensis* Bark reddish-brown. Racemes dense (buds more or less contiguous), 1.5-5cm × 3-5mm. with papillose rhachis. Bracts entire, equalling or often exceeding calyx. Sepals very finely denticulate (needs microscope). Petals 1.25-1.5mm, pink, obovate, caducous. All year, esp. Apr. - July. Common around the coast, often planted on beaches for shelter. **D** Ll (**Ma**, I) FE II 293

3. *T. gallica* Bark blackish to purplish-brown. Racemes lax (green gaps between flowers apparent), 2-5cm × 3-5mm. Bracts not exceeding calyx, usually to below mid-calyx. Rhachis of raceme completely glabrous. Sepals almost entire. Petals 1.5-1.75mm, elliptic to slightly elliptic-ovate. Apr. - Sept. Damp places near sea: possibly commonest in the Campos area. K D Ll (**Ma**, Mi) FE II 293

4. *T. boveana* Typically *T. boveana* has racemes 5-15cm × 8-9mm, bracts exceeding calyx, and 4-merous flowers. (Detail a) after illustration of *T. boveana* in Baum: others from a specimen identified by Baum as *T. boveana*, and fitting his decription in all respects except for the rather short raceme and the presence of some 5-petalled flowers (all with 4 calyx-lobes). B and Ll list this species. (**Ma**) Not Bl in FE II 293

FRANKENIACEAE: *FRANKENIA*

Annual or perennial procumbent herbs, sometimes woody at base. Leaves opposite, entire. Flowers sessile. Petals and sepals 5, stamens 6 in two whorls of 3, the inner longer.

5. *Frankenia pulverulenta* Annual Sea-heath. Procumbent silver-haired annual. Leaves obovate, more or less inrolled. Flowers pale violet in leafy terminal and axillary spikes. May. **K D** (**Ma**, Mi, I) FE II 295

6. *F. laevis* Sea-heath. Procumbent perennial. Flowers few, solitary or in small clusters throughout upper parts of main stems and branches, usually facing towards tips of procumbent branches, pink. Apr. - May. K **D** Ll (**Ma**, Mi, I) FE II 295

7. *F. hirsuta* Procumbent perennial. Leaves strongly inrolled and usually curved, back outwards. Flowers in dense corymbiform clusters, facing up to the sky, pink. Calyx densely covered with broad-based long white hairs. Apr. - May. K **D** (**Ma**, Mi, I) FE II 295

Hybrids of *Frankenia* species, which are common, lead to difficulty in identification.

Also recorded from Mallorca:
Tamarix parviflora This is 4-merous like *T. boveana*, but the racemes are only 3-5mm in diameter. H and Ll treat as alien. Not Bl in FE II 293
Elatine macropoda K and D record for Mi only. B and Ll give (**Ma**, ?Mi) FE II 295

Minorca only:
Elatine hydropiper Not Bl in FE II 296

Plate 42

CUCURBITACEAE: *ECBALLIUM*
CACTACEAE: *OPUNTIA*
LYTHRACEAE: *LYTHRUM*
TRAPACEAE: *TRAPA*
MYRTACEAE: *MYRTUS, EUCALYPTUS*
PUNICACEAE: *PUNICA*

CUCURBITACEAE: *ECBALLIUM*

1. *Ecballium elaterium* Procumbent perennial. Whole plant fleshy and hispid. May - Oct. **K D** (**Ma**, Mi, I) FE II 297

CACTACEAE: *OPUNTIA*

2. *Opuntia ficus-indica* Prickly Pear. Erect, woody cactus, up to 5m. Fruit edible. May - July. Native of tropical America. **K D** (**Ma**) FE II 300

LYTHRACEAE: *LYTHRUM*

3. *Lythrum junceum* Hairless, straggling perennial of damp places. Petals 5-6mm. Stamens 12, some exceeding sepals. Apr. - June. **K D** (**Ma**, Mi, I) FE II 301
4. *L. hyssopifolia* Grass poly. Annual like 1, but smaller. Petals 2-3mm. Stamens usually 4-6, not exceeding sepals. Apr. - June. **K D** (**Ma**, Mi, I) FE II 301
5. *L. borysthenicum* Annual. Petals minute and fugaceous. Calyx broadly bell-shaped. Mar. - Apr. Rare. From Mallorcan specimen, though not previously recorded here. (**Ma**, Mi) Not Bl in FE II 302

TRAPACEAE: *TRAPA*

6. *Trapa natans* Water Chestnut. Aquatic herb with floating rosettes of diamond-shaped leaves. Solitary flowers and edible fruit in leaf axils. June - July. Native of SE Europe. (From garden specimen). K (quotes Barceló 1867-1877). D Ll (Ma) FE II 303

MYRTACEAE

MYRTUS

7. *Myrtus communis* Myrtle. Branched evergreen shrub, up to 5m, usually much less here. May - June. **K D** (**Ma**, Mi, I) FE II 303

EUCALYPTUS

8. *Eucalyptus species*. Gum tree. Tall graceful trees with bluish leathery leaves. Flowers have numerous stamens, but petals are fused in bud and fall when flower opens. May - July. Many species introduced from Australia and Tasmania, two more or less naturalised. **D.** Ll lists *E. camaldulensis* and *E. globulus* (**Ma**) FE II 304

PUNICACEAE: *PUNICA*

9. *Punica granatum* Pomegranate. Shrub or small tree. Cultivated for (fairly) edible fruit and widely naturalised. Roadsides (fruiting freely on shrubs less than 1m high). May - June. Native of SW Asia. K **D** Ll (**Ma**, I) FE II 305

Dubious records for Mallorca:
Lythrum thymifolia ?Ll (?Ma, ?Mi). Bl in FE II 301
Lythrum tribracteatum B (quotes Garcia, collecting 1905) 'A verificar'. Ll omits. Not Bl in FE II 301

In other islands:
Citrullus colocynthis Ibiza. Not Bl in FE II 298
Lythrum portula ?Minorca. FE II 302

110

Plate 43

ONAGRACEAE: *OENOTHERA, EPILOBIUM*
HALORAGACEAE: *MYRIOPHYLLUM*
THELIGONACEAE: *THELIGONUM*
ARALIACEAE: *HEDERA*
UMBELLIFERAE (1): *BOWLESIA, NAUFRAGA, ERYNGIUM, ECHINOPHORA*

ONAGRACEAE

OENOTHERA

1. *Oenothera rosea* Distinguished from *Epilobium* species by shape of fruit. June - July. (From garden specimen). D. B (naturalised at Sa Granja 1976). Ll treats as alien.Native of America. (Ma) FE II 308

EPILOBIUM

2. *Epilobium hirsutum* Great Hairy Willow-herb. Flowers up to 2 cm, petals shallowly notched. Stigma 4-lobed. Damp places. May - Sept. **K D** (**Ma,** Mi) FE II 309
3. *E. parviflorum* Small Hairy Willow-herb. Like 2, but flowers 9mm or less, petals deeply notched. Damp places. May - Aug. **K D** (**Ma,** Mi, I) FE II 309
4. *E. tetragonum* subsp. *tournefortii* Stems leafy, with numerous axillary shoots. Petals 6-8mm, shallowly notched. Stigma entire. May - Sept. Common in seasonally damp places. **K D** (**Ma,** Mi) FE II 310

HALORAGACEAE

MYRIOPHYLLUM

5. *Myriophyllum verticillatum* Whorled water-milfoil. Aquatic perennial rooted in mud. Flowers in spike, held above water, with pinnate or pectinate bracts exceeding flowers even at apex. Fresh water. May. (From British specimen). K **D** (**Ma**) FE II 312
6. *M. spicatum* Spiked Water-milfoil. Similar to 5, but upper bracts entire and shorter than flowers. May. Common in suitable habitats. K **D** (**Ma,** Mi) FE II 312

THELIGONACEAE

THELIGONUM

7. *Theligonum cynocrambe* Leafy annual, superficially like *Parietaria* species, but hairless and slightly succulent. Flowers unisexual, in axillary clusters. Mar.- Apr. Common. **K D** (**Ma,** Mi, I) FE II 312

ARALIACEAE

HEDERA

8. *Hedera helix* Ivy. Common on buildings, rocks and trees. Sept. - Nov. **K D** (**Ma,** Mi, I) FE II 314

UMBELLIFERAE

BOWLESIA

9. *Bowlesia incana* Procumbent annual with star-shaped hairs, especially on fruit and backs of leaves. Native of America. Apr. - May. (From Duvigneaud's Mallorcan specimen). **D** (Ma) Not Bl in FE II 319

NAUFRAGA

10. *Naufraga balearica* Minute plant, discovered 1967, recently found in Corsica too. (From garden specimen). May. **D** (Ma) FE II 319

ERYNGIUM

11. *Eryngium maritimum* Sea Holly. Robust, prickly. Maritime sands. June - Oct. **K D** (**Ma,** Mi, I) FE II 322
12. *E. campestre* Field Eryngo. As above, but less robust and prickly. Inland. May - Sept. **K D** (**Ma,** Mi, I) FE II 323

ECHINOPHORA

13. *Echinophora spinosa* Leaves stiff and spiny. Rays 5-8. Maritime sands, very rare. July - Aug. (Specimen from Spanish mainland). K **D** (Ma, Mi, I) FE II 324

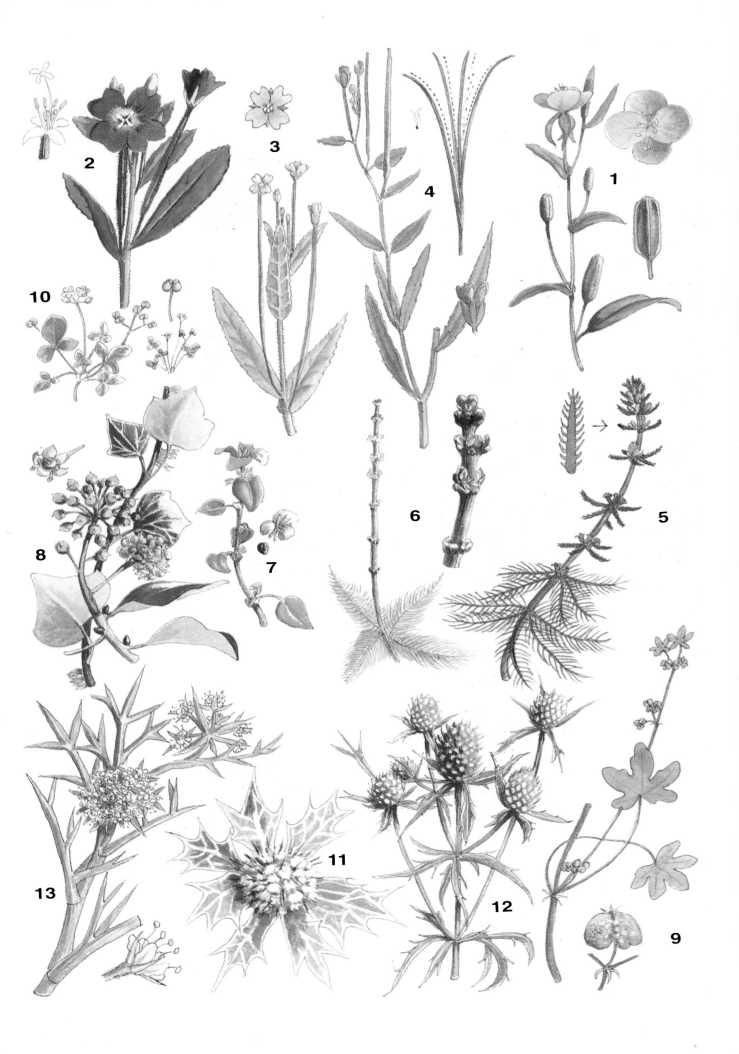

Plate 44

UMBELLIFERAE (2) *(ANTHRISCUS), SCANDIX, (BIFORA),*
SMYRNIUM, BUNIUM, PIMPINELLA, (BERULA), CRITHMUM,
OENANTHE, FOENICULUM

SCANDIX

1. *Scandix pecten-veneris* Shepherd's Needle. Branched hairless
   annual, up to 50cm, usually quite small. Beak of longer than
   seed-bearing part. Feb.- May. Common. **K D** (**Ma**, Mi, I) FE II
   327

SMYRNIUM

2. *Smyrnium olusatrum* Alexanders. Hairless biennial, up to
   1.5m. Leaves shining. Feb.- May. Common. **K D** (**Ma**, Mi, I) FE
   II 328

BUNIUM

3. *Bunium bulbocastanum* Great Pignut. Hairless perennial, up
   to 100cm. Basal leaves arising from subterranean part of stem.
   Leaves 3-pinnate, segments narrow spathulate.Rays 10-20.
   Bracts and bracteoles 5-10. Inner side pedicels minutely
   toothed. Sepals absent or minute. Apr.- May. Local. (Specimen
   from Spanish mainland). **K D** (**Ma**) FE II 329
4. *B. pachypodum* Erect or ascending perennial, up to 60cm.
   Rays 6-15, bracts 6-8, bracteoles 3-6. Fruiting pedicels almost
   as thick as fruit. May - June. Occasional in mountains. **D** (**Ma**)
   FE II 329

PIMPINELLA

5. *P. bicknelli* Perennial up to 50cm. Leaves ternate to biternate,
   with pinnatisect segments. Apr.- June. Local in mountains,
   often with *Urtica atrovirens*. Knoche only found it 'recouvertes
   d'une innombrable quantité de pucerons grisâtres et poisseux,
   qui rongeaient les tiges et les feuilles succulentes', which turned
   out to be aphids: but thriving now, and possibly commoner
   than Knoche's account would suggest. **K D** (**Ma**, endemic) FE
   II 332

CRITHMUM

6. *Crithmum maritimum* Rock Samphire. Leaves fleshy, more or
   less circular in section. July - Jan. Local, maritime rocks. **K D**
   (**Ma**, Mi, I) FE II 333

OENANTHE

7. *Oenanthe globulosa* subsp. *globulosa*. Branched hairless
   perennial to 50cm. Rays 3-6. Fruit globular. Apr.- Aug. Marshy
   places near sea. (Fruit × 2). **K D** (**Ma**, Mi) FE II 338
8. *O. lachenalii* Parsley Water Dropwort. Perennial, up to
   100cm. Rays 5-15. Fruit egg shaped. Apr.- Aug. Marshy places
   near the sea. (Fruit from Minorcan specimen, × 2). **D** (**Ma**, Mi)
   FE II 339

FOENICULUM

9. *Foeniculum vulgare* subsp. *piperitum* Fennel. Perennial up to
   250m. Leaf segments filiform. June - Aug. Very common,
   roadsides and waste places. (× 1/2). **K D** (**Ma**, Mi, I) FE II 341

The following are also recorded from Mallorca:
Anthriscus caucalis K (quotes Bianor: 'rochers ombragées avec
   Urtica atrovirens). Also seen in one 2m square patch in a high
   place by Bonafè. Ll (Ma, Mi) FE II 326
Scandix australis Resembles 1, but beak of fruit not clearly
   differentiated from seed-bearing part. Carpophore usually bifid
   at top. (see Alomar, Rita & Rosselló 1986) (Ma) Not Bl in FE
   II 327
Bifora testiculata K (quotes Barceló 1867-1877). Ll (Ma, I) FE II
   328
B. radians K (quotes Barceló 1867-1877). Ll (Ma) FE II 328
Smyrnium perfoliatum K (quotes Willkomm (1873), adds 'A
   vérifier. ! Jamais retrouvé'). Ll omits. Not Bl in FE II 328
Bunium alpinum subsp. *macuca* ?D Ll (Ma) Not Bl in FE II 329
Pimpinella tragium Perennial up to 50cm. Basal leaves pinnate
   (rarely bipinnate) cauline leaves few, small. Rays 5-15. Bracts
   and bracteoles absent or few. Fruit shortly tomentose. July Aug.
   Very local. K D Ll (Ma) FE II 331
Berula erecta Stoloniferous aquatic perennial, to 100cm, usually
   less. Submerged leaves 3-4-pinnate with linear lobes, aerial
   leaves pinnate with more or less ovate deeply serrate segments.
   May - July. In shallow water. Rare. (From British specimen).
   K D Ll (Ma, Mi, I) FE II 333

In Minorca:
Pimpinella lutea Not Bl in FE II 331

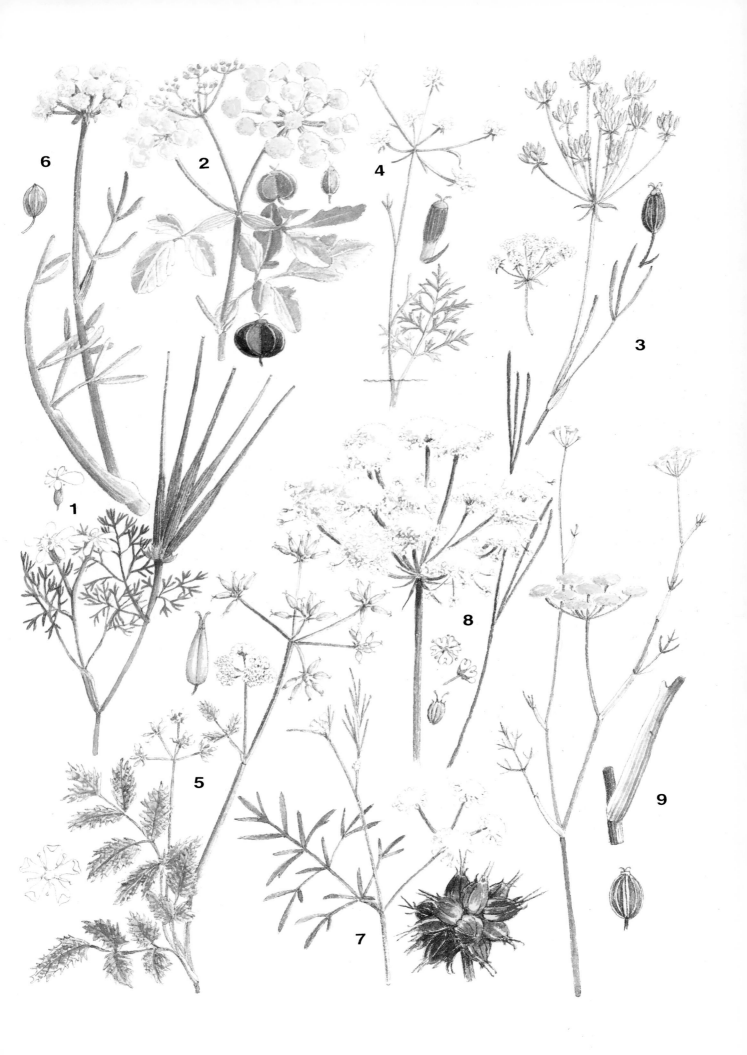

Plate 45

UMBELLIFERAE (3): *(ANETHUM), KUNDMANNIA, CONIUM, (MAGYDARIS), BUPLEURUM, APIUM, PETROSELINUM, RIDOLFIA, (SISON), AMMI*

KUNDMANNIA

1. *Kundmannia sicula* Hairless perennial, to 70cm. Inflorescence usually drooping in bud. Bracts and bracteoles numerous, long, linear. Apr.- June. Locally common field weed. **K D** (**Ma,** Mi) FE II 342

CONIUM

2. *Conium maculatum* Spotted Hemlock. Almost hairless perennial, up to 2.5m, much branched, with numerous fairly small umbels. Lower part of stem often purple-spotted. Rays 10-20. Bracts 5-6, bracteoles 3-6 on outside of umbel. May - Aug. Widespread. **K D** (**Ma,** Mi, I) FE II 342

BUPLEURUM

3. *Bupleurum lancifolium* Hairless annual up to 75cm. Upper leaves perfoliate. Rays 2-3. Fruit 3-5mm, ovate to globular, tuberculate. Mar. - July. Rare, if at all here. (From Italian specimen). K may have seen it (uncertain of identification). D Ll (Ma, Mi, I) FE II 346

4. *B. baldense* Hairless yellowish-green annual to 75cm. Mar. July. Common. **K D** (**Ma,** Mi, I) FE II 347

5. *B. semicompositum* Hairless, glaucous annual to 30cm. Rays 3-6. May - Sept. Dry ground, usually near the sea. Fairly common. **K D** (**Ma,** Mi, I) FE II 348

6. *B. barceloi* Shrub up to 40cm. Basal leaves linear-lanceolate, stems almost leafless. May - Aug. Fairly common but often inaccesible in rocky places. **K D** (**Ma,** I endemic) FE II 350

APIUM

7. *Apium graveolens* Hairless biennial up to 1m. Leaves shining. Umbels with very short stalks or none. Bracteoles 0. Common in marshy ground near sea. May - July. **K D** (**Ma,** Mi, I) FE II 351

8. *A. nodiflorum* Fool's Watercress. Procumbent or ascending perennial up to 1m. Bracteoles 5-7. May - July. Common in wet places. **K D** (**Ma,** Mi, I) FE II 351

PETROSELINUM

9. *Petroselinum crispum* Parsley. Hairless biennial. May - June. Occasional escape from cultivation. K D (**Ma,** Mi, I) FE II 352

RIDOLFIA

10. *Ridolfia segetum* Hairless annual to 1m. Leaves 3-4 pinnate, with filiform segments: upper ones often reduced to sheath only. Rays 10-60, bracts and bracteoles absent. Fruit about 2mm. June - Aug. Field weed. Common. K D (**Ma,** I) FE II 352

AMMI

11. *Ammi visnaga* Annual or biennial up to 1m. leaves 1- to 3-pinnate with narrowly linear lobes. Rays very numerous. Bracts 1-2-pinnatisect; bracteoles slender and tapering. May June. Rare. (From garden specimen × 1/2). K (quotes Barceló 1867-1877). D Ll FE II 353

12. *A. majus* Hairless annual to 1m. Rays 15-60. Bracts trifid or pinnatisect with very narrow lobes. May - July. Common, often a field weed growing with *Ridolfia segetum*. **K D** (**Ma,** Mi) FE II 353

Others recorded for Mallorca:

Anethum graveolens **K** D adds ? FE II 341

Magydaris panacifolia Pubescent perennial. Basal leaves simple or shallowly lobed. Cauline leaves pinnate, with 3-5 broad, crenate obtuse segments. Petals white. Fruit ovoid, hairy. Rare. **K D** FE II 344

Bupleurum tenuissimum Resembles *B. semicompositum*, but most umbels have only 2 or 3 rays. Local (Prof. Llorens). Not Bl in FE II 348

Sison amomum Doubtful. Ll omits. D (quotes FE). Bl in FE II 352

In other islands:

Magydaris panacifolia subsp. *femeniesii* Bolós & Vigo Minorca: endemic subsp. cf. FE II 345 (Subsp. not described)

Bupleurum rigidum Ibiza. Not Bl in FE II 349

Plate 46

UMBELLIFERAE (4): *LIGUSTICUM, (CAPNOPHYLLUM), FERULA, PASTINACA, TORDYLIUM, LASERPITIUM, THAPSIA, TORILIS, (TURGENIA), (ORLAYA), DAUCUS, PSEUDORLAYA*

LIGUSTICUM

1. *Ligusticum lucidum* subsp. *huteri* Subglabrous perennial. Leaves 3-5-pinnate, basal like cauline but with smaller terminal segments. Rays 11-16. Bracts few or 0, bracteoles 5-8. Umbel enlarged in fruit. (Fruit and leaf segment × 2. Other details show size of segments of basal leaf and of lateral umbel in flower rays of umbels terminating main branches 20 mm. July. Rare. **K** D (**Ma,** endemic subsp.) FE II 356

FERULA

2. *Ferula communis* Giant Fennel. Robust perennial. Stem up to 3m. Terminal umbels surrounded by denser and smaller stalked umbels. May.- June. Local. (× about 1/20). **K D** (**Ma, Mi, I**) FE II 358

PASTINACA

3. *Pastinaca lucida* Shining Parsnip. Robust biennial to 1m. Basal leaves (shown here) simple, cordate. Lower cauline leaves pinnate, upper entire, shining bright green. May - Aug. Common in mountains. (Main illustration × about 0.75). **K D** (**Ma, Mi,** endemic) FE II 364

TORDYLIUM

4. *Tordylium apulum* Annual. Rays 3-8. Bracts and bracteoles ciliate. Outer petal of outer flowers enlarged. Apr.- Aug. Rare. (Flowers of Greek specimen with details × 2). **K** D (**Ma, Mi**) FE II 367

LASERPITIUM

5. *Laserpitium gallicum* Curry-scented perennial 160 cm. Leaves up to 5-pinnate. Rays 20-50: bracts and bracteoles numerous. Corolla white. June - Sept. Local in mountains. (Pinna from 3-pinnate leaf × 2/3: 4-winged fruit × 1, dorsal and end-on: from Spanish mainland). K **D** Ll (**Ma**) FE II 370

THAPSIA

6. *Thapsia villosa* Hairy perennial up to 2m. (From garden specimen x 1/15: fruit × 1). K: 'la forme des îles Baléares se rapproche beaucoup du *T. villosa*'. **D** (gives '*Thapsia villosa* L. subsp.'). Ll omits. Probably does not occur here, records = 7. FE II 370

7. *Thapsia gymnesica* Rosselló & Pujadas. Stems solitary, 60-80cm. Basal leaves withering before flowering: blade up to 50cm, 4-pinnate, segments rounded, margins revolute. Stem with sheaths only. Umbels terminal, rays 5-10, raylets 20-30. Bracts and bracteoles 0. Petals yellow. Fruit as 6, but not all winged. May - July. Dry places, local. **K D,** though not by this name. (**Ma, Mi,** endemic) Not described in FE

TORILIS

8. *Torilis nodosa* Knotted Hedge-parsley. Annual, often procumbent. Peduncle short or absent, rays short, concealed by fruit. Fruits at centre of umbel tuberculate, at periphery with inner mericarp tuberculate, outer spiny. Mar.- May. **K D** (**Ma, Mi, I**) FE II 371

9. *T. webbii* Jury Resembles 8, but leaves bipinnate, peduncles longer, and both mericarps spiny. Locally common. (**Ma**) Described by S.L. Jury in *Botanical Journal of the Linnaean Society* (1987), 95: 293-299.

10. *T. arvensis* Field Hedge-parsley. Annual up to 1m. Bracts 0-1, outer petals generally longer than inner. Inner mericarp tuberculate and outer spiny. May - June. Fairly common. **K D** (**Ma, Mi**) FE II 371

DAUCUS

11. *Daucus carota* Wild Carrot. Several subsp. here: subsp. *major* common, with pubescent leaves, flattish umbels becoming strongly contracted in fruit (main illustration). (Lower details subsp. *drepanensis*, nearly glabrous with fleshy green leaves (small segment × 1) and large globular heads (× 1/4) which remain convex in fruit. Common, especially near sea). Mar. Apr. **K D** (**Ma, Mi, I**) FE II 374

PSEUDORLAYA

12. *Pseudorlaya pumila* Resembles *Daucus* sp., but bracts linear or sometimes 3-fid. Fruit 7-10mm. Apr.- May. Local on maritime sands. **K D** (**Ma, Mi, I**) FE II 375

Other species recorded from Mallorca:
Capnophyllum peregrinum Ll lists (**Ma**) Not Bl in FE II 358
Torilis japonica Dubious. Bl not excluded in FE II 371
T. leptophylla Annual, slightly resembling *T. nodosa*, but erect, with peduncles >2 cm. Rays 2-3, short but easily visible. K D Ll (**Ma**) FE II 371
Turgenia latifolia B (quotes Bianor). D and Ll omit. Not Bl in FE II 372 *Orlaya daucoides* (L.) Greuter (*O. kochii*) B Ll (**Ma, Mi**) Not Bl in FE II 372

In Ibiza:
Elaeoselinum asclepium Ibiza FE II 368
Thapsia garganica Ibiza FE II 370

Plate 47

PYROLACEAE: *MONOTROPA*
ERICACEAE: *ERICA, ARBUTUS*
PRIMULACEAE: *PRIMULA, CYCLAMEN, ASTEROLINON,
(GLAUX), ANAGALLIS, SAMOLUS, CORIS*

PYROLACEAE: *MONOTROPA*

1. *Monotropa hypopitys* Yellow Bird's Nest. Saprophytic plant without chlorophyll. May - Sept. Local, but increasing, under *Quercus ilex*. K **D (Ma)** FE III 5

ERICACEAE

ERICA

2. *Erica arborea* Tree Heath. Tall branched shrub. Feb.- May. Local in sheltered places in the Sierra. **K D (Ma,** Mi, I) FE III 7

3. *E. multiflora* Low shrub. Usually some flowers; mainly Aug. - Sept. Common in dry rocky places. **K D (Ma,** Mi, I) FE III 7

ARBUTUS

4. *Arbutus unedo* Strawberry tree. Tree or shrub (flowering when only 1m or so). Oct.- Jan. Common in hilly regions. **K D (Ma,** Mi, I) FE III 11

PRIMULACEAE

PRIMULA

5. *Primula vulgaris* subsp. *balearica* Mallorcan Primrose. Very like the widespread subsp. *vulgaris* (absent here), but flowers paler and more scented. Local, in pockets where snow stands in winter. Apr.- July. **K D** (Ma) FE III 16

CYCLAMEN

6. *Cyclamen balearicum* Some flowers almost throughout year. Apr. - May. Common in rocky places. **K D (Ma,** Mi, I) FE III 25

ASTEROLINON

7. *Asterolinon linum-stellatum* Small and easily overlooked. Apr. Local, in dry stony places. K **D (Ma,** Mi, I) FE III 27

ANAGALLIS

8. *Anagallis tenella* Bog Pimpernel. Stems creeping, rooting at nodes. Apr.- Sept. Rare in marshy places. (From British specimen). **K D** (Ma) FE III 28

9. *A. arvensis* Scarlet Pimpernel. Annual. Flowers blue or red. Petals fringed with glandular hairs. Maritime plants are often rather fleshy. Apr.- May. Common. **K D (Ma,** Mi, I) FE III 28

10. *A. foemina* Similar, but always blue. Petals without glandular hairs or with very few. Widespread, but much less common than 9. Apr. - May. My Mallorcan specimen was quite distinctive, and seemed to be this species. **D** ?Ll (gives ?Ma, ?Mi, ?I) FE III 28

11. *A. monelli* Perennial. Stem terete (stem in 9 and 10 is quadrangular). Flowers blue. Apr.- May. (From garden specimen). **D** Ll omits. (?Ma, ?I) Not Bl in FE III 28

SAMOLUS

12. *Samolus valerandi* Brooklime. Damp places, brackish or fresh water. May - June. Common in suitable habitats. **K D (Ma,** Mi, I) FE III 29

CORIS

13. *Coris monspeliensis* Much branched. May. Local in sandy places. **K D (Ma,** Mi, I) FE III 29

Also recorded for Mallorca:
Glaux maritima K (quotes Barceló 1867-1877). Ll omits.?Bl in FE III 28

In Minorca:
Erica scoparia FE III 8
Lysimachia minoricensis Endemic. FE III 27
Anagallis minima Bl excluded in FE III 28

Plate 48

PLUMBAGINACEAE: *LIMONIUM*

This is a difficult genus, and a high proportion of plants are hybrids persisting by apomixis. Upwards of 30 species and subspecies are recorded for Mallorca, many of them endemic to Mallorca or to the Balearic Islands: others occur only in Minorca, Ibiza or the smaller islands. The classification is constantly being revised, and it is not generally possible to give an exact FE equivalent for Knoche's names or for the names used by M. Erben in his recent classification, used here (see bibligraphy: essential reading for any serious study of this genus).

The plants are mostly perennials. The shape of the basal leaves are important for identification, also the general form and pattern of branching of the inflorescence, including non-flowering branches with a single reduced scale at the tip (see B1, bottom right), and sterile branches which have imbricate reduced bracts at the tip (B2). The branches of the inflorescence usually have a small scale at the base, and the shape and size the largest of these is occasionally helpful in identification.

The inflorescence is a panicle with terminal spikes of 1-5-flowered spikelets. The number of spikes per centimetre and the form of the bracts are important. Each spikelet is enveloped below by 3 bracts. The middle one is often hidden, but the inner bracts is longer than the outer, and both these are easily seen. The relative lengths of these bracts and their anatomy in terms of size and shape, width of hyaline border, arrangement of nerves and whether these stop short of the edge of the bract or run out beyond the edge are important.

The plants illustrated here have been identified by M. Erben, and the names are those he uses. The illustrations are intended to give some idea of the variation in form within this genus, and are not adequate for identification. Erben's papers should be consulted for precise information (see bibliography). The specimens were chosen to show a wide range of forms, and characteristically 3 out of 5 are hybrids, (× 3/4 - 1, details × about 4).

1. *Limonium minutum* (L.) Chaz. (cf *L. minutum* and *L. caprariense* in FE III 43) × *L. virgatum* (Willd.) Fourr. (cf *L. oleifolium* subsp. *oleifolium* FE III 46) Leaves small, papillose-hairy, in cushion-like rosettes at apex of short woody branches. Inflorescence is zig-zag, with a few short sterile branches at base. Spikelets 1-3-flowered, hardly curved. Aug.Sept. Rocky places.

2. *L. camposanum* Erben spec. nov. × *pseudoebusitanum* Erben (cf *L. inarimense* subsp. *ebusitanum* FE III 45). Plant has numerous long broad 1-veined spathulate leaves with small mucro. Branches all fertile, up to 7cm, with 7-9 spikelets per cm each with 2-4 flowers. Tip of coloured part of bract excurrent nearly to edge of membranous margin. Aug. - Sept. Rocks in Campos area.

3. *L. virgatum* (Willd.) Fourr. (cf *L. oleifolium* in FE III 46) Leaves are linear to spathulate with 1 vein, on long basal branches. Numerous sterile branches present. Spikelets about 4 per cm, curved, with 1 or 2 flowers. Inner bract has reddish-brown margin, more or less hyaline near apex. Aug. - Sept. Common in sandy saline soils.

4. *L. connivens* Erben (cf *L. duriusculum* FE III 46) A fairly compact plant with few stems. Leaves rounded at the ends, slightly curved under at edges, mostly 1-veined, but larger ones may have a few pinnately arranged smaller veins. Branching starts near base of stem, rather short straight branches coming off in a regular zig-zag arrangement at an angle of 50-70°. There are 4-6 2-4-flowered spikelets per cm (ie spikelets more or less contiguous). Long uncinate teeth of calyx in fruit are striking. Aug. - Sept. (× about 3/4) Mainly on East coast.

5. *L. echioides* This species at least is easily identified, and its specific name derives from the name Linnaeus used (though the genus was *Statice*, not *Limonium).* A bushy much-branched annual with small curved spikelets (1-2 per cm). The inner bract is tuberculate. Apr. - May. Fairly common on beaches. FE III 50

Plate 49

OLEACEAE: *FRAXINUS, OLEA, PHILLYREA*
GENTIANACEAE: *BLACKSTONIA, CENTAURIUM*

OLEACEAE

FRAXINUS

1. *Fraxinus angustifolia* Ash. Tree resembling *Fraxinus excelsior*, the common Ash of northern Europe, but with brown rather than black buds. Locally common. (× 1/2) K lists as cultivated plant. **D** (**Ma,** introduced) FE III 54

OLEA

2. *Olea europaea* Olive. Tree up to 15m. Underside of leaves scaly. Flowers in axillary panicles. Drupe green. Introduced, common only as cultivated plant, but wild plants with spiny lower branches may also be found. May - June. K lists as cultivated plant. **D** (**Ma,** Mi, I) FE III 55

PHILLYREA

3. *Phillyrea angustifolia* Shrub, to 2.5m. Underside of leaves without scales. Leaves with 4-6 pairs of veins, lower running a long way up the leaf, rather obscure. Flowers in short axillary racemes, calyx thick, shallowly lobed. Drupe blue-black, 6-8mm, ovoid at first, then globose. Mar.- June. Fairly common in dry, rocky places. (× 2/3, details × 5). **K D** (**Ma,** Mi, I) FE III 55

4. *P. latifolia* Like 3, but up to 15m. Juvenile leaves more or less ovate, mature leaves lanceolate to elliptical, 7-11 pairs of veins, not prominent, but easily seen, short and clearly forked distally. Drupe globose, 7-10mm. Mar.- June. Not common. (× 1/2: left hand detail juvenile leaf × 1 from garden specimen). **K D** (**Ma**) FE III 55

GENTIANACEAE

BLACKSTONIA

5. *Blackstonia perfoliata* Yellow-wort. Hairless, glaucous annual. Very variable (several subspecies occur here). Corolla with 6-12 lobes. Jan.- Sept. Common in a wide variety of habitats. **K D** (**Ma,** Mi) FE III 56

CENTAURIUM

6. *Centaurium erythraea* subsp. *erythraea* Common Centaury. Hairless biennial, to 50cm. Rosette leaves present at flowering time, obovate. Flowers in corymbiform cyme, the calyx 1/2-3/4 as long as corolla-tube. Apr.- Aug. Local. **K D** (**Ma,** Mi) FE III 57

7. *C. pulchellum* Hairless annual, without basal rosette at flowering time. Stem with 2-4 internodes, usually dichotomously branched from below the middle. Flowers in dichasial cyme, often deep pink or white. Apr.- May. Fairly common in dry places. **K D** (**Ma**) FE III 59

8. *C. tenuiflorum* Hairless annual, sometimes with weak leaf-rosette. Stem with 5-9 internodes, branched above. Branches strict. Calyx nearly equalling corolla-tube. Apr.- May. Very common, especially near the sea. **K D** (**Ma,** Mi, I) FE III 59

Hybrids occur between 6, 7 and 8. Angles of divarication of inflorescence branches vary from less than 15° (?strict = *C. tenuifolium*) to about 30° (?patent = *C. pulchellum*). These do not seem to show any regular pattern of association with more or less cauline internodes, or branching above or below the middle of the stem.

9. *C. spicatum* Hairless annual or biennial. Stem often branched from base or middle. Inflorescence a spike or very short-stalked raceme. June - Oct. Very local in dry saline habitats. **K D** (**Ma,** Mi, I)) FE III 59

10. *C. maritimum* Hairless annual or biennial. Flowers yellow (less common) or pinkish-yellow (var. *erubescens* Willk.). Dry grassy places mainly near sea. Apr. - July. **K D** (**Ma**) FE III 59 (upper illustration here probably *C. bianoris* (Sennen) Sennen, whose status is uncertain, possibly *C. maritimum* × *C. tenuiflorum* common endemic plant of Mallorca and Ibiza).

Other species in Mallorca:
Jasminum fruticans Rare in Arta region (Prof. Llorens). Not Bl in FE III 53
Centaurium quadrifolium López & Jarvis subsp. *barrelieri* (Duf.) López. Ll lists for Ma. Not described in FE

In Minorca, or recorded for Bl unspecified:
Centaurium linariifolium Smythies records from Bl. D quotes FE. ?Bl in FE III 59
Cicendia filiformis Minorca. FE III 56
Centaurium enclusense Minorca endemic. FE III 58

Plate 50

APOCYNACEAE: *NERIUM, VINCA*
ASCLEPIADACEAE: *GOMPHOCARPUS, CYNANCHUM, VINCETOXICUM*
RUBIACEAE: *SHERARDIA, CRUCIANELLA, ASPERULA*

APOCYNACEAE

NERIUM

1. *Nerium oleander* Oleander. Shrub, up to ca 2m here. May June. From garden specimen. Formerly native in Mallorca, now probably only as introducton, though sometimes in apparently wild situations. K lists as cultivated in Mallorca, wild in Ibiza. **D** (**Ma,** I) FE III 68

VINCA

2. *Vinca difformis* Periwinkle. Creeping perennial. Dec.- July. Common in hedgerows in cultivated areas. **K D** (**Ma,** Mi, I) FE III 69

ASCLEPIADACEAE

GOMPHOCARPUS

3. *Gomphocarpus fruticosus* Bristly Silkweed. Shrub, to 2m. June - July. Occasional. **K D** (Introduced **Ma,** I) FE III 70

CYNANCHUM

4. *Cynanchum acutum* Stranglewort. Woody climber. June - Aug. Shrubby places, not common. (From Greek specimen). **K D** (Ma, Mi, I) FE III 71

VINCETOXICUM

5. *Vincetoxicum nigrum* Twining perennial. May - Aug. Fairly common in northern part of mountain range. (× 1/3). (**Ma,** Mi) FE III 71
6. *V. hirundinaria* subsp. *intermedium* Perennial herb up to 1m, sometimes twining. May - July. Occasional in mountains. (Main illustration from Mallorcan specimen, detail from garden specimen, possibly a different subspecies). **K D** (**Ma,** Mi) FE III 72

RUBIACEAE

SHERARDIA

7. *Sherardia arvensis* Field Madder. Procumbent annual. Mar. - July. Very common in open grassy places and field margins. **K D** (**Ma,** Mi, I) FE IV 3

CRUCIANELLA

8. *Crucianella maritima* Woody perennial, up to 50cm, usually less. May - Oct. Locally common in higher parts of beaches. **K D** (**Ma,** Mi, I) FE IV 4
9. *C. angustifolia* Hairless annual, lowermost leaves linear-lanceolate. Corolla 3-5mm long, pale yellow, exceeded by free bract, which is lomg pointed and lanceolate. Bracteoles easily visible. May - July. Occasional. (From garden specimen × 1/2). K **D** Ll (Ma, I) FE IV 4
10. *C. latifolia* Annual, stems slightly hairy. Lowermost leaves obovate-elliptical. Bracts slightly connate, concealing bracteoles. Corolla 5-7.5mm long, yellowish-purple, exceeding bract. May- June. Widespread in rocky places. (× 1/2). K **D** (**Ma,** I) FE IV 4

ASPERULA

11. *A. laevigata* Scrambling perennial. Apr.- July. Occasional in damp places. **K D** (**Ma,** Mi) FE IV 12
12. *A. arvensis* Annual. Apr.- May. Rare. (From garden specimen. Found later as street weed in Puerto Alcudia, looking similar, but more robust with many more flowers). K H Ll (**Ma,** Mi, I) FE IV 13

Other possible species for Mallorca:
Asperula cynanchica K (quotes Barcelò 1867-1877). Ll lists (Ma, I). FE IV 10

In Ibiza only:
Asperula paui Font Quer (cf. *A. aristata* FE IV 6)

Plate 51

RUBIACEAE (2): *GALIUM, VALANTIA, RUBIA*

GALIUM

1. *Galium elongatum* Straggling weak plant, with stout stems and long internodes. Middle stem leaves up to 3.5cm, rough on margin and midrib, blunt. Inflorescence dense. Corolla pure white. May - June. Local in wet places. (× 1, detail corolla × 3). K D (**Ma, Mi, I**) FE IV 21

2. *G. lucidum* Stoloniferous perennial, erect or ascending. Longest leaves 10-30 × 1-2mm, straight, usually shorter than the internodes. Inflorescence dense. Corolla white, 3-5mm diameter. Apr.- June. Occasional in mountain areas and Alcudia peninsula. (Part of inflorescence, slightly enlarged. Details × 3). **K** D (**Ma, I**) FE IV 25

3. *G. cinereum* Stoloniferous perennial, resembling 2, but glaucous, Stems erect or ascending. Leaves up to 8 -15 × 0.5-2mm, shorter than the internodes. Inflorescence dense, much branched. Corolla white, lobes apiculate. Apr.- June. Locally common in rocky places in mountain areas. (Upper and lower part of stem × 1; 5 internodes between omitted). **K** D (**Ma**) FE IV 25

4. *G. crespianum* Erect or ascending almost glabrous perennial. Leaves bright green, shining, the longest 3-4cm, curved, and usually exceeding the internodes. Flowers ochre to yellow (not white, in spite of FE description), in a dense pyramidal inflorescence. May - Sept. Locally common in rocky places. (× 1, details × 3). **K** D (**Ma, I**, endemic) FE IV 25

5. *G. balearicum* Stoloniferous perennial, stems up to 10cm, usually less. Leaves dark green, up to 5mm long, lanceolate to ovate with a short hyaline point. Flowers few. Corolla about 1.5mm, purplish red, segments not apiculate. Very local in rock crevices. (× 1, details of flower × 6, detail of plant as seen in rock crevice × 2). **K** D (**Ma**, endemic) FE IV 30

6. *G. setaceum* Slender annual. Upper leaves linear, lower linear lanceolate. Flowers minute, purple. Fruit densely covered in fine bristles. Apr.- May. Local, dry rocky places. (× 1, detail of flower × 4). **K** D (**Ma**) FE IV 34

7. *G. aparine* Goosegrass, Cleavers. Straggling annual. Leaves 6-8 in a whorl with rough edges covered in downwardly pointing bristles. Corolla up to 1.7mm, greenish-white. Fruit green or purplish, covered in hooked bristles. Mar.- Apr. Common in cultivated ground. (× 1, detail of flower × 4). K D (**Ma, Mi, I**) FE IV 35

8. *G. tricornutum* Rough Corn Bedstraw. Scrambling annual, stems rough with downward curved prickles. Flowers often in threes, the central hermaphrodite and the lateral male. Corolla creamish, with acute lobes. Fruit 3-5mm diameter, with fruiting pedicels strongly recurved. Male flowers often develop small vestigial fruit. Apr.- May. Common, cultivated ground. (× 1, slightly enlarged). **K** D (**Ma, Mi, I**) FE IV 35

9. *G. verrucosum* Annual, erect or ascending. Flowers mostly in 3-flowered axillary cymes, the lateral 2 male, the central hermaphrodite flower developing characteristic warty fruit. Fruiting pedicels often recurved. Mar.- Apr. Common, cultivated ground. (× 1, details slightly enlarged). **K D** (**Ma, Mi, I**) FE IV 35

10. *G. parisiense* Scrambling slender annual up to 40cm. Stems rough with prickles directed downwards. Peduncles 1-3 × length pedicels. Inflorescence widely divaricate in fruit. Corolla 0.5-1mm, lobes acute, erect, greenish inside and reddish outside. Fruit 0.8-1mm, glabrous or with curved hairs, finely papillose. Locally common, especially at sides of roads. May. (× 1, corolla and fruit × 3). **K** D (**Ma, Mi**) FE IV 35

11. *G. divaricatum* Much branched slender annual. Stems with sparse downwardly directed prickles, nearly smooth above. Peduncles 3 -7 × length of filiform pedicels. Pedicels deflexed in fruit. Flowers minute, bright yellow or reddish-yellow. Fruit up to 0.7mm, glabrous, finely papillose. Apr.- May. Local in dry rocky places. (× 1. Upper detail to show pedicels recurved in fruit slightly enlarged, lower details of flower and fruit × 10). **K** D (**Ma, Mi**) FE IV 36

12. *G. murale* Small annual, up to 20cm. Leaves in whorls of 4-6. Corolla ca 0.7mm, greenish. Fruit up to 1.5mm, cylindrical, with hooked bristles at the apex and along lower margin. Mar. - Apr. Common on walls and rocks. (× 1, details flower and fruit × 6).**K** D (**Ma, Mi, I**) FE IV 36

VALANTIA

13. *Valantia hispida* 13 and 14 are annuals with 3-flowered axillary cymes of small yellowish flowers. Peduncles and pedicels become thickened, deflexed and coalesced to enclose fruit of the hermaphrodite central flower (outer two are male). *V. hispida* is usually erect, fruit has 15-25 soft hyaline bristles at apex. Common, walls and rocky places. (× 1, details × 2). **K** D (**Ma, I**) FE IV 38

14. *V. muralis* Variable here, often small erect annual up to about 10cm. Fruit differs from that of 13 in having a hard bristly horn projecting from the top of the fruit. On sea shores there is a distinctive prostrate form with a rosette of stems with very regular imbricate fleshy leaves between rows of fruits, superficially like a large version of *Selaginella denticulata*. Apr.- May. Common in dry places. (× 1, detail of flower × 5). **K** D (**Ma, Mi, I**) FE IV 38

RUBIA

15. *Rubia peregrina* Climbing perennial. Leaves ovate-elliptical, dark and shining, in whorls of 4-8. Flowers 5-merous. Corolla greenish yellow. Fruit a black berry. Apr.- Sept. Common in thickets and on walls. (Left, × 1/2, and lower flower × 2). **K** D (**Ma, Mi, I**) FE IV 38

16. *R. angustifolia* L. Resembles *R. peregrina*, but has curved linear leaves, prickly on both sides and with revolute margins. It may be a distinct species. (Right, × 1/2, and upper flower × 2). **K D** (**Ma, Mi, I**) FE IV 38

Other possible species in Mallorca:
Galium debile ?Bl in FE IV 21
G. palustre 'All except...?Bl...' in FE IV 21 (? after Knoche's '*G. palustre* subsp. *elongatum*', = *G. elongatum*). D (quotes FE). Ll omits. Probably not in Bl.
Rubia tinctorum (not native) FE IV 38.

Possibly in Ibiza:
Galium corrudifolium ?Ibiza. Bl in FE IV 25

Plate 52

CONVOLVULACEAE: *CUSCUTA, CRESSA, CALYSTEGIA, CONVOLVULUS, IPOMOEA*
BORAGINACEAE (1) *HELIOTROPIUM*

CUSCUTA Dodder.

Annual parasites, with clusters of small flowers along twining leafless stems. Only *C. epithymum* is common.

1. *Cuscuta campestris* Stems stout, yellowish. Flowers 2-3mm, glomerules 10-12mm. Stigmas capitate. Not Bl in FE. Native of N. America. **K** Hansen. (From Greek specimen, enlarged). (Ma, Mi, ?I) FE III 75
2. *C. epithymum* subsp. *kotschyi* Flowers ca 2.5mm, usually pinkish. Glomerules 5-6mm diameter. Calyx lobes keeled, fleshy, (but not nearly semicircular in cross section: see *C. planiflora* below). Stigmas elongate. Apr.- May. Common, mainly on dwarf shrubs. (Slightly enlarged). **K D** (**Ma,** Mi, I) FE III 77
3. *C. epithymum* subsp. *epithymum* Flowers 3-4mm, usually white. Glomerules 7-10mm. Calyx lobes acute or acuminate, membranous. Stigmas elongate, stigmas and styles together much longer than ovary. Common, often on Leguminosae. (Slightly enlarged). **K D** (**Ma,** Mi, I) FE III 77

CRESSA

4. *Cressa cretica* Branched greyish shrublet. Saltmarshes. Apr. May. Local. **K D** (**Ma,** I) FE III 78

CALYSTEGIA Bindweed.

5. *Calystegia soldanella* Sea Bindweed. Perennial rhizomatous plant, not or hardly climbing. May. Maritime sands. **K D** (**Ma,** Mi, I) FE III 78
6. *C. sepium* Bellbine. Climbing perennial. May - Sept. Common. **K D** (**Ma,** Mi, I) FE III 78

CONVOLVULUS Bindweed.

7. *Convolvulus lineatus* Silvery slightly bushy perennial with many appressed hairs. Basal leaves on shoots widened and scarious at base. May. Rare. (From garden specimen). K (quotes Bianor 1914 1917). D B gives 2 locations. Ll (Ma, I) FE III 81
8. *C. cantabrica* Shrubby perennial with spreading hairs at least below. Basal leaves as 8. May - Oct. Locally common, mainly on sandy soils. **K D** (**Ma,** Mi) FE III 81
9. *C. tricolor* Herbaceous annual or perennial, erect, not twining. K (quotes Barceló 1867-18770) D FE III 81

10. *C. siculus* Annual or short-lived perennial. Stems trailing, rarely twining. Leaves stalked. Mar.- June. Rare. (From Cretan specimen: detail from Mallorcan specimen found subsequently). K D Ll (**Ma,** Mi, I) FE III 81
11. *C. arvensis* Bindweed, Cornbine. May - Sept. Very common. **K D** (**Ma,** Mi, I) FE III 81
12. *C. althaeoides* Mallow-leaved Bindweed. Two subspecies here: subsp. *althaeoides* with mostly patent hairs and broad lobed leaves, and subsp. *tenuissimus* with almost entirely appressed hairs and narrow leaf-lobes (detail on right). Mar. July. Both are common. **K D** (**Ma,** Mi, I) FE III 82

IPOMOEA Morning Glory.

Many cultivated tropical species of *Ipomoea* occur here with showy blue, purple and violet flowers. The following species is probably native:

13. *Ipomoea sagittata* Climbing or creeping perennial. Leaves arrow-shaped. Sepals rounded or notched with a terminal mucro. July - Sept. Usually on *Arundo*. (Specimen from Spanish mainland). K lists for Minorca only. **D** records. Ll treats as alien. (Ma, Mi, I) FE III 82

BORAGINACEAE (1): *HELIOTROPIUM*

14. *Heliotropium europaeum* Heliotrope. Much branched annual, up to 4ocm. May - Oct. Locally common roadside and street weed. **K D** (**Ma,** Mi, I) FE III 85
15. *H. curassavicum* Hairless, fleshy procumbent marine perennial. May - Sept. Fairly common on higher parts of beaches. Native of N. and S. America. K **D** (Introduced **Ma,** Mi, I) FE III 86

Other species recorded for Mallorca:
Cuscuta planiflora Flowers 1.5-2.5mm, white. Calyx lobes swollen, nearly semicircular in cross-section. **D** (Ma) FE III 77
C. approximata Flowers 3-4mm. Calyx tube golden-yellow, shiny and reticulate when dry, the lobes with terminal fleshy appendage. **D** ?Ll (?Ma) Not Bl in FE III 77
Calystegia silvatica D (quotes FE). Ll omits. Dubious. Bl in FE III 79
Convolvulus pentapetaloides Annual or short-lived perennial. Leaves sessile, more or less linear. Corolla blue with yellow centre. **K D** Ll (Ma, I) FE III 81

In other islands:
Convolvulus valentinus Ibiza. Not Bl in FE III 81
Heliotropium supinum Minorca. FE III 86.

Plate 53

BORAGINACEAE (2) *LITHOSPERMUM, NEATOSTEMA, BUGLOSSOIDES, ALKANNA, ECHIUM, NONEA, (SYMPHYTUM), ANCHUSA, BORAGO, (MYOSOTIS), (LAPPULA), CYNOGLOSSUM*

LITHOSPERMUM Gromwell.

1. *Lithospermum officinale* Erect perennial. Leaves with conspicuous lateral veins beneath. Corolla yellowish-white, with 5 longitudinal folds inside. Nut shining white. May - Aug. Rare. (From British specimen). K **D** Ll (Ma) FE III 86

NEATOSTEMA Yellow Gromwell.

2. *Neatostema apulum* Bristly annual. Corolla with glandular hairs inside and outside. May - Aug. Occasional in dry shady places. **K D** (**Ma**, I) FE III 86

BUGLOSSOIDES Gromwell.

3. *Buglossoides arvensis* Small hairy annual resembling 1. Corolla white, with 5 longitudinal bands of hairs inside. Nut brownish. Feb.- Oct. Occasional in grassy places. **K D** (**Ma**, Mi, I) FE III 87

ALKANNA Alkanet.

4. *Alkanna lutea* Hispid annual, with glandular hairs and bristles with white bulbous bases. Leaves elliptical. Corolla hairless on outside, with cylindrical tube and funnel-shaped limb with a ring of hairs in throat. Local. May - June. **K D** (**Ma**, Mi, I) FE III 96

ECHIUM Bugloss.

5. *Echium asperrimum* Rough bugloss. Intricately branched biennial, up to 1m, hispid with stinging bristles. Corolla 13-18mm, deep pink. Mouth oblique, tube much wider at mouth than base (characterstic of *Echium*). stamens long-exserted, with red filaments. May - Sept. Rare. (Small illustration of specimen from rubbish tip near Arenal shows habit; larger illustration shows tip of branch slightly reduced). K D Ll (**Ma**, Mi, I) FE III 98
6. *E. italicum* Pale bugloss. Roughly hispid biennial with a branched pyramidal inflorescence up to 1m. Corolla 10-12mm, pale blue or pink, or white. Stamens long-exserted, with pale filaments. May - Sept. Common in waste and grassy places. (Small illustration shows habit; larger one top of inflorescence slightly reduced). **K D** (**Ma**, Mi, I) FE III 98
(Intermediates between 5 and 6 probably occur here: FE III 98)
7. *E. plantagineum* Tall much branched annual or biennial, softly hairy. Corolla 18-30mm, deep blue, reddish or purple, with hairs on the veins and margins. 2 stamens usually exserted. Apr. - July. Common near the sea. **K D** (**Ma**, Mi, I) FE III 99
8. *E. sabulicola* Bristly biennial or perennial, often procumbent. Similar to 9, but corolla uniformly hairy outside. 2 stamens usually exserted, shorter than in 7. Apr.- July. Common in sandy places near the sea. **K D** (**Ma**, Mi, I) FE III 99
9. *E. parviflorum* Annual or biennial, usually erect, up to 40cm. Corolla 10-30mm, stamens included. Calyx 6-8mm, lobes narrow, enlarging in fruit to up to 15mm, × 3-6mm at base. Mar. - June. Common. K **D** (**Ma**, Mi, I) FE III 100
10. *E. arenarium* Ascending biennial, up to 25cm, usually less. Corolla 6-11mm, all stamens included. Calyx 5-7mm, enlarging in fruit up to 10mm, × 2-3mm wide at base. Mar.- June. Common on sandy ground near the sea. **K D** (**Ma**, I) FE III 100

NONEA

11. *Nonea vesicaria* Hispid and glandular-pubescent annual or biennial. Corolla funnel-shaped, brownish-purple. Lobes erect, not spreading. Apr.- May. Rare. (From Portuguese specimen). **D** (Ma, I) FE III 103

ANCHUSA Alkanet.

12. *Anchusa azurea* Blue Alkanet. Tall perennial, easily distinguished from *Echium* species by the regular actinomorphic corolla. Nutlets longer than wide. Common field weed. May - Aug. **K D** (**Ma**, Mi, I) FE III 108

BORAGO Borage.

13. *Borago officinalis* Hispid annual, distinguished from *Echium* and *Anchusa* species by very short corolla tube and cone of fused blackish anthers. May - Sept. Common, especially by road sides. **K D** (**Ma**, Mi, I) FE III 109

CYNOGLOSSUM Hounds Tongue.

14. *Cynoglossum creticum* Blue Hound's Tongue. Biennial. Corolla actinomorphic with short tube. Mar.- May. Common, roadsides and field margins. **K D** (**Ma**, Mi, I) FE III 120
15. *C. cheirifolium* Biennial. Apr.- May. Locally common, often in dry grazed turf. **K D** (**Ma**, Mi, I) FE III 120

Other possible species for Mallorca:
Echium creticum. K ('forme maritimum', probably *E. plantagineum*). D quotes FE. Ll lists for Ma. FE III 99
Symphytum tuberosum K (quotes Cambessèdes 1824-1827). B gives one location. Ll lists for Ma, Mi. FE III 104
Anchusa undulata Pubescent biennial or perennial. Setae not conspicuously white or tubercle-based. Calyx lobed to not more than 2/3. K (quotes Barceló 1867-1877). D omits. B gives 2 locations. Ll lists for Ma, Mi. Not Bl in FE III 107
A. officinalis K lists this 'selon mes notes'. He seems to add this only in cases of doubt (?no specimen). D lists for Ma. H doubts. Ll omits. FE III 107
A. arvensis K and B (quote Barceló 1867-1877, who records it as very rare). D and Ll omit. FE III 108
Asperugo procumbens K (quotes Barceló 1867-1877). D and Ll omit. Not Bl in FE III 110
Myosotis arvensis B gives one location. D quotes FE. Ll lists for Ma and Formentera. Bl not excluded in FE III 112
Myosotis ramosissima **K** D B quotes many records, but not recent ones. Ll lists for Ma. FE III 112
Lappula squarrosa K (quotes Bianor 1914-1917). ?D. Ll lists for Ma. ?Bl in FE III 118

In Minorca:
Cerinthe minor FE III 94

Plate 54

VERBENACEAE: *VITEX, VERBENA, LIPPIA*
CALLITRICHACEAE: *CALLITRICHE*
LABIATAE (1): *TEUCRIUM*

VERBENACEAE.

VITEX

1. *Vitex agnus-castus* Chastity bush. Shrub, up to ca 15m here. Flowers pink or blue: petals often reflexed. Aug.- Oct. Uncommon, stream beds. **K D (Ma,** Mi, I) FE III 122

VERBENA

2. *Verbena officinalis* Vervain. Slender perennial. May - Oct. Common, dry roadsides, waste ground. **K D (Ma,** Mi, I) FE III 123

LIPPIA

3. *Lippia nodiflora* Creeping perennial. Flowers white. May. - Sept. (From garden s pecimen). Rare, shores. **K D (Ma,** Mi, I) FE III 123

4. *L. canescens* As above, but often woody at the base. Flowers lilac. July - Aug. Rare. (Specimen from Spanish mainland). **D** (Native of S. America, introduced Ma). FE III 123

CALLITRICHACEAE: *CALLITRICHE*

The morphology of this genus varies with the habitat. Only aquatic forms are shown here, but these too are variable.

5. *Callitriche stagnalis* Water starwort. Plant of fresh water, with floating rosettes of leaves. Submerged leaves elliptical, stalked. Flowers axillary, minute, monoecious. Fruit with erect or spreading styles. Mar.- Sept. (From British specimen). **K D** (Ma, Mi) FE III 125

6. *C. brutia* Submerged leaves linear, often notched at the apex. Styles deflexed, appressed to sides of fruit. (Specimen from Spanish mainland). K lists for Minorca only. **D** (Ma, Mi) FE III 125

LABIATAE (1): *TEUCRIUM*

7. *T. asiaticum* Dwarf shrub with distinctive foul smell. Apr. - Sept. Common in north eastern mountains. **K D (Ma,** Mi endemic) FE III 132

8. *T. scordium* Water germander. Hairy perennial, garlic-scented when crushed. Damp stream banks. Rare. May - Sept. (From Cretan specimen). **K D** (Ma, Mi) FE III 132

9. *T. botrys* Cut-leaved germander. Small annual. Apr.- May. Occasional in mountains. K **D (Ma)** FE III 132

10. *T. chamaedrys* Wall germander. Shrubby rhizomatous perennial. May - Sept. Fairly common in hilly areas. **K D (Ma,** Mi) FE III 132

11. *T. flavum* subsp. *flavum* (with ca 20mm leaves, velvety beneath) and subsp. *glaucum* (with leaves ca 10mm, glaucous beneath). Shrubby perennial. Rather uncommon in hilly districts. (From garden specimen: subsequently found in Mallorca, but not in flower: both were subsp. *flavum*). May Aug. **K D (Ma,** I) FE III 132

12. *T. marum* Cat Thyme. Small shrub with white woolly stems. Rather like 14, but larger, and not spiny. (Specimen from Spanish mainland). K lists for Ma. H (quotes a record in 1984). D quotes FE. Ll gives ?Ma, ?Mi. FE III 133

13. *T. balearicum* (Pau) Castroviejo, & Bayón. Prickly shrublet forming neat hemispherical 'hedgehog' with tiny, greyish triangular leaves. May - July. Common in mountains. **K D (Ma** endemic) (Not described in FE, but cf. *T. subspinosum* FE III 133)

14. *T. cossonii* subsp. *cossonii* Dwarf shrub, leaves and stems greyish with branched hairs. Resembles *T. polium* subsp. *capitataum*, but leaves have less than 3 crenations on each side. Calyx 5-6mm. Rare in rock crevices. (From garden specimen). First described 1972. **D** (Ma endemic) FE III 134

15. *T. dunense* Sennen Woolly, compact shrublet with simple heads of white or pinkish-red flowers. Up to 5 crenations on each side of leaves. Calyx up to 5mm May - July. Common in sandy places in mountains and near sea, including higher parts of beaches. **K D (Ma)** (cf. *T. polium* subsp. *polium* in FE III 134)

16. *T. capitatum* L. differs from *T. dunense* in longer spreading stems and compound heads of pink flowers. May - June. Common in similar habitats, also sometimes inland. **K D (Ma,** Mi, I) (cf. *T. polium* subsp. *capitatum* and *pii-fontii* in FE III 134)

Also recorded from Mallorca:
Verbena supina Shortly bristly annual, usually procumbent. Stems quadrangular with rounded angles separated by narrow grooves. Corolla lilac, about equalling calyx, in short spikes. D lists for Mi only. Ll gives Ma, Mi. Not Bl in FE III 123
Teucrium campanulatum K (quotes Barceló 1867-1877). D Ll (Ma) FE III 131
T. polium L. subsp. *aguilasense* Puech. Ll (Ma) ?no FE equivalent
T. polium L. subsp. *purpurascens* (Bentham) Puech. Ll (Ma) (cf. subspecies of *T. polium* as described in FE III 134)

In other islands:
Callitriche truncata Minorca Not Bl in FE III 124
C. lenisulca Clavaud Minorca (not described in FE)
Teucrium subspinosum (endemic Minorca) FE III 132
T. cossonii subsp. *vedranense* Llorens. (endemic Ibiza)

Plate 55

LABIATAE (2) *AJUGA, SCUTELLARIA, PRASIUM, MARRUBIUM, SIDERITIS, PHLOMIS, LAMIUM, MOLUCCELLA, BALLOTA*

AJUGA Bugle.

1. *Ajuga iva* Tufted perennial, woolly-haired. Flowers occasionally purple. Fairly common in dry places. May - Oct. **K** D (**Ma,** Mi, I) FE III 129

2. *A. chamaepitys* Ground pine. Usually annual. Leaves tripartite with linear segments. May - Sept. Rare in mountains. (From garden specimen). K D and Ll list. (Ma). FE III 129

SCUTELLARIA Skullcap.

3. *Scutellaria balearica* Stems decumbent. Flowers few, corolla about 6mm. May. Rather local in moist shady places in mountains. **K D** (**Ma** endemic) FE III 136

PRASIUM

4. *Prasium majus* Small shrub with shining glabrous leaves. May. Very local. **K D** (**Ma,** Mi) FE III 137

MARRUBIUM Horehound.

5. *Marrubium vulgare* Aromatic, woolly-haired perennial. Stamens included in corolla-tube. Corolla-tube included in calyx. Apr. - Sept. Common in waste places. (Main illustration × 1/2). **K D** (**Ma,** Mi, I) FE III 138

SIDERITIS

6. *Sideritis romana* Hairy annual. Apr. - Aug. **K D** (**Ma,** Mi, I) FE III 143

PHLOMIS

7. *Phlomis italica* Straggling shrub, densely covered in star-shaped hairs. Flowers usually uniformly dull pink (these with dark lower lip were found on N. side of Puig Roig). May - June. Common in mountains. **K D** (**Ma,** Mi endemic) FE III 145

LAMIUM

8. *Lamium amplexicaule* Henbit. Annual. Feb. - Oct. Weed of gardens and recently cultivated ground. **K D** (**Ma,** Mi, I) FE III 148

MOLUCCELLA

9. *Moluccella spinosa* Bells of Ireland. From garden specimen. (K quotes Barceló 1867-1877). D (Ma, garden escape) FE III 149

BALLOTA Horehound.

10. *B. nigra* subsp. *foetida* Perennial. Calyx limb regularly dentate, lobes 5. May - Sept. Occasional field weed. K **D** Ll (**Ma,** Mi) FE III 150

Also recorded for Mallorca:
Ballota hirsuta Calyx limb irregularly dentate, lobes 10 or more. K D Ll (Ma, I) FE III 150

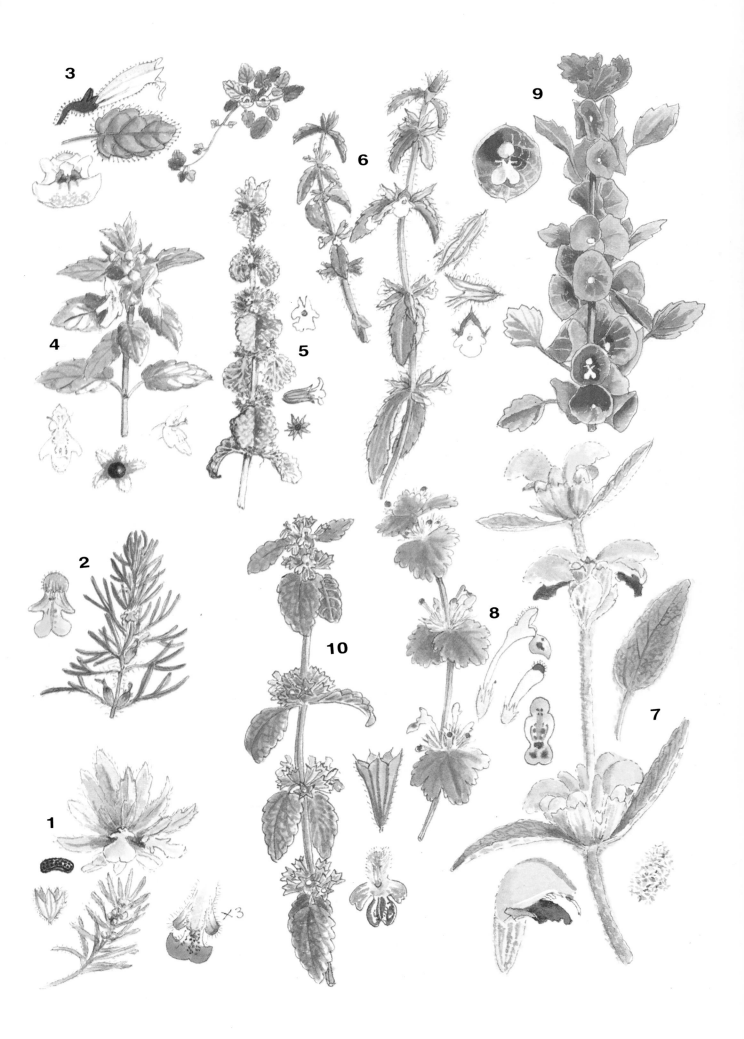

Plate 56

LABIATAE (3) *STACHYS (NEPETA), PRUNELLA (MELISSA), SATUREJA, MICROMERIA, CORIDOTHYMUS (ORIGANUM), THYMUS, MENTHA, ROSMARINUS, LAVANDULA, SALVIA*

STACHYS Woundwort

1. *Stachys germanica* Downy woundwort. White hairy perennial up to 1m. Knoche's account suggests flowers are often (?always) white here. Stamens and corolla tube well exserted from calyx. up to 1m. Apr. - Aug. Rare. (From garden specimen). K **D** (**Ma**) FE III 153
2. *S. ocymastrum* Hairy annual, up to 50cm. Mar. - June. Common in cultivated areas. **K D** (**Ma**, Mi, I) FE III 157
3. *S. arvensis* Annual. Mar. - May. Occasional in mountain areas. (Specimen here differed from FE description in ascending habit and lobed upper lip of corolla). **K D** (**Ma**) FE III 157

PRUNELLA Self-heal.

4. *Prunella laciniata* Perennial, up to 30cm. This specimen, from Teix, only had entire leaves. July. Higher parts of mountains, not common. K **D** (**Ma**) FE III 162

SATUREJA.

5. *Satureja ascendens* (Jordan) Maly (*Calamintha sylvatica* subsp. *ascendens*) Common Calamint. Perennial. Calyx with 13 veins, lower two teeth up to 3.5mm, long-ciliate. Hairs in mouth of calyx hardly exserted (details of calyx, side-view and from below, × 2). Aug. - Oct. Locally common in mountain areas. **K D** Ll (**Ma**, Mi, I) FE III 166
6. *S. calamintha* (L.) Scheele (*C. nepeta* subsp. *glandulosa*) Resembles 5, but calyx shorter, with lower 2 teeth 1-2mm, rarely ciliate, and hairs in mouth of calyx further exserted. Aug. - Oct. Very rare. (Calyx × 2, from Italian specimen). D's *C. nepeta* subsp. probably refers to *S. rouyana*). K seems to treat the 2 species separately and to have seen both. B (gives one high location). ?Ll. (?Ma, ?I) FE III 166

S. rouyana Briq. (*Calamintha rouyana*) Strong-smelling pubescent herb. Sterile branches prostrate, flowering stems ascending. Leaves grey green, blunt, hairy on both sides. Flowers in axillary cymes, exceeding the leaves. Calyx with hairs in throat which protrude between the teeth. Corolla twice length calyx, bright blue. (Description after Barceló's '*C. nepeta* Link. & Hoffm.': K gives '*C. nepeta* Barc. as alternative name for his *C. rouyana* Rouy) The distinctive feature seems to be the bright blue corolla: Knoche mentions that the leaves are often reddish beneath. **K D** ('*C. nepeta* subsp.') Very rare. (Ma endemic) Appears in FE index as 5 or 6 above). Not illustrated.

MICROMERIA

7. *Micromeria filiformis* Dwarf shrub, prostrate or ascending. Leaves ovate-triangular, the lower cordate at base. Flowers white, often in pairs, sometimes in pedunculate cymes of up to 4 flowers. A very variable plant which has been divided into several subspecies. Of these subsp. or var. *rodriguezii* is distinctive and endemic. May - June. Common in dry stony places. **K D** (**Ma**, Mi, I) FE III 168
8. *M. microphylla* Very much like 1. Usually erect or ascending. Lower leaves rounded or wedge-shaped at base. Verticillasters of up to 6 or 7purple flowers. May - June. Local. **K D** (**Ma**) FE III 168
9. *M. nervosa* Like 1 and 2, but leaves larger (up to 1cm), sometimes more or less linear in the inflorescence. Calyx with long, dense, spreading hairs. (× 1 1/2). Apr. - June. **K D** (**Ma**, I) FE III 169

CORIDOTHYMUS Thyme.

10. *Coridothymus capitatus* (L.) Reichenb. fil. (previously included in *Thymus* or *Thymbra*). Dwarf shrub, to 50cm. Calyx flattened, 2-lipped (front and back, × 6, below and to left of portion of plant × 1). June - Oct. Local, mountains S. of Sóller. **K D** (**Ma**, I) FE III 174

THYMUS

11. *Thymus richardii* subsp. *richardii* June - July. Much branched shrublet.

Leaves 7-12 × 3-6mm. Inflorescence capitate. Corolla 7-9mm. Very rare. K D (Ma endemic) FE III 180

MENTHA Mint.

12. *Mentha pulegium* Penny-royal. Perennial. Lower two calyx teeth longer and narrower than upper (equal in other species here). Apr.Aug. Common where water stands seasonally. **K D** (**Ma**, Mi) FE III 184
13. *M. aquatica* Flowers in a dense terminal head, usually with other dense whorls below. July - Oct. (From British specimen). **K D** (**Ma**, Mi, I) FE III 185

(The next two are sometimes difficult to distinguish. Many hybrids occur, and many species and hybrids are cultivated. Scent is often distinctive).

14. *M. suavolens* Apple-scented Mint. Variable perennial. Leaves with more or less rounded, rugose. Flowers usually pale. Whorls crowded except at the base. May - Oct. Local. K D (**Ma**, Mi, I) FE III 185
15. *M. spicata* Spearmint. Leaf length usually more than twice width, leaves not rugose. Whorls of flowers usually more widely spaced than in 14, flowers usually a deeper colour. **K D** (**Ma**, I) FE III 186

ROSMARINUS Rosemary.

16. *Rosmarinus officinalis* Rosemary. Shrub, either erect or trailing, variable in size, up to 2m but flowering when only a few centimetres high. Common. Jan. - Mar. **K D** (**Ma**, Mi, I) FE III 187

LAVANDULA Lavender.

17. *Lavandula dentata* Leaves toothed. Bracts broad, deep purple. Locally common in dry, rocky places. Jan. - May. **K D** (**Ma**, I) FE III 188

SALVIA Sage.

18. *Salvia verbenaca* Leaves deeply lobed or pinnatifid. Bracts in inflorescence shorter than calyx. Some flowers cleistogamous. Feb. - June. Common. **K D** (**Ma**, Mi, I) FE III 192

Other records for Mallorca:

Likely, but mostly rare:
Lavandula stoechas Resembles 17, but with entire leaves. See Rita J. et al. (1985) (Ma, Mi, I) FE III 187
Nepeta cataria K lists for Mi only. B (quotes Garcia, collecting 1905), Ll lists for Ma, Mi. FE III 159
Prunella vulgaris Ll lists. H gives for Mi. (Ma, Mi, I) Not Bl in FE III 162
Acinos arvensis K (quotes Willkomm 1873). B (quotes Barceló as having seen it alive). Ll records for Ma. FE III 166
Micromeria graeca Resembles 7 and 8, but the small leaves are linear in the inflorescence. K and B (quote Hermann 1912). Ll lists. (Ma, I) FE III 169
Satureja barceloi (Willk.) Pau (*Thymus inodorus* Desf., *Micromeria inodora*) K (quotes Barceló 1867-1877). D Ll (Ma, I) FE III 170)
Origanum vulgare L. subsp. *virens* (*O. virens*) K thought introduced, though it was evidently locally common in Barceló's time. Ll lists. (Ma). FE III 171
Thymus herba-barona Loisl. Ll lists. Recent record. (Ma) Not Bl in FE III 180
Salvia viridis Ll lists. (Ma). Not Bl in FE III 192

Unlikely, or transient garden escapes:
Melissa officinalis K D H Ll (Ll treats as alien). (Ma, Mi, I) FE III 162
Lavandula latifolia Probably introduced. ?Bl in FE III 188
Salvia officinalis K D B Ll treat as alien. FE III 189
S. sclarea Clary. K (quotes Willkomm 1873). B gives two locations. Ll treats as alien. FE III 190

In other islands:
Stachys brachyclada Ibiza FE III 157
Nepeta nepetella Minorca (also dubious old records for Ma) FE III 160
Thymus vulgaris Ibiza FE III 176
Thymus richardii subsp. *ebusitanus* endemic Ibiza FE III 180

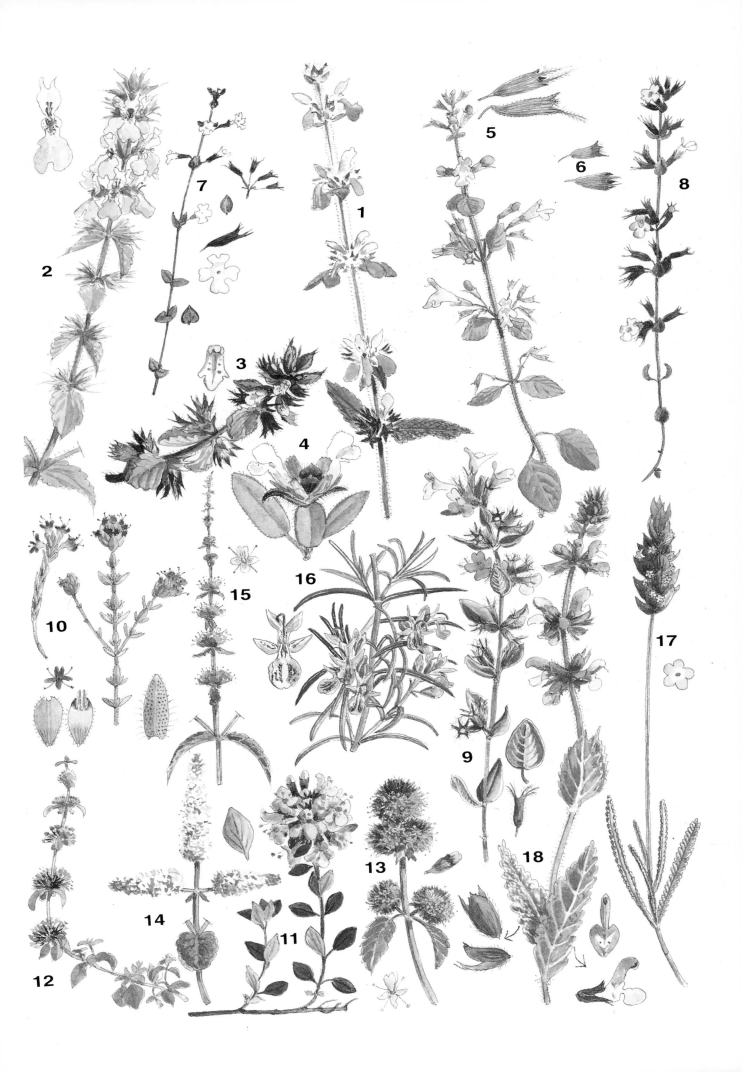

Plate 57

SOLANACEAE: *LYCIUM, HYOSCYAMUS, WITHANIA, SOLANUM, LYCOPERSICON (MANDRAGORA), (DATURA), NICOTIANA*

LYCIUM Tea tree.

1. *Lycium intricatum* Much branched spiny shrub to 2m. May. - Sept. Very local. **D** (**Ma**) Not Bl in FE III 194

HYOSCYAMUS Henbane.

2. *Hyoscyamus albus* Annual to perennial sticky herb up to about 50cm. May - Sept. Common in waste places. **K D** (**Ma**, Mi, I) FE III 195

WITHANIA

3. *Withania somnifera* Grey stellate-tomentose shrub to 1.2m. Flowers in clusters of 4-6; corolla ca 5mm. Apr. - Aug. Not common. (Specimen from Spanish mainland). **K D** Ll (**Ma**, Mi, I) FE III 195
4. *W. frutescens* Glabrous to sparsely hairy shrub to 1.8m. Flowers usually solitary, rarely up to 3 together. Apr. - Aug. Rare. (Specimen from Spanish mainland). K records from Ibiza only. **D** Ll (**Ma**, Mi, I) FE III 195

SOLANUM

5. *Solanum nigrum* Black Nightshade. Annual to 70cm, variably hairy. Mar. - May. Very common, waste places. **K D** (**Ma**, Mi, I) FE III 197
6. *S. luteum* (including *S. villosum* Miller and *S. alatum* Moench, treated in FE as two subspecies, one villous, one more or less glabrous). Very like 5, but fruit red. Mar. - May. Common. **K D** (**Ma**, Mi, I) FE III 197

7. *S. dulcamara* Woody Nightshade. Scrambling perennial. Apr. - June. Rare. (From British specimen). B gives one location. **K D** Ll (Ma, I) FE III 198
8. *S. bonariense* Shrub to 3m. May - Aug. Commonly cultivated, more or less naturalised near houses. Introduced from S. America. **D** (**Ma**) FE III 199
9. *S. linneanum* Hepper & Jaeger (*S. sodomeum)* Prickly stellate-pubescent shrub, to 3m or more. Sept. - June. Local near the sea. Introduced from Africa. **K D** (**Ma**, I) FE III 199

LYCOPERSICON

10. *Lycopersicon esculentum* Tomato. Apr. - Aug. Common casual. (**Ma**) FE III 199

NICOTIANA Tobacco.

11. *Nicotiana glauca* Shrub Tobacco. Glabrous, glaucous shrub to 6m. May - Oct. Fairly common, especially in the south. Introduced from S. America. **D** (**Ma**, I) ?Bl in FE III 201

Others recorded from Mallorca:
Lycium europaeum K (quotes Barcelò 1867-1877). D lists. Ll treats as alien. Bl in FE III 194
Solanum ottonis Hyl. Ll lists for Ma. (cf. *S. suboblatum*, not Bl in FE III 197
Mandragora autumnalis K (quotes Bianor 1910-1914). Old record, probably no recent records. ?Bl in FE III 200
Datura stramonium H and Ll list. (Ma, I). Bl excluded in FE III 200

Also in other islands:
Datura innoxia Ibiza. Not Bl in FE III 200
Nicotiana rustica ?Ibiza. ?Bl in FE III 201

Plate 58

SCROPHULARIACEAE: (1) *VERBASCUM, SCROPHULARIA, ANTIRRHINUM, MISOPATES, CHAENORRHINUM*

VERBASCUM Mullein.

1. *Verbascum creticum* Tall greyish biennial. Flowers solitary in the axil of each bract. Upper petals with reddish blotches at base. Mar. - May. Rare. (Detail only × 1/2, specimen from Spanish mainland). K **D** Ll (Ma, Mi, I) FE III 209
2. *V. thapsus* subsp. *crassifolium* Greyish biennial. Inflorescence usually unbranched. Bracts and upper leaves long-decurrent. At least lower bracts with several axillary flowers. Filaments of upper stamens with white hairs, filaments of lower two sometimes glabrous. May - July. Locally common around Sóller and Lluc. (× 1/10: details × 1). K **D (Ma)** FE III 211
3. *V. boerhavii* Woolly biennial. Inflorescence usually unbranched. Flowers in clusters. Calyx 6-9mm, with oblong to linear lobes. Stamens with violet hairs. May - July. Locally common, especially near Lluc. (× 1/10: details × 1). K **D** Ll **(Ma)** FE III 211
4. *V. sinuatum* Grey woolly biennial, with wavy-edged, round lobed pinnatifid basal leaves. Inflorescence much-branched. Flowers in clusters of up to 10. Calyx 2-4 mm. Stamens 5, with violet-haired filaments. Apr. - Oct. Common, roadsides and waste places. (Plant × 1/20: leaf from 1st year rosette × 1/4, part of inflorescence × 1/2). K **D (Ma,** Mi, I) FE III 213

SCROPHULARIA Figwort.

5. *Scrophularia peregrina* Annual. Leaves irregularly saw-toothed. Apr. - July. Common in NW mountains, occasionally elsewhere. K **D (Ma,** Mi, I) FE III 218
6. *S. auriculata* Water Betony. Perennial. Stems winged. Apr. - July. Common in damp situations. K **D (Ma,** Mi, I) FE III 219
7. *S. ramosissima* Small shrubby perennial, woody at base. Stems up to about 30cm, a great many on each plant, patent, ascending and erect. Persistent dead stems rigid and hard and therefore prickly, not spiny. Leaves toothed, pinnate or bipinnate, dark green and shining. Flowers crimson or crimson and white up to 4mm. Apr. - July. Local on beaches. K **D (Ma)** FE III 220

(A note in *FE* comments that 'Plants from Islas Baleares referred to this species are in many features transitional to *S. canina*'. The main difference between the two plants here is one of habit).

8. *S. canina* Perennial, up to 1m, with less than 10 sparingly branched erect stems. Flowers with broad white margin, more than 4mm (?subsp. *bicolor* as described in FE for S.E. Europe only). Apr. - May. Common, roadsides. K **D (Ma,** Mi, I) FE III 220

ANTIRRHINUM

9. *Antirrhinum majus* Snapdragon. Perennial. Apr. - May. ?Usually garden escape. K **D (Ma)** FE III 223

MISOPATES

10. *Misopates orontium* Weasel's Snout. Annual. Apr. - May. Common, walls and roadsides. K **D (Ma,** Mi, I) FE III 224

CHAENORRHINUM

11. *Chaenorrhinum origanifolium* subsp. *origanifolium* May. - July. Rare, mountain peaks. (From garden specimen). K **D (Ma)** FE III 225
12. *C. rubrifolium* subsp. *rubrifolium* April - May. Rare, sandy places. (Illustration after line drawing in Knoche's Flora Balearica coloured after description: actual size of corolla up to 13mm, of fruit 0.4-0.5mm). K **D** Ll (Ma, I) FE III 226

Other records for Mallorca:
Verbascum blattaria Ll lists for Ma. Not Bl in FE III 208
V. virgatum K (quotes Barcelò 1867-1877). B gives one location. Ll omits. Bl in FE III 208
V. nigrum K (quotes Barcelò 1867-1877, but questions record). B (recorded once in 1962). D lists. Ll omits. Bl in FE III 216

In Ibiza:
Chaenorrhinum origanifolium subsp. *crassifolium* FE III 225
C. formenterae Gand. (*C. rubrifolium* subsp. *formenterae* Ibiza and Formentera endemic subspecies) FE III 226

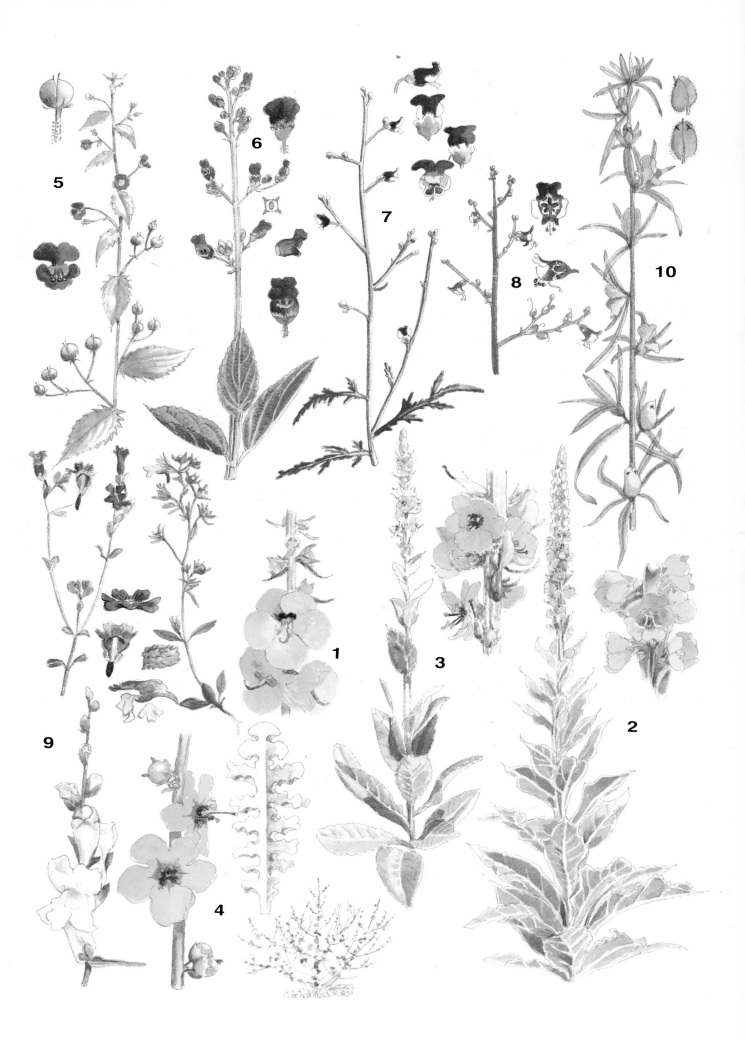

Plate 59

SCROPHULARIACEAE (2) *LINARIA, CYMBALARIA, KICKXIA*

LINARIA Toadflax.

1. *Linaria triphylla* Glabrous, glaucous annual, to 45cm. Leaves in whorls or some opposite or alternate. Flowers white, yellow or violet, with yellow boss and violet spur. Apr. - May. Common, fields and wayside near the sea. (Slightly enlarged). **K D** (**Ma**, Mi, I) FE III 230

2. *L. chalepensis* Glabrous annual, to 40cm. Flower white to greenish white. Spur 8-11mm. Upper calyx lobe much shorter than others. Apr. Rare. (From Greek specimen × 2/3). K **D** Ll (Ma, Mi, I) FE III 231

3. *L. repens* Glabrous perennial. Corolla white to pale violet with violet veins. Boss white, sometimes very slightly yellow-tinged at base. (From British specimen). K (quotes Barceló 1867-1877). Ll lists. ?Bl in FE III 231

4. *L. pelisseriana* Glabrous, glaucous annual to 50cm. Apr. - May. Rare. K lists for Mi only. (Specimen from Spanish mainland). **D** Ll (Ma, Mi) FE III 232

5. *L. aeruginea* subsp. *pruinosa* Ascending glaucous perennial. Inflorescence with reddish stalked glands, especially calyx. Apr. - July. Local, in higher parts of mountains. (Slightly enlarged). **K D** (**Ma**, endemic subsp.) FE III 233

CYMBALARIA

6. *Cymbalaria muralis* Trailing perennial. Leaves with 5-9 lobes, hairless at maturity. Corolla up to 15mm, usually with yellow boss. Apr. - Aug. Common on walls, probably introduced. **K D** (**Ma**, Mi, I) FE III 237

7. *C. aequitriloba* subsp. *aequitriloba* Resembles 6, but leaves hairy at maturity, with 3-5 lobes. Boss on corolla always white or pale violet. Apr. - July. Common in damp shady places in mountains. (Larger illustration × 1 1/2, not the same specimen as smaller illustration, × 1). Rather variable here, including earlier erroneous records of *Cymbalaria hepaticifolia* (Poir.) Wettst. (Hansen 1985) **K D** (**Ma**, Mi) FE III 237

KICKXIA Fluellen.

8. *Kickxia cirrhosa* Annual, up to 90cm, stems very slender. Corolla violet. May - June. Sandy places near the sea. (Left hand illustration × 1, right × 3). **K D** (**Ma**, Mi) FE III 238

9. *K. commutata* Procumbent perennial, up to 70cm long. Leaves broadly ovate below, with sagittate to hastate base in peripheral part of plant. Pedicels long, glabrous except just below calyx. Corolla whitish, 11-15mm, with white or slightly yellowish lower lip and purple-spotted palate. (× 1 1/2). May - July. Occasional in short grass. **K D** (**Ma**, Mi, I) FE III 238

10. *K. spuria* subsp. *integrifolia* (numerous lateral flowering branches were present in the peripheral parts of this specimen). Glandular pubescent annual. Leaves with rounded or cordate base: petiole very short. May - Sept. Local in grassy places. **K D** (**Ma**, Mi, I) FE III 239

11. *K. lanigera* Procumbent densely villous annual. Leaves broadly ovate, usually cordate in distal part of stem. Corolla 8-11mm, bluish white with violet upper lip. Pedicels very hairy, longer or shorter than corolla. May - Sept. Occasional in grassy places. **K D** (**Ma**, I) FE III 239

Other possible species in Mallorca:
Linaria arvensis B (cultivated species). D Bl in FE III 236
L. simplex K (quotes Porta and Rigo 1885). B (possibly cultivated). D Ll (Ma, Mi) Bl in FE III 236
L. micrantha Glaucous annual. Corolla 2.5-5mm, lilac-blue. Spur 1mm or less. K lists for Ib only. D B Ll (Ma, I) FE III 236
Kickxia elatine Ll lists. (Ma, I). FE III 238

In other islands:
Linaria pedunculata Formentera FE III 228
Cymbalaria aequitriloba subsp. *fragilis* Minorca (endemic) FE III 237

Plate 60

SCROPHULARIACEAE (3) *DIGITALIS, ERINUS, VERONICA, SIBTHORPIA, PARENTUCELLIA, BELLARDIA*

DIGITALIS Foxglove.

1. *Digitalis minor* L. (*D. dubia* Rodr.) Like *D. purpurea*, but smaller and very hairy. May - July. Common in rock crevices in mountains. **K D** (**Ma,** Mi endemic) FE III 240

ERINUS

2. *Erinus alpinus* Small villous perennial with inconspicuous pinkish flowers. May - June. Local in rocky places in mountains. (Specimen from Spanish mainland). **K D** (Ma) FE III 241

VERONICA Speedwell.

3. *Veronica anagalloides* Annual. Calyx segments appressed to fruit. Capsule not emarginate (though appears so when beginning to dehisce). Apr. - Sept. Wet ditches, pond margins. **K D** (**Ma,** Mi, I) FE III 248

4. *V. anagallis-aquatica* Usually perennial. Lower leaves often stalked. Upper leaves sessile, all more or less amplexicaul. Bracts linear, equalling pedicels or shorter. Fruit orbicular or longer than broad. Apr. - Sept. Common in wet places. (Main illustration × 1/2, details × 3). **K D** (**Ma,** Mi, I) FE III 249

5. *V. catenata* Like 4, but all leaves sessile. Bracts lanceolate, usually exceeding pedicels. Fruit broader than long. Apr. Sept. Occasional in wet places. (Fruit and corolla × 4 from British specimen. Corolla × 4). K lists for Ibiza only. **D** ?Ll (?Ma, I) Not Bl in FE III 248

6. *V. arvensis* Erect annual. Leaves ovate, crenate, upper sessile, lower shortly petiolate. Corolla 2-3mm, all lobes deep blue. Capsule usually glabrous apart from marginal cilia, flat. Feb. - June. Common in dry places. **K D** (**Ma,** Mi) FE III 249

7. *V. verna* Erect annual. Lower leaves lanceolate or ovate, shortly petiolate. Upper leaves sessile, pinnatifid with narrow lobes. Corolla 3mm, deep blue. Capsule glandular-hairy, flat. Rare. (Garden specimen from British seed). D Seen by B in 1977. Ll lists. (Ma) Not Bl in FE III 249

8. *V. polita* Procumbent annual. Flowers 4-8mm, blue, the upper lobe usually darker. Capsule rounded, not flat or keeled. Dec. - June. Fairly common. **K D** (**Ma,** Mi, I) FE III 250

9. *V. persica* Buxbaum's Speedwell. Annual. Corolla 8-12mm. Capsule 2 lobed with widely divergent lobes, strongly keeled. Mar. - May. Very common, usually in cultivated ground. **D** (**Ma,** I) FE III 250

10. *V. hederifolia* subsp. *hederifolia* Annual. Leaves rather fleshy. Calyx lobes acute, cordate at base, with long cilia on the margins, erect in fruit. Corolla blue with white centre, upper lobe usually darker than others. Capsule 4-lobed, with long cilia, otherwise glabrous. Jan. - Mar. Common in cultivated ground. (Slightly reduced: details × 2). B also records subsp. *triloba* with mainly 3 lobed leaves and dark blue flowers. K **D** (**Ma,** Mi, I) FE III 250

11. *V. cymbalaria* Procumbent annual. Rather like 10, but corolla white. Calyx lobes patent in fruit, obtuse. Capsule ciliate. Jan. - Apr. Common in cultivated areas. **K D** (**Ma,** Mi, I) FE III 250

SIBTHORPIA

12. *Sibthorpia africana* Creeping perennial. Corolla up to 7mm, leaves up to 15mm. Jan. - Sept. Common in damp shady places in mountains. **K D** (**Ma,** Mi, I, endemic) FE III 252

PARENTUCELLIA

13. *Parentucellia viscosa* Annual. Apr. - July. Common in grassy places. **K D** (**Ma,** Mi, I) FE III 269

14. *P. latifolia* Annual. Mar. - May. Local, sandy places, often under pine trees. **K D** (**Ma,** Mi) FE III 269

BELLARDIA

15. *Bellardia trixago* Annual. Lower lip sometimes yellow. Apr. - July. Common in grassy places. **K D** (**Ma,** Mi, I) FE III 269

Also recorded for Mallorca:
Veronica beccabunga Resembles 4, but stems decumbent, rooting at nodes. Leaves thick, all petiolate. Ll lists. (Ma, Mi). Bl excluded in FE III 248
V. praecox K (quotes Willkomm 1867-1877). B (quotes Willkomm and adds that nobody else has found it). Ll omits. Very dubious. ?Bl in FE III 248

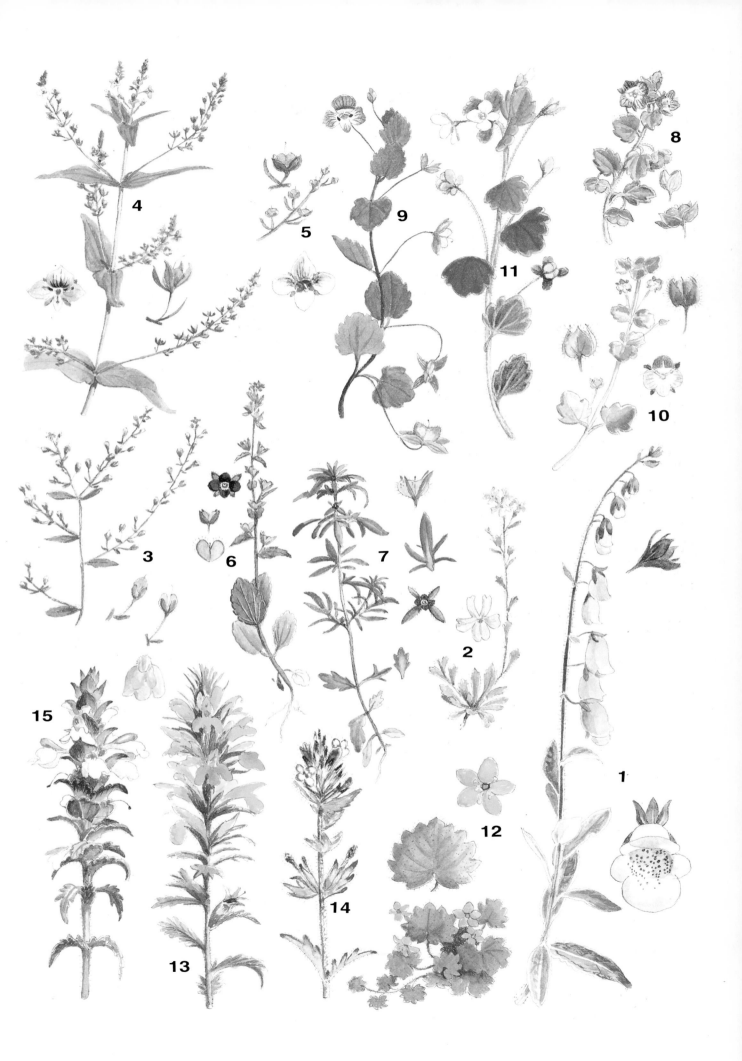

Plate 61

GLOBULARIACEAE: *GLOBULARIA*
(ACANTHACEAE: *ACANTHUS)*
OROBANCHACEAE: *OROBANCHE*

GLOBULARIACEAE: *GLOBULARIA*

1. *Globularia cambessedesii* Herbaceous perennial. Apr. - May. Local in rock crevices in northern mountains. **K D** (**Ma** endemic) FE III 282
2. *G. alypum* Small shrub. Heads up to 2.5cm.Corolla usually blue, occasionally white with pinkish base. Most of year, best Oct. - Apr. Locally common in dry scrub in hills. **K D** (**Ma**, Mi, I) FE III 283

OROBANCHACEAE: *OROBANCHE* Broomrape.

These are difficult to identify and variable. For definite identification live specimens should be used with a key. Illustrations here offer only tentative identification.

3. *Orobanche ramosa* Three rather ill-defined subspecies are recorded here. Main illustration and upper detail are subsp. *nana*, which seems commonest here, the two lower details are from a much-branched plant with numerous flowers, ?subsp. *mutelii* or *ramosa*. Apr. - Oct. Common. **K** and **D** (both only record subsp. *ramosa* for Ma). Bonafè records all three subspecies in the **text** of his book, but not in his *Tabulae Plantarum* Appendix II. Ll does not differentiate between subspecies. (**Ma**, Mi, I) FE III 288
4. *O. rosmarina* Possiby not previously recorded. Found by F. Rumsey, illustrations from his photographs. (Ma) Not Bl in FE III 288
5. *O. crenata* Corolla opening out at mouth, with large rounded and frilled lobes, white or pale pinkish- purple with darker veins. Apr. - June. **K D** (**Ma**, Mi, I) FE III 290
6. *O. loricata* (= *O. picridis* Schulyz ex Koch.) Long bracts often conspicuous. Corolla white or yellowish white with violet markings, usually glandular pubescent. May - July. **K D** (**Ma**) FE III 291

7. *O. minor* Resembles 6, but cluster of buds at top of immature inflorecence usually more domed than in 6 (which is usually broadly spire-shaped). Bracts less conspicuous than in 6. Flowers small, yellowish, usually purple tinged. June - Sept. **D** Ll (**Ma**) Not Bl in FE III 291
8. *O. clausonis* whole plant yellowish, glandular-pubescent. Calyx segments connate for about half their length, bifid with broad triangular teeth. Stigma orange or purple. Rare, possibly not previously recorded. (Illustration from Ma specimen, identified by F. Rumsey) (**Ma**) Not Bl in FE III 291
9. *O. hederae* Corolla creamish, sometimes purple-tinged, usually glabrous, with spreading lobes. May - July. Not common. (Main illustration from Mallorcan specimen: detail from British specimen). **K D** (**Ma**, Mi, I) FE III 292

(*O. balearica* Sennen & Pau is 9 according to Med-Checklist, though Knoche treats as two species).

10. *O. gracilis* Corolla yellow outside, shining dark red inside. May. - July. Rare. (From Greek specimen × 3/4). **K D** Ll (Ma, ?I) FE III 293

Also recorded from Mallorca:
Acanthus mollis Bear's Breech. Tall herbaceous perennial, somewhat resembling a large *Orobanche*, but with green pinnate leaves. May - July. Common garden escape, usually near houses. K D (**Ma**, Mi) FE III 283
Orobanche purpurea Smythies and B list. B adds 'A verificar'. Ll omits. ?Bl in FE III 289
O. foetida Corolla dark purplish-red outside, shining dark red inside. **K** D (Ma, Mi, I) FE III 293

In other islands:
Orobanche ramosa subsp. *mutelii* Ibiza. FE III 288
O. lavandulacea Ibiza. FE III 288
O. latisquama Ibiza. FE III 292
O. sanguinea Minorca. FE III 293

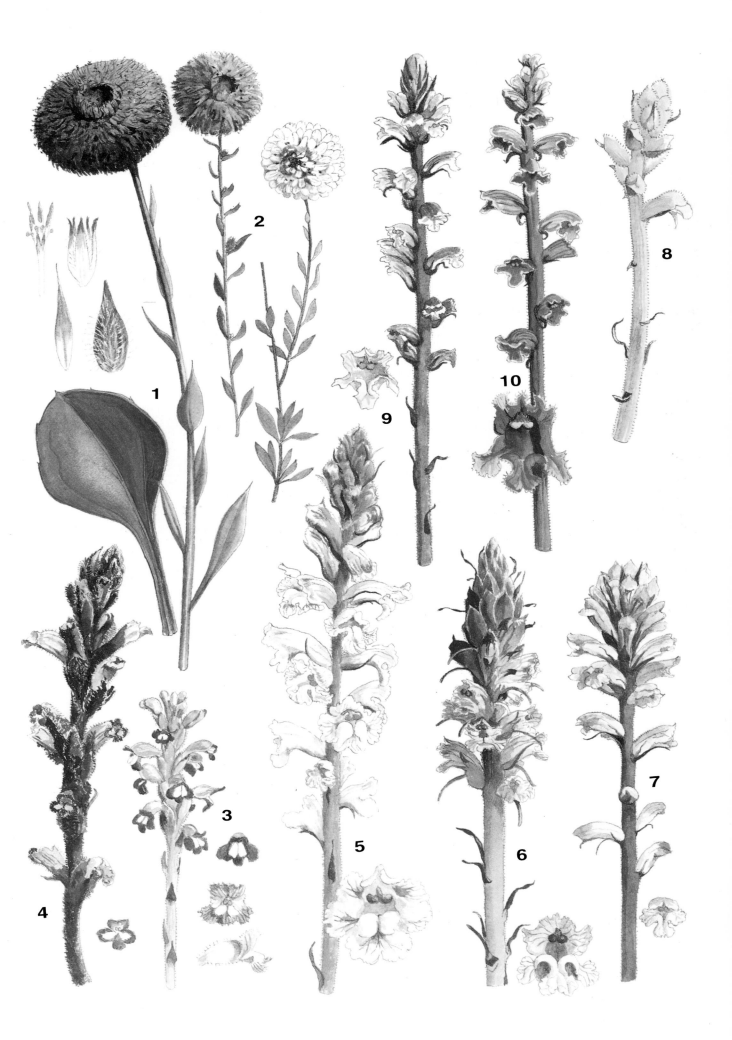

Plate 62

PLANTAGINACEAE: *PLANTAGO*
CAPRIFOLIACEAE: *SAMBUCUS, VIBURNUM, LONICERA*

PLANTAGINACEAE: *PLANTAGO*

1. *Plantago major* Plantain. Leaves broad, abruptly contracted into stalk. Anthers purple, becoming yellowish. Apr. - Nov. Common, waysides and waste places. **K D** (**Ma,** Mi, I) FE IV 39

2. *P. coronopus* subsp. *coronopus* Buck's horn plantain. Leaves hairy, not fleshy, pinnate. Bract subtending flower with broad base and long, narrow apex.Apr. - Oct. Common near the sea. **K D** (**Ma,** Mi, I) FE IV 40

Also here: *P. coronopus* subsp. *purpurascens* with purplish spikes. Bracts subtending flower ovate, subacute. Not common. D Ll (Ma, endemic subsp.). FE IV 40

3. *P. crassifolia* Leaves fleshy, glabrous or slightly hairy, usually with a few small teeth. Bract subtending flower short, rounded. Damp saline soils. Apr. - Oct. **K D** (**Ma,** Mi, I) FE IV 40

4. *P. lanceolata* Ribwort plantain. Perennial. Spike very dense. Bracts glabrous or shortly hairy, in this specimen (and often here) with long scarious point. Anterior sepals connate for most of length, glabrous or shortly hairy. Corolla lobes glabrous. Common in grassy places. Apr. - Nov. **K D** (**Ma,** Mi, I) FE IV 42

5. *P. lagopus* Rather like 4, but sometimes annual. Bracts and calyx densely villous with long hairs. Corolla- lobes usually sparsely hairy, long-acuminate. Apr. - May. In grassy places. **K D** (**Ma,** Mi, I) FE IV 43

6. *P. albicans* Perennial. Leaves densely silvery-haired, often wavy. Flower spike narrow, elongated, usually interrupted below. Stamens long exserted, with pale whitish anthers. Apr. - June. Local in dry places. **K D** (**Ma,** Mi, I) FE IV 43

7. *P. bellardii* Hairy annual, bright green, becoming grey-green on drying. Spike oval. Flowers white. Calyx lobes and bracts pointed. May - June. Local in dry stony or sandy ground. **K D** (**Ma,** Mi, I) FE IV 43

8. *P. afra* Annual, glandular-pubescent above. Leaves opposite. Flower spikes axillary. Apr. - June. Locally common in dry places. **K D** (**Ma,** Mi, I) FE IU 44

CAPRIFOLIACEAE

SAMBUCUS

9. *Sambucus ebulus* Danewort. Stout perennial, stems up to 2m (upper part stem much reduced, flower slightly enlarged, fruit × 1). July. - Sept. Locally common, especially round Lluc (where it seems to be a troublesome weed). **K D** (**Ma,** Mi, I) FE IV 44

VIBURNUM

10. *Viburnum tinus* Laurustinus. Shrub. Mature flower clusters white, buds pinkish. Dec. - Mar. Mountain rocks and roadsides in mountain areas. **K D** (**Ma**) FE IV 45

LONICERA

11. *Lonicera pyrenaica* subsp. *majoricensis* Small shrub. Flowers nearly actinomorphic. June. Rare in mountains. **K D** (**Ma,** endemic subsp.) FE IV 46

12. *L. implexa* Honeysuckle. Climbing shrub, sweetly scented. Apr. - June. Common, road sides and bushy places. **K D** (**Ma,** Mi, I) FE IV 47

Other species recorded for Mallorca:
Plantago serraria K (quotes Willkomm (1873), but adds 'A vérifier'). Ll omits. ?Bl in FE IV 40
P. argentea K (quotes Gandoger (1899), but adds 'Je crois qu'il s'agit d'une forme du précédent', i.e. *P. lanceolata*). Ll omits. ?Bl in FE IV 42
Sambucus nigra Introduced Ma, escaped in one locality (Bonafè). Bl excluded in FE IV 44

In Minorca:
Plantago macrorhiza D Not Bl in FE IV 40

Plate 63

VALERIANACEAE: *VALERIANELLA, FEDIA, CENTRANTHUS*
DIPSACACEAE: *CEPHALARIA, DIPSACUS, SCABIOSA*
(KNAUTIA)
CAMPANULACEAE: *CAMPANULA, LEGOUSIA, TRACHELIUM,*
SOLENOPSIS

VALERIANACEAE

VALERIANELLA

1. *Valerianella discoidea* Petals 5, blue. Fruit very hairy, surmounted by 'crown' with tips of teeth curled, filled with woolly hairs. Apr. - May. Common, disturbed ground. **K D** (**Ma**, Mi, I) FE IV 50
2. *V. eriocarpa* Petals 5, blue. Fruit and 'crown' slightly hairy. Teeth of crown short and straight, usually 5 or 6, but missing or very small sometimes - a variation which has been named *'V. muricata'* (Steven ex Bieb.) J. W. Loudon. This usually seems to have untoothed leaves; it is not a distinct species in FE. Apr. - May. Occasional in waste places. K D (**Ma**, Mi, I) FE IV 51
3. *V. microcarpa* Petals 4, pink. Fruit has only very small rim of calyx. Apr. - May. Common in waste ground. **K D** (**Ma**, Mi, I) FE IV 51

FEDIA

4. *Fedia cornucopiae* Annual. Easily distinguished from 5 and 6 by larger flowers with red markings. Apr. - June. (From Portuguese specimen). Mainly in the south. **K D** (Ma) FE IV 52

CENTRANTHUS

5. *Centranthus ruber* Dustman's breeches. Robust perennial. Spur at base of corolla tube. Stamen 1 only. Apr. - Sept. Common, usually as garden escape. **K D** (**Ma**, I) FE IV 55
6. *C. calcitrapae* Annual. Also has spur, but this is minute and difficult to see. Apr. - July. Common. **K D** (**Ma**, Mi) FE IV 56

DIPSACACEAE

CEPHALARIA

7. *Cephalaria squamiflora* subsp. *balearica* Robust perennial. Flowers always white. Aug. Rare in mountains. **K D** (Ma, I, endemic subsp.). FE IV 57

DIPSACUS

8. *Dipsacus fullonum* (= *D. sylvestris* Hudson.) Teasel. Tall prickly biennial. May - July. **K D** (**Ma**) FE IV 59

SCABIOSA

9. *Scabiosa cretica* Woody-based perennial. Leaves entire, mostly basal. Rocky places. May - July. Local on rocks in mountain areas. **K D** (**Ma**, Mi, I) FE IV 69
10. *S. maritima* L. (= *S. atropurpurea* L.) Straggling biennial. Upper leaves pinnately lobed. May - Sept. Common, roadsides and grassy scrub. **K D** (**Ma**, Mi, I) FE IV 71

CAMPANULACEAE

CAMPANULA

11. *Campanula erinus* Annual bellflower. May - June. Fairly common on walls and in dry sandy places. **K D** (**Ma**, Mi, I) FE IV 88

LEGOUSIA

12. *Legousia falcata* Leaves hairless. Calyx lobes curved, about 3 × length corolla. Apr. - May. Fairly common in mountain areas. K D (**Ma**) FE IV 94
13. *L. hybrida* Venus's Looking Glass. Leaves hairy. Calyx lobes straight, about twice length corolla. Apr. - May. **K D** (**Ma**, Mi) FE IV 94

TRACHELIUM

14. *Trachelium caeruleum* Throatwort. Perennial, superficially resembling 5, but without spurred corolla, and with 5 stamens. May - Sept. Locally common garden escape. B Ll (**Ma**) Bl not specified in FE IV 94

SOLENOPSIS

15. *Solenopsis minuta* (L.) Presl. subsp. *balearica* (Wimmer) Meikle. Perennial. Flowers lilac. Mar. - Apr. Rare. (From garden specimen). **K D** Ll (**Ma**) *Laurentia tenella* A. DC. in FE IV 102
16. *S. laurentia* (L.) Presl. Annual. Flowers blue. Mar. - Apr. Mistakenly included here. D and Ll record for Mi, I, but not Ma. (From Greek specimen). *Laurentia michelii* A. DC. in FE IV 102

Other plants recorded for Mallorca:
Valerianella coronata ?Confused with 1 above. K includes only *V. discoidea*, given as subsp. D (quotes FE). Ll omits. Bl in FE IV 49

V. costata K (quotes Porta and Rigo 1885). D (quotes FE). Ll lists. Bl in FE IV 51

V. carinata K (quotes Hermann 1912). D (quotes FE). B gives two (high) locations. Ll omits. (?Ma) FE IV 50

V. echinata K (quotes Barcelò 1867-1877). D (quotes FE). Ll lists. (Ma). Bl in FE IV 51

V. dentata K (quotes Barcelò 1867-1877). ?D and ?Ll (?Ma, ?Mi, ?I) Bl in FE IV 51

V. rimosa B (quotes Garcias, collecting 1905). Ll lists. (Ma). Not Bl in FE III 51

Knautia integrifolia K B and Ll list. ?D. Bl in FE IV 67
Scabiosa stellata K (quotes Barceló 1867-1877) B and Ll list. ?B. Bl in FE IV 70

Scabiosa monspeliensis Recently recorded (Rita J. et al. 1985). (Ma) Not Bl in FE IV 71

In other islands only:
Campanula dichotoma Ibiza FE IV 84

Plate 64

COMPOSITAE (1): *EUPATORIUM, SOLIDAGO, BELLIS, BELLIUM, ASTER, ERIGERON, CONYZA, FILAGO, LOGFIA*

EUPATORIUM

1. *Eupatorium cannabinum* Hemp Agrimony. Perennial, up to 2m. Florets all tubular, in heads of 5-6 arranged in dense corymbs. May - July. Rare. (From British specimen × 1/20) K quotes Bianor (1910-1914) D. Ll treats as alien. (Ma) FE IV 109

SOLIDAGO

2. *Solidago virgaurea* Golden Rod. Heads with up to 12 ligules. October. ?rare now, though recorded from many places by K (flowering late in year). (From British specimen × 1/2). B says cultivated. **K** D Ll (Ma, I) FE IV 110

BELLIS

3. *Bellis annua* Annual Daisy. Leaves not all basal. Involucral bracts in 2 rows. Ligules white, commonly becoming pale violet or pinkish. Oct. - May. Very common. **K D (Ma,** Mi, I) FE IV 111

4. *B. sylvestris* Robust perennial. Leaves forming basal rosette. Ligules white. Oct. - Mar. Widespread. **K D (Ma,** Mi) FE IV 112

BELLIUM

5. *Bellium bellidioides* Perennial. Leaves all basal. Involucral bracts in one row. Apr. - Sept. Common. **K** D **(Ma,** Mi, I) FE IV 112

ASTER

6. *Aster squamatus* Glabrous annual or biennial, up to 1m or more. Aug. - Sept. Common on saline soils. Native of S. America, introduced. (× 1/20, detail top left × 2/3, others enlarged). **D (Ma,** Mi, I) FE IV 115

7. *A. tripolium* ssp. *pannonicus* Sea Aster. Fleshy annual or perennial. Sept. - Nov. Common in brackish marshes. **K** D **(Ma,** Mi, I), FE IV 115

ERIGERON

8. *Erigeron karvinskianus* Perennial with lax leafy branches. Leaves entire, or lower ones 3-lobed. Involucral bracts in several rows, with long fine points. Ligules white, becoming reddish-purple. May - Oct. (Garden specimen). **D** Ll (Native of Mexico, introduced **Ma**) FE IV 117

CONYZA

9. *Conyza canadensis* Canadian Fleabane. Branched, leafy annual, slightly hairy with spreading hairs. Ligules 0.5-1mm, purple, usually slightly exceeding pappus. June - July. Fairly common. (Part of inflorescence). **K** D (Native of N. America, introduced **Ma,** ?I) FE IV 120

10. *C. bonariensis* Similar to 9 but hairy, with ligules up to 0.5mm, usually shorter than pappus. All year. Common in waste places. K D (Native of central America, introduced **Ma,** Mi I) FE IV 120

The form *C. floribunda* Kunth with a narrow cylindrical inflorescence and very short branches is also common here. (Lower detail shows flower). **D** (Ma, Mi, I) FE IV 120

FILAGO

11. *Filago vulgaris* Cudweed. Greenish-white to greyish densely tomentos annual, usually erect. Leaves widest in lower half. Heads terete, in 10-12mm globose clusters of 20-40, not overtopped by leaves. Involucral bracts with fine yellow arista. Pappus well-developed. Apr. - June. Rare. (From British specimen). **K** D (Ma, Mi, I) FE IV 121

12. *F. pyramidata* Annual, much branched from base, stems prostrate or ascending. Leaves entire, widest in upper half, greyish-white tomentose. Heads in sharply 5-angled clusters of 8-20, often overtopped by subtending leaves. Involucral bracts all similar, softly hairy on back and with short recurved arista. Pappus well-developed. Apr. - June. Dry waysides and sandy places, common and rather variable. **K** D **(Ma,** Mi. I) FE IV 122

LOGFIA

13. *Logfia gallica* Heads in small clusters overtopped by leaves. Involucral bracts not aristate, forming a star in fruit. May. - June. Local. (From British specimen). K **D** (Ma, Mi, I) FE IV 124

Also in Mallorca:
Conyza sumatrensis (Retz) Walker. Ll lists. Not described in FE.
F. congesta Resembles 12, but heads usually in clusters of 3-6., very numerous. Involucral bracts hairy only on margin, inner bracts obtuse. Hermaphrodite florets 4-6, without pappus or with only 1-4 hairs. Mar. - June. Trampled places, mainly in the south. **D** Ll (Ma, I) FE IV 122

In Formentera:
Filago fuscescens Not Bl in FE IV 122

154

Plate 65

COMPOSITAE (2): *EVAX, BOMBYCILAENA, GNAPHALIUM, HELICHRYSUM, PHAGNALON,*

EVAX

1. *Evax pygmaea* subsp. *pygmaea* Annual, green to silvery, with short lateral branches terminated by rosettes of leaves 5-15 × 2-5(-8)mm, which enclose clusters of 1 or more heads of small florets, inner few florets functionally male, outer numerous and female. Heads surrounded by narrow brownish aristate involucral bracts. Apr. - May. Common in dry places. **K D (Ma, Mi, I) FE IV 124**

2. *Filago (Evax) petro-ianii* Rita & Dittrich sp. nov. Very small annual. Stem short with or without procumbent axillary branches. Cauline leaves linear, rosette leaves ca 6mm × 2mm, apical part with revolute margins and pale, acuminate tip. Heads about 4mm diameter, solitary or forming flat cushion-shaped cluster with 3-5 peripherally inserted heads. Involucral bracts and smaller but similar involucral scales dark aristate. Rare, S. Mallorca near the sea. (First found by Dr Juan Rita in 1986: see Dittrich M. and Rita J. in Kit Tan (ed.) *'Plant Taxonomy, Phytogeography and Related Subjects - The Davis and Hedge Festschrift'* pp 1-9 Edinburgh University Press (1989) Illustration × 3 (Ma, endemic) Not in FE.

BOMBYCILAENA

3. *Bombycilaena ?erecta* Erect silvery-white annual. Heads small, in terminal and axillary clusters. Inner involucral bracts pouched, each enclosing one of the peripheral florets. Rare in mountains. (Plant illustrated here was collected near one of higher peaks. It appears to be *B. erecta*, lacking the brownish-yellow colouration of heads in *B. discolor*. The leaves are undulate). Not Bl in FE IV 125

K gives *"Micropus erectus* var *bombycinus* Lag. or *M. bombycinus* Lag." Do both species of *Bombycilaena* occur?. FE equates *M. bombycinus* Lag. with *Bombycilaena discolor*. Ll lists only *M. discolor* (also for Mi, I) (?**Ma**) FE IV 125

GNAPHALIUM

4. *Gnaphalium luteo-album* Silvery-white annual. Clusters of heads yellowish, terminal. April. Rare. (From garden specimen: found later in Mallorca, where it looked much the same). K D (**Ma**, Mi, I) FE IV 128

HELICHRYSUM

5. *Helichrysum stoechas*
   1) Subsp. *stoechas* Perennial shrub. Very variable. Height commonly 5-50cm. Densely white woolly to green and almost glabrous. Leaves sometimes aromatic, usually less than 25mm long. Heads egg-shaped just before flowering. Apr. - May. Common in dry places. **K D (Ma,** Mi, I) FE IV 129

6. 2) variety or subsp. *decumbens* (Status uncertain, see FE). Shrub, usually less than 15cm. Leaves less than 1cm, broad linear or spathulate, not or scarcely aromatic. Heads in dense globular clusters. Apr. - May. Local in sandy places near the sea. (**Ma**, Mi, I) FE IV 129

7. *H. rupestre* Plant silvery, not aromatic. Leaves linear, most exceeding 30mm, basal usually much more. Rather uncommon. Feb. - May. **K D (Ma,** I) FE IV 129

8. *H. ambiguum* Rather like 7, but lower leaves exceeding 7mm wide. Small scarious bracts resembling involucral bracts on branches of inflorescence. Apr. - May. Local in mountain areas. **K D (Ma,** Mi endemic) FE IV 130

9. *H. italicum* subsp. *microphyllum* Inner involucral bracts at least 5 × length of outer. Always curry - scented. Uncommon in mountains (specimen was found exactly where Knoche found it). **K D (Ma,** I) FE IV 130

PHAGNALON

10. *Phagnalon sordidum* Dwarf shrub. Leaves linear, inrolled. May. - June. Walls and dry rocky places. Locally common. **K D (Ma,** Mi, ?I) FE IV 133

11. *P. rupestre* Dwarf shrub. Heads solitary. Outer involucral bracts with flat margins. Apr. - May. Common on walls and in dry rocky places. **K D (Ma,** Mi, I) FE IV 133

12. *P. saxatile* Similar to 10, but margins of middle involucral bracts undulate. Locally common. **K D (Ma,** I) FE IV 133

Plate 66

COMPOSITAE: (3) *INULA, DITTRICHIA, PULICARIA, JASONIA, PALLENIS, ASTERISCUS, AMBROSIA, XANTHIUM*

INULA

1. *Inula conyza* Plougman's Spikenard. Perennial, 30-120cm. Ligules 0 or very small. May - Aug. Rare. (From British specimen). K (quotes Bianor 1910-1914). B gives two locations. D lists. Ll treats as alien. (Ma) Bl in FE IV 136
2. *I. crithmoides* Golden Samphire. Fleshy maritime shrub, up to 100cm. May - July. Common on saline soils. **K D** (**Ma,** Mi, I) FE IV 136

DITTRICHIA

3. *Dittrichia viscosa* Large, resin-scented perennial. Leaves clasping stem. Ray florets much longer than involucre. Aug.Oct. Common. **K D** (**Ma,** Mi, I) FE IV 137
4. *D. graveolens* Annual. Ray florets not or hardly exceeding involucre. Aug. - Oct. Local. K D Ll (**Ma,** Mi, I) FE IV 137

PULICARIA

5. *Pulicaria odora* Perennial. Stems 20-70cm, sparingly branched. Heads usually solitary. Stem leaves clasping stem, with small auricles. July - Oct. Common in damp places. (× 3/4). **K D** (**Ma,** Mi, I) FE IV 137
6. *P. dysenterica* Fleabane. Perennial. Stems to 60cm, white woolly. Heads in dense cluster. Leaves clasping stem, with pronounced auricles. June - Oct. Common in damp places. **K D** (**Ma,** Mi, I) FE IV 137
7. *P. vulgaris* Annual. Leaves lanceolate to elliptical, margins wavy. July - Oct. Rare. (From garden specimen). **D** Ll (Ma, Mi) Not Bl in FE IV 137
8. *P. sicula* Annual. Leaves in middle and upper part of stem linear, not wavy. July - Oct. Local in places flooded in winter. **K D** (**Ma,** Mi) FE IV 137

JASONIA

9. *Jasonia glutinosa* (*Chiliadenus glutinosus* (L.) Fourr.) Small sticky perennial. Stems 10-45 cm. Inner bracts scarious except for green mid vein, cilate. Outer bracts green, glandular-hairy. Ligules absent. July. (Specimen from Spanish mainland × 1 1/2. Details of involucral bracts × 3). Rock crevices. K **D** Ll (Ma) FE IV 138

PALLENIS

10. *Pallenis spinosa* Perennial. Stems rigid, heads surrounded by large, spreading, spine-tipped outer involucral bracts. Ligulate florets in 2 rows. Apr. - June. Common. **K D** (**Ma,** Mi, I) FE IV 139

ASTERISCUS

11. *Asteriscus aquaticus* Annual, usually without a stem or with a very short stem, but sometimes with a branched stem up to 50cm. Outer involucral bracts with a long, leaf-like apex much exceeding the ligules, which are more or less erect, in 2 rows like *Pallenis*. Apr. - June. Widespread in rocky and sandy places. (Both × 1). **K D** (**Ma,** Mi, I) FE IV 139
12. *A. maritimus* Perennial. Ligules broad and longer than involucral bracts. Mar. - July. Maritime sands and rocks, fairly common. **K D** (**Ma,** Mi, I) FE IV 139

AMBROSIA

13. *Ambrosia maritima*. American Wormwood. Dark greenish-grey perennial with creeping rhizomes. Sept. - Oct. (Terminal part of 40cm specimen, slightly reduced. Details of male heads × 2). Not listed by K, D, or Ll. B (quotes Bianor and adds 'A verificar'). Illustration from Mallorcan specimen. (**Ma**) Not Bl in FE IV 142

XANTHIUM

14. *Xanthium strumarium* Cocklebur. Spineless annual. Fruit covered in hooked spines. June - Aug. Local in seasonally damp places. K D (**Ma,** Mi) FE IV 143
15. *X. spinosum* Spiny cocklebur. Annual with long straight spines at base of each leaf. June - Sept. Local. Native of S. America. (× 3/4). **K** D (**Ma,** Mi, I) FE IV 143

Also recorded from Mallorca:
Tagetes minuta (A.A.Butcher, private communication) Not Bl in FE IV 144

Plate 67

COMPOSITAE (4): *SANTOLINA, ANTHEMIS, ACHILLEA, CHAMAEMELUM, (ANACYCLUS), (OTANTHUS), CHRYSANTHEMUM, (COLEOSTEPHUS), COTULA, GYMNOSTYLES, ARTEMISIA, (DORONICUM)*

SANTOLINA

1. *Santolina chamaecyparissus* subsp. *magonica* Bolòs, Molinier & Monts. Lavender Cotton. Blue-grey aromatic shrub. Apr. - Aug. Very local near sea, commoner in mountains. (Detail of head × 2, of floret × 6). **K D** (**Ma**, Mi endemic subsp.) FE IV 145 (subsp. not described)

ANTHEMIS

2. *Anthemis maritima* Perennial. Leaves fleshy. Involucral bracts with broad scarious margin. May - Aug. Local on sea-shores. (Slightly reduced: inner involucral bract × 3). **K D** (**Ma**, Mi, I) FE IV 151

3. *A. arvensis* Corn Chamomile. Annual or biennial. Leaves with terminal segments acute and mucronate. Receptacular scales with short stiff point all over receptacle. Achene with prominent ribs. Apr. - June. Common. (Detail of receptacle with achenes removed × 1, of achene × 6, other details × 2). **K D** (**Ma**, Mi, I) FE IV 153

4. *A. cotula* Stinking Mayweed. Annual, closely resembling 3, but but narrow receptacular scales only at the apex of conical receptacle. Ribs of achenes covered in granular tubercles. May. - Sept. Occasional, roadsides, waste places. (Detail of dried fruiting receptacle with some achenes removed × 2, of disc floret and receptacular scale × 4, of achene × 6). **K D** (**Ma**, Mi, I) FE IV 155

ACHILLEA

5. *Achillea ageratum* Perennial, commonly up to about 50cm. May. - Sept. Locally common in hilly areas. **K D** (**Ma**, I) FE IV 164

CHAMAEMELUM

6. *Chamaemelum mixtum* Pubescent annual. Leaves 1-pinnate. Involucral bracts with broad scarious border. Tube of disc florets sac-like at base, enclosing apex of achene. Uncommon. (Specimen from Spanish mainland: detail of involucral bract × 2, tubular florets and achenes × about 4). D Ll (Ma, Mi) Not Bl in FE IV 165

CHRYSANTHEMUM

7. *Chrysanthemum segetum* Corn Marigold. Glabrous, usually glaucous annual. Leaves somewhat fleshy, subentire to incise-dentate, the upper amplexicaul. Head very like yellow form of 8. Apr. - June. Not common. (From British specimen). **K D** (Ma, Mi) FE IV 168

8. *C. coronarium* Crown Daisy. Glabrous or slightly hairy annual. Most leaves bi-pinnatisect. Inner involucral bracts with broad scarious apical appendage covering bud. Ligules uniformly bright yellow or pale yellow peripherally and bright yellow centrally. Mar. - July. Common. (Details × 1 1/2). **K D** (Ma, Mi, I) FE IV 169

COTULA

9. *Cotula coronopifolia* Hairless annual. Apr. - Aug. Local in wet places. D (Native of S. Africa, introduced **Ma**) FE IV 177

GYMNOSTYLES

10. *Gymnostyles stolonifera* Woolly annual with procumbent stems rooting at the nodes. Outer florets without a corolla. Rare. (Specimen from Spanish mainland: detail of leaf × 2, achene × 5). **D** (Native of S. America, introduced Ma, Mi) FE IV 178

ARTEMISIA

11. *Artemisia arborescens* Shrubby Wormwood. Aromatic whitish perennial. Stems woody below. Apr. - June. Local, inland. (Small branch flowering stem × 1, detail × 2). **K D** (Ma, Mi, I) FE IV 180

12. *A. caerulescens* Greyish-green aromatic shrub. Two subspecies here, differing mainly in the shape of the ultimate segments of the pinnatisect leaves (elongate, generally more than 0.7mm wide in subsp. *caerulescens* (illustrated here), very short and 0.4-0.7mm wide in subsp. *gallica* June - Oct. Subsp. *caerulescens* common in saltmarshes. **K D** (**Ma**) FE IV 181

Others in Mallorca:

Anacyclus clavatus Distinguished from *Anthemis* species by broadly 2-winged outer achenes. K (quotes Mas y Guindal 1908). Ll (Ma, I) FE IV 168

Otanthus maritimus Densely white-tomentose perennial without ligulate florets. Tubular florets have 2 spurs at base which partially enclose ovary. K (quotes Barcelò 1867-1877). Ll (Ma, I) FE IV 168

Coleostephus myconis D Llorens et al. (1991) treat as alien. Not Bl in FE IV 174

Cotula australis Ll (Ma) (Australia and New Zealand) Not Bl in FE IV 177

Petasites fragrans Bl (introduced) in FE IV 188

Doronicum grandiflorum K (quotes Marès and Vigineix 1850-1853). D. Ll treats as alien. Not Bl in FE IV 191

In other islands:

Leucanthemum paludosum Ibiza FE IV 177

Plate 68

COMPOSITAE (5): *SENECIO, CALENDULA, ARCTOTHECA, GAZANIA, CARLINA, ATRACTYLIS, ARCTIUM, STAEHELINA*

SENECIO

1. *Senecio bicolor* Subsp. *cineraria*. Dusty Miller. Densely white-tomentose shrubby perennial. May - June. Mediterranean plant, cultivated and widely naturalised in Mallorca. K **D** (**Ma,** Mi) FE IV 194

2. *S. leucanthemifolius* Fleshy annual.

a) Subsp. *crassifolius* Yellow flowers. Mar. - May. Abundant on one area of rocky coast. Not Mallorca in FE: not listed for Mallorca by K or D. Ll includes for Ma. (**Ma,** I) FE IV 203

3. b) Subsp. (*S. rodriguezii* Willk. ex Rodr.) Jan. - July. Lilac flowers. Widespread in rocky places near the coast. (**Ma** endemic) **K D** FE IV 204 (not treated as separate species).

4. *S. vulgaris* Groundsel. Annual. Common weed of cultivated ground. Feb. - June. **K D** (**Ma,** Mi, I) FE IV 204

CALENDULA

5. *Calendula arvensis* Field Marigold. Annual, often whitish-woolly. Feb. - Oct. Very common. **K D** (**Ma,** Mi, I) FE IV 207

ARCTOTHECA

6. *Arctotheca calendula* Annual. Ligules greenish-purple on the underside. May. - June. South African plant, occasionally naturalised. D (**Ma**) Not Bl in FE IV 208

GAZANIA

7. *Gazania rigens*. Perennial. May - July. Another South African introduction, widely planted and occasionally naturalised. **D** (**Ma,** Mi) Not Bl in FE IV 208

CARLINA

8. *Carlina corymbosa* Perennial, with stems arising from underground rhizome. Inner involucral bracts brownish-yellow above. June - Oct. Very common. (Heads often larger than in illustration). **K D** (**Ma,** Mi, I) FE IV 209

9. *C. lanata* Annual. Inner involucral bracts reddish-purple above. May - August. Less common than 8, but fairly widespread. **K D** (**Ma,** Mi, I) FE IV 211

ATRACTYLIS

10. *Atractylis cancellata* Annual, slender or fairly robust. Leaves whitish woolly. Apr. - June. Common in rocky places. **K D** (**Ma,** Mi, I) FE IV 211

XERANTHEMUM

11. *Xeranthemum inapertum* Annual. Florets more or less concealed by inner involucral bracts, which are held erect. June - July. (From Greek specimen). **K** D (**Ma**) FE IV 212

ARCTIUM

12. *Arctium tomentosum* (*Arctium chabertii* Briq. & Cavillier) Subsp. *balearicum* Arènes. Erect biennial up to 1.5m. Petioles solid. Each main branch of inflorescence corymbose. Involucral bracts with hooked spiny apices. July. Very local. (From garden specimen). **K D** Bonafè lists several locations. Ll. (**Ma,** endemic subsp.) Subsp. not described in FE IV 215)

STAEHELINA

13. *Staehelina dubia* June - Aug. Shrubby perennial. Occasional in dry rocky places. **K D** (**Ma,** Mi, I) FE IV 217

Other plants recorded for Mallorca:
Senecio linifoliaster López Ll lists. (Ma, I) Not in FE
Carlina vulgaris K quotes Chodat (1903). Llorens et al. (1991) omit. Not Bl in FE IV 210
Arctium lappa K gives only 'var. *minus*' (see below) Bl not excluded in FE IV 215
A. minus Differs from 12 in the hollow petioles and racemose branches with solitary terminal heads. K Ll lists for Ma. Bl not excluded in FE IV 215

In other islands:
Senecio gallicus ?Ibiza FE IV 203
S. lividus Cabrera and Minorca. FE IV 204
S. viscosus Minorca. FE IV 204
S. elegans South African, ?naturalized Bl in FE IV 205
Calendula tripterocarpa Ibiza. FE IV 207
Atractylis humilis Minorca and Ibiza FE IV 211

Plate 69

COMPOSITAE (6): *CARDUUS, CIRSIUM, PICNOMON,*
NOTOBASIS, GALACTITES, TYRIMNUS, ONOPORDUM

CARDUUS

1. *Carduus tenuiflorus* Sea Thistle. Annual or biennial up to 75cm. Stem with continuous prickly wings. Apr. - May. Common. **K D** (**Ma,** Mi, I) FE V 231

2. *C. pycnocephalus* Annual. Stem unwinged below heads, which may be solitary or in clusters of 2-3. Mar. - June. **K D** (**Ma,** Mi, I) FE IV 231

CIRSIUM

3. *Cirsium echinatum* Perennial thistle, up to 40cm. Middle leaves decurrent on stem for up to 1cm, upper rather less, stem otherwise unwinged. Heads in corymb overtopped by 2-8 subtending leaves. Involucre up to 4cm. June - Aug. Common in mountain areas. **K D** (**Ma**) FE IV 237

4. *C. vulgare* Spear Thistle. Stem winged: middle leaves at least decurrent for whole internode. May - Oct. Common. **K D** (**Ma,** Mi, I) FE IV 237

5. *C. arvense* Creeping Thistle. Perennial, up to 1m, with creeping rootstock. May - Sept. Common weed of cultivated ground. **K D** (**Ma,** I) FE IV 242

PICNOMON

6. *Picnomon acarna* Greyish woolly-haired annual, up to 50cm. Heads almost concealed by upper leaves. Florets purple. Local. (From Cretan specimen × 1/2). K quotes Bianor (1910-1914). B D Ll (Ma) FE IV 242

NOTOBASIS

7. *Notobasis syriaca* Annual, up to 1m or more. Uppermost cauline leaves surrounding and often exceeding heads. May. - June. Not common. (× 1/4, detail of head × 1). K D (**Ma,** Mi, I) FE IV 242

GALACTITES

8. *Galactites tomentosa* Annual. Leaves white-veined and variegated. Outer florets large, spreading. Mar. - July. Common, a major field weed. **K D** (**Ma,** Mi, I) FE IV 244

TYRIMNUS

9. *Tyrimnus leucographus* Annual, up to 60cm. Leaves white-veined above, grey-woolly below. Heads solitary on long peduncles. June - July. Rare. (Specimen from Spanish mainland). K **D** B (quotes Barceló 1867 - 1877, and Willkomm, 1873) (Ma) FE IV 244

ONOPORDUM

10. *Onopordum illyricum* subsp. *illyricum* Biennial, up to 150cm, with densely spiny white-woolly stem. Leaves with at least 8 pairs of lobes. Heads much enlarged in fruit. June - July. Locally common. (× about 1/10, details × 1). **K D** (**Ma**) FE IV 247

Also recorded from Mallorca:
Onopordum macranthum Differs from 10 in the sparsely spiny stem and leaves with 5-7 pairs of lobes. June - July. D Very rare. Not Bl in FE IV 247

In Ibiza only:
Carduus bourgeanus subsp. *bourgeanus* Not Bl in FE

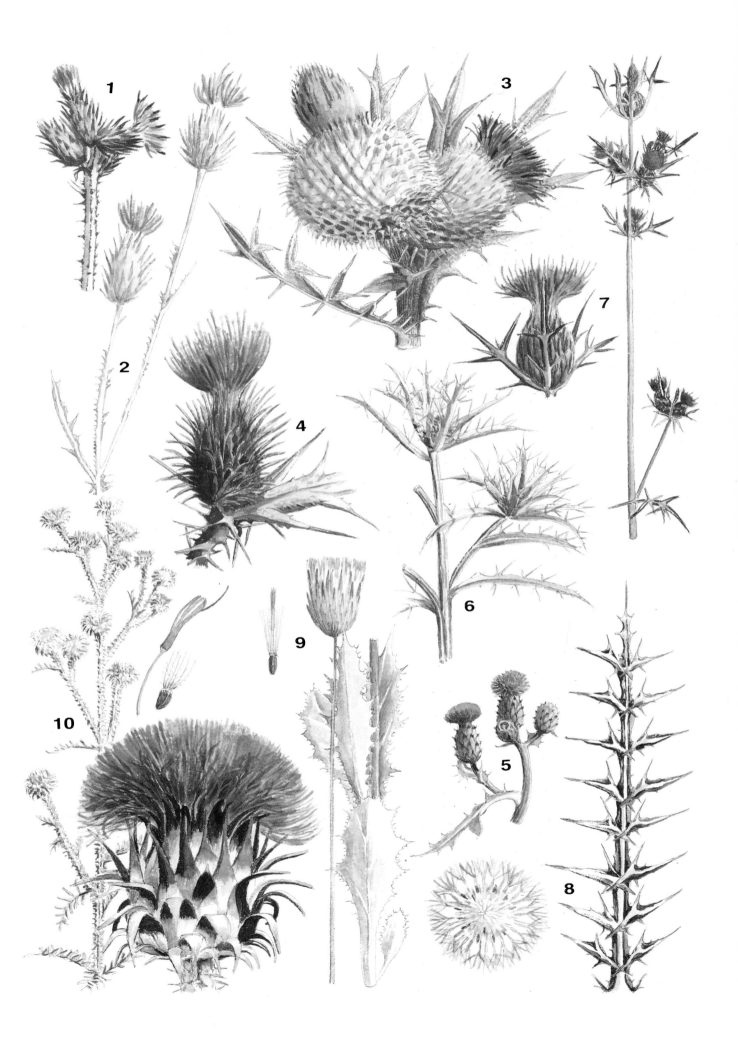

Plate 70

COMPOSITAE (7): *CYNARA, SILYBUM, CHEIROLOPHUS, LEUZEA, MANTISALCA, CENTAUREA, CRUPINA, CARTHAMUS.*

CYNARA

1. *Cynara cardunculus* Cardoon. Robust prickly perennial. May - Aug. Local. Stony and waste places. **K D** (**Ma,** Mi, I) FE IV 248

SILYBUM

2. *Silybum marianum* Milk Thistle. Annual or biennial, up to 1.5m. May - Aug. Common in waste places. **K D** (**Ma,** Mi, I) FE 249

CHEIROLOPHUS

3. *Cheirolophus intybaceus* Shrubby perennial, up to 60cm, with branched, leafy stems. Lower stem-leaves narrow pinnatifid, upper narrow entire. Outer achenes without a pappus (unlike *Centaurea*). June - Aug. Rare. (Specimen from Spanish mainland: head and middle stem leaf × 1: middle involucral bract enlarged). K **D** (Ma, I) FE IV 250

LEUZEA

4. *Leuzea conifera* Usually perennial. May - Aug. Local. Stony ground. **K D** (**Ma,** Mi, I) FE IV 252

MANTISALCA

5. *Mantisalca salmantica* Biennial or perennial, glabrous above, slightly woolly below. Stems with slender branches, leafless above. Basal leaves pinnately lobed, cauline dentate to pinnatisect. Involucral bracts black distally, with a single, often reflexed, apical spine up to 3mm. Apr. - Oct. Rare. Roadsides and waste places. (From Portuguese specimen). **K** D Ll (Ma) FE IV 254

CENTAUREA

6. *Centaurea calcitrapa* Star Thistle. Shrubby perennial. Lower leaves pinnatisect. May - Sept. Common. **K D** (**Ma,** Mi, I) FE IV 282

7. *C. aspera* Rough Star-Thistle. Perennial. May - Sept. Common. **K D** (**Ma,** Mi, I) FE IV 285

8. *C. melitensis* Maltese Star-Thistle. Annual or biennial. May. - June. Local in waste places. **K D** (**Ma,** Mi, I) FE IV 285

9. *C. diluta* Perennial. Involucral bracts with shortly decurrent orbicular-ovate appendages, irregularly fimbriate, with a rigid filiform spine in the apical notch. May - June. (Head only, from Mallorcan specimen). Described in FE as native SW Spain, frequent casual elsewhere. Possibly not previously recorded. (**Ma**) FE IV 285

CRUPINA

10. *Crupina* species. Tall slender branched annual, leafy below. Heads with more than 15 florets, but often with only one achene developing in each head. Pappus with outer row of blackish scabrid hairs and inner row of dark, lanceolate scales. (Specimens here seem intermediate between *C. vulgaris* and *C. crupinastrum* as described in FE). May - June. Local in dry places. **K D** (**Ma**) FE IV 301

CARTHAMUS

11. *Carthamus lanatus* Glandular annual. Very variable. Heads always solitary, often on diffusely branched bushy plant, also in more or less racemose inflorescence. May - Sept. Dry waste places and cultivated ground. **K D** (**Ma,** Mi, I) FE IV 308

Also possibly in Mallorca:
Centaurea balearica Small shrub, differing from other species in the terminal segment of the pinnatisect summer leaves with 3 apical spines. Known from several sites in Minorca, once recorded from Mallorca. Recently raised as new genus: *Femeniasia balearica* (Rodr. Fem) Susanna 1987. FE IV 273
C. solstitialis B 'A verificar'. Ll omits. Bl in FE IV 284

In other islands:
Cynara humilis ?Ibiza Not Bl in FE IV 248
Centaurea collina Ibiza ?Bl in FE IV 263
C. hyalolepis Ibiza Not Bl in FE IV 282
C. seridis subsp. *maritima* ?Ibiza. ?Bl in FE IV 283
C. cyanus Minorca Not Bl in FE IV 300

Plate 71

COMPOSITAE (8): *CARDUNCELLUS, SCOLYMUS, CICHORIUM, CATANANCHE, TOLPIS, HYOSERIS, HEDYPNOIS, RHAGADIOLUS*

CARDUNCELLUS

1. *Carduncellus pinnatus* Perennial, acaulescent, or with stalk up to 20cm. Leaves usually glabrous apart from cottony-hired rhachis. Apr. - May. Rocky places in mountains. Rare. K lists for Ibiza only. (From Sicilian specimen). **D** B (quotes D). Ll (**Ma,** I) FE IV 303

2. *C. caeruleus* (usually) cottony-haired perennial with unbranched stem up to 60cm. Involucral bracts with short glands. Apr. - May. Local, field margins, grassy places. K **D** (**Ma,** Mi, I) FE IV 304

SCOLYMUS

3. *Scolymus maculatus* Annual, up to 90cm. Stems with continuous toothed and spiny wings with thickened white margin. June - July. Waste places, not common. (From garden specimen). K (quotes Barcelò 1867 1877) D (Ma, Mi) FE IV 304

4. *S. hispanicus* Spanish Oyster Plant. Robust biennial or perennial, up to 80cm. Stems with interrupted spiny wings, not much thickened at the margin. June - July. Locally common. **K D** (**Ma,** Mi, I) FE IV 304

CICHORIUM

5. *Cichorium intybus* Chicory. Apr. - Sept. Common, branched form to 120 cm widespread in grassy places, 1-flowered acaulescent plants common in mountain areas and dry places. **K D** (**Ma,** Mi, I) FE IV 304

CATANANCHE

6. *Catananche coerulea* Cupidone. Perennial. Very rare, misrecorded or extinct, ?seen only once (by Knoche on Puig Major in 1912). Ll omits. (From garden specimen). **K** D (Ma) FE IV 305

TOLPIS

7. *Tolpis barbata* Annual. Leaves toothed, hairy, mainly in basal rosette. Dry sandy and grassy places. Rare. (From garden specimen). K lists for Minorca only. B D (Ma, Mi) FE IV 306

HYOSERIS

8. *Hyoseris scabra* Annual. Stems usually swollen, procumbent from centre of leaf-rosette. Marginal achenes enfolded by involucral bracts, with pappus of short hairs. Middle achenes broader, flattened and winged, inner narrow terete, both with pappus of pale narrow scales. Mar. - May. Common in dry places. **K D** (**Ma,** Mi, I) FE IV 307

9. *H. radiata* Perennial. Achenes resemble those of 8, but all wih pappus of rigid hairs and linear scales, generally longer on the inner achenes. Mar. - June. Common. **K D** (**Ma,** Mi, I) FE IV 307

HEDYPNOIS

10. *Hedypnois cretica* Variable annual, stems branched or simple. Outer achenes incurved, usually enclosed in hardened involucral bracts. Common. May - June. **K D** (**Ma,** Mi, I) FE V 307

RHAGADIOLUS

11. *Rhagadiolus stellatus* Star Hawkbit. Annual. Stems branched. Outer involucral bracts hardening in fruit and enclosing achenes, which spread to form characteristic star. May - June. Fairly common. **K D** (**Ma,** Mi, I) FE IV 308

In Ibiza only:
Carduncellus monspeliensium FE IV 303
C. dianius FE IV 303

168

Plate 72

COMPOSITAE (9): *UROSPERMUM, HYPOCHAERIS, LEONTODON, PICRIS, SCORZONERA, TRAGOPOGON*

UROSPERMUM

1. *Urospermum dalechampii* Softly hairy perennial. Leaves hispid, lower pinnatifid or entire, upper lanceolate to ovate, amplexicaul. Heads solitary, up to 5cm wide. Ligules pale yellow with black-tipped teeth, (giving black centre to immature head), outer ligules often reddish on reverse. (Achene × 2, pappus very pale reddish-brown - often apparently white unless compared with achene of *U. picroides*). Apr. - June. Common. **K D (Ma,** Mi, I) FE IV 308

2. *U. picroides* Annual. Leaves prickly, at least on veins beneath. Ligules deep yellow, without black teeth. Pappus snow-white. Common. (Achene × 2). **K D (Ma,** Mi, I) FE IV 308

HYPOCHAERIS

3. *Hypochaeris achryophorus* Annual. Stems hispid at least above, often branched, but small apparently scapose plants very common. Involucral bracts in several rows, hispid. Fully opened head very characteristic, with very numerous florets in many rows with short, imbricate ligules. Achenes beaked, with pappus in 2 rows, outer much shorter than inner. Apr. - June. Common. (Achene × 2). **K D (Ma,** Mi, I) FE IV 309

LEONTODON

4. *Leontodon tuberosus* Tuberous-rooted perennial. Stems simple, with rigid simple or long-stalked bifid or trifid hairs. Leaves dentate or pinnatifid, narrowed to more or less dentate petiole. Involucral bracts in several rows, glabrous or with bifid hairs, often confined to the midline. Outer ligules with greenish stripe on back. Achenes minutely transversely ridged, outer curved with pappus of very short hairs, inner straight with pappus of longer plumose hairs. May - June. Occasional. (Achenes × 2). **K D (Ma,** Mi, I) FE IV 315

5. *L. taraxacoides* Lesser Hawkbit. Resembles 4, but not tuberous-rooted. Heads usually drooping in bud. Involucral bracts usually hairy all over (hairs as in 4). Outer ligules greyish-violet on outer face. Outer achenes with pappus of short scales, inner beaked with pappus of hairs. Apr. - June. Two subspecies here:

subsp. *taraxacoides* Perennial, inner achenes with 1mm beak. Locally common. (From British specimen: achenes × 2). **K D** (Ma, Mi, I) FE IV 315

subsp. *longirostris* Annual, inner achenes with 2-3mm beak. (Not illustrated). **D** (Ma, Mi, I) FE IV 315

PICRIS

6. *Picris echioides* Bristly Ox-tongue. Bristly annual or biennial. Stems much-branched. Heads numerous, with broad heart-shaped outer involucral bracts. Achenes with minute transverse ridges, inner straight, outer curved. May - Sept. Common. (Achene × 1+). **K D (Ma,** Mi, I0 FE IV 316

SCORZONERA

7. *Scorzonera laciniata* (= *Podospermum laciniatum* (L.) DC) Annual to perennial. Basal leaves pinnatisect. Involucre 7-20mm, much enlarged in fruit. Ligules equalling or up to 1 1/3 × involucral bracts. Apr. - June. Occasional. (Flowering head from garden specimen: fruiting heads, somewhat reduced, from Mallorca). **K D (Ma,** Mi, I) FE IV 318

TRAGOPOGON

8. *Tragopogon porrifolius* Salsify. Biennial, up to 125cm. Leaves broadly linear. Peduncles inflated. Ligules lilac to deep violet or purple. Achenes with beak about equalling wing, separated from pappus of plumose hairs by an annulus. Apr. - June. Common escape from cultivation for edible cylindrical roots. (Achene × 4/5). **K D (Ma,** I) FE IV 323

9. *T. hybridus* Glabrous annual. Flowering head resembles 8, but ligules reddish-lilac. Beak of achenes without a ring, outer with a pappus of 5 unequal stiff hairs, inner with pappus of plumose hairs. Waste grassy places. May - June. (Flowering head only). **K D (Ma,** Mi) FE IV 325

Also recorded from Mallorca:
Hypochaeris radicata K Bl excluded in FE IV 309
Scorzonera hispanica Salsify. Formerly cultivated, as 8 above. K quotes Barceló (1867-1877) D (Ma, Mi, I) FE IV 320

In other islands:
Hypochaeris glabra Minorca FE IV 309
Scorzonera baetica subsp. *ebusitana* Bolòs & Vigo Ibiza Subsp. not described, and not Bl in FE IV 320

Plate 73

COMPOSITAE (10): *REICHARDIA, LAUNAEA, AETHEORHIZA, SONCHUS, LACTUCA*

REICHARDIA

1. *Reichardia tingitana* Glabrous annual or perennial. Involucral bracts heart-shaped with broad scarious border. Mar. - May. Common, mainly in waste ground and on roadsides. **K D** (**Ma**, Mi, I) FE IV 325
2. *R. picroides* Resembles 1, but ligules without purple base. Scarious border of involucral bracts narrow. Mar. - May. Common in similar places. **K D** (**Ma**, Mi, I) FE IV 325

LAUNAEA

3. *Launaea cervicornis* Spiny dwarf shrub, much branched. May. - June. Exposed rocky ground near the sea, commonest in north. **K D** (**Ma**, Mi endemic) FE IV 326

AETHEORHIZA

4. *Aetheorhiza bulbosa* subsp. *bulbosa* Stoloniferous perennial, with blackish stalked glands at base of involucre and top of stem. Involucral bracts linear-lanceolate, abruptly narrowed to blunt apex. May - June. Common in grassy places. **K D** (**Ma**, Mi, I)
5. *Aetheorhiza bulbosa* subsp. *willkommii* resembles 4, but heads are generally smaller with narrow linear involucral bracts gradually tapering to acute apex. Fairly common, especially in rocky places in the north. **K D** (**Ma**, I endemic) FE IV 326

SONCHUS

6. *Sonchus asper* Spiny Sow-thistle. Weedy, branched annual or perennial with shiny glabrous leaves. Achenes strongly compressed and often winged, smooth between ribs. May June. Head, characteristic upper stem leaf with rounded auricle, and achene shown here. Occasional, roadsides and waste places. **K D** (**Ma**, Mi, I) FE IV 327
7. *S. tenerrimus* Very variable annual, biennial or perennial, not always easily distinguished from 8. At least upper leaves pinnatisect with many lobes, which are either linear or strongly contracted at the base. Auricles of upper leaves are usually large and wavy rather than toothed. Achenes not strongly compressed, unwinged, ridged or tuberculate between ribs and abruptly contracted at base. May - June. Very common, especially by roadsides and in waste places in towns. **K D** (**Ma**, Mi, I) FE IV 327
8. *S. oleraceus* Sow-thistle. Resembles 6 and 7. Upper stem leaves with pointed auricles. Heads usually pale yellow in flower. Achenes like those of 7, but gradually narrowed at base. Head, auricle of upper leaf and achene shown here. May - June. Common, in similar habitats to 5 and 6. **K D** (**Ma**, Mi, I) FE IV 327
9. *S. maritimus* Rhizomatous perennial to 60cm, stems little branched or unbranched.Subsp. *maritimus* (of damp saline habitats) has large bright orange-yellow heads with ovate outer involucral bracts. Subsp. *aquatilis* (of damp not saline habitats: not illustrated) is usually more branched, and has smaller yellower heads with lanceolate outer involucral bracts. June - Oct. Local in suitable habitats. **K D** (**Ma**, Mi, I) FE IV 327

LACTUCA

10. *Lactuca viminea* Biennial or perennial with (usually) many stems up to 100cm. Inflorescence much-branched. Stem leaves with elongated, narrow, closely appressed auricles. Heads small, usually with 5 florets. June - Sept. Local, in rocky mountain scrub and near sea. (Leaf and small part of inflorescence). **K D** (**Ma**) FE IV 329
11. *L. serriola* Prickly lettuce. Annual or biennial, up to 180 cm. Usually one stem with a few axillary branches below. Inflorescence much branched. Leaves entire or pinnatifid, held vertically, often in one plane. Involucre 8-12mm. Achenes olive-grey with white beak. June - Aug. Common, roadsides, waste places. (Part of small plant × 3/4). **K D** (**Ma**, Mi) FE IV 330
12. *L. tenerrima* Perennial. Heads with 12-20 florets. Ligules bluish lilac. Occasional in mountain scrub. **K D** (**Ma**) FE IV 331

Other species recorded in Mallorca:

Reichardia intermedia K's *Picridium vulgare* Desf. 'la forme intermedium' or *Picridium intermedium* Willk. might be taken for this species. However Duvigneaud only quotes FE, and if this plant occurs here at all it must be very rare. Knoche states that it is commonest plant in Balearic Islands. This throws some doubt on his identification. (?Ma, ?Mi, ?I) FE V 325

Lactuca saligna Upper cauline leaves oblong to linear with sagittate base. Inflorescence spike-like panicle of numerous heads with 6-15 pale yellow florets. Achenes pale brown, 7-8-ribbed, with beak 1 + -3 × length body. K and D record from Mi only. B and Ll list. (Ma, Mi). FE IV 330.

L. virosa Leaves dentate to pinnatifid with wide lobes. Inflorescence pyramidal. Heads with about 15 pale yellow florets. Achenes blackish, narrowly winged and 5-ribbed, with beak as long as body. K (quotes Bianor 1910-1914). B and Ll list. (Ma). FE IV 330.

Recorded from Minorca:
Sonchus arvensis ?Mi Not Bl in FE IV 330

Plate 74

COMPOSITAE (11): *TARAXACUM, CHONDRILLA, LAPSANA, CREPIS, ANDRYALA, HIERACIUM*

TARAXACUM Dandelion

Some plants of the genus *Taraxacum* produce little or no pollen, and set viable seed asexually, (= apomixis). This perpetuates mutations. Others reproduce sexually. The field is outside the scope of this book. One common species is illustrated to represent the genus. Others found by Duvigneaud are listed at the end of this section.

1. *Taraxacum ?obovatum* **K D** (**Ma**, I) FE IV 335

CHONDRILLA

2. *Chondrilla juncea* Slightly shrubby biennial or perennial with grey-green arching branches from (usually) single stem. Cauline leaves few, usually bract-like. Heads numerous, with 9-12 florets. Occasional in scrub, not common. (× 1). **K D** (**Ma**, Mi) FE IV 343

LAPSANA

3. *Lapsana communis* Nipplewort Annual. Lower leaves with large terminal and small lateral lobes. May. Rare. (From British specimen, × 1/4, details × 1, but a larger specimen was collected later in Mallorca in a neglected garden). ?K ?D Ll treats as alien. (**Ma**) FE IV 344

CREPIS Hawk's-beard.

4. *Crepis triasii* Perennial. Leaves mostly basal, with yellowish hairs. Involucral bracts greyish hairy outside, glabrous inside. Common in rock crevices in the mountains. (Main illustration × 1/3, details × 1 and achene × 4). **K D** (**Ma**, Mi, endemic) FE IV 351

5. *C. foetida* Annual up to 50cm. Stem branched from base or middle. Heads 1 to many. Ligules reddish-purple on outside. Involucral bracts lnear to linear-lanceolate, outer 0.5 - 0.7 × inner. Receptacle with linear scales. Outer achenes stout, with or without short beak: inner long and slender with slender beak. (Specimen from Spanish mainland × about 1/6, head × 1, achenes enlarged). **D** Ll (Ma, I) FE IV 354

6. *C. pusilla* Acaulescent annual. Capitula in sessile cluster. Achenes of two kinds. (From Greek specimen: upper details × 3 show, left to right, outer involucral bract, and inner involucral bract enclosing outer achene, from outside and inside. Lower detail shows inner achene × 4). **D** Ll (Ma) Not Bl in FE IV 355

7. *C. vesicaria* subsp. *vesicaria* Usually biennial or perennial. Stems up to about 1m, usually much-branched. Outer involucral bracts broadly ovate. All achenes with a beak as long as the achene. Common. (Plant × 1/10, details × 1). **K D** (**Ma**, I) FE IV 356

ANDRYALA

8. *Andryala integrifolia* Annual to perennial. Stems up to 80cm, much branched. Whole plant covered in stellate and simple eglandular hairs, upper part of plant, especially involucral bracts, with long yellowish glandular hairs too. Occasional garden escape. (× 1/10, details × 1). (**Ma**) Not Bl in FE IV 358

HIERACIUM Hawkweed

Hieracium, like *Taraxacum*, commonly produces seed by apomixis. However *Hieracium* species are not common here, though several species have been recorded. The general form of plants of this genus resembles that of *Crepis*, but the involucral bracts are in several irregularly imbricate rows (only two in *Crepis*), and the pappus is usually brownish rather than whitish.

9. *Hieracium amplexicaule* Stems up to 50cm, with stellate hairs and dense brownish glandular hairs. Basal leaves present at flowering-time, all leaves with dense brownish glandular hairs like the stem. Ligules with dense simple hairs at the apex. (Specimen from Spanish mainland × about 1/3, head × 1). **B D** Ll (Ma) Bl in FE IV 396

Other species recorded for Mallorca include:
Taraxacum obovatum (Willd.) DC **K D**
T. balearicum van Soest **D** (Not described in FE).
T. cupreum van Soest **D** (Not described in FE).
T. marginellum H. Lindb. fil. (FE index gives this as *T. erythrospermum* group, though here Bl is excluded). **D** FE IV 338
T. mediterraneum van Soest **D** (Not described in FE).
T. miniatum H. Lindb. fil. (FE index gives this as *T. erythrospermum* group, though here Bl is excluded). **D** FE IV 338
T. retzii van Soest (FE index gives this as *T. fulvum* group, though Bl is not included in the list for this group. **D** FE IV 338
Crepis bellidifolia ?Bl in FE IV 357
Hieracium pilosella Bl in FE IV 368
H. glaucinum **D** Not Bl in FE IV 377
H. eliseanum **D** (Ma) FE IV 381
H. aragonense **D** Not Bl FE IV 383

In other islands:
Species of *Taraxacum* and *Hieracium*
Andryala ragusina Ibiza. FE IV 358

174

Plate 75

ALISMATACEAE: JUNCAGINACEAE: POTAMOGETONACEAE

ALISMATACEAE

ALISMA

1. *Alisma plantago-aquatica* Glabrous perennial, up to about 1m. Leaves mostly subcordate or truncate at base, occasionally cuneate. Flowers white or lilac, usually opening after midday. Style arising below middle of fruit. Lateral pericarp thickish, opaque. May. Rare in fresh water. (From British specimen: main illustration and leaf × 1/4, flower × 2). **K D** (Ma) Bl excluded in FE V 2

2. *A. lanceolatum* As above, but leaves always cuneate at base. Flowers pink, usually opening in the morning. Style arising near top of fruit. Lateral pericarp thin, translucent. (Terminal part of inflorescence × 1 superimposed on leaf × 1/4). **D (Ma, Mi, I)** FE V 2

DAMASONIUM

3. *Damasonium alisma* Glabrous annual or perennial up to about 30cm. Apr. In water or on mud. Rare. (Main illustration from Mallorcan specimen, detail of flower × 2 from British specimen). **D** (Ma) FE V 3

JUNCAGINACEAE: *TRIGLOCHIN*

4. *Triglochin bulbosa* subsp. *barrelieri* Arrow-grass. Perennial up to about 20cm. Mar. - May. Locally common in saline mud. (Main illustration × 1/2, details slightly enlarged). K **D (Ma, Mi)** FE V 6

POTAMOGETONACEAE: *POTAMOGETON* Pondweed.

5. *Potamogeton coloratus* Floating leaves thin, somewhat translucent: petiole not longer than the lamina. Submerged leaves similar but narrower. Fruit 1.5-1.75mm, green. Common, usually in calcareous water in mountain areas. (Fruit × 4). **K D (Ma,** Mi, I) FE V 9

6. *P. crispus* Leaves all submerged, minutely serrulate. Mature leaves undulate. Fruit 4-5mm with long beak, dark olive. Occasional, ponds and streams. (From British specimen: fruit × 4). **D** Ll (Ma, Mi) FE V 10

7. *P. pectinatus* Submerged and floating leaves all similar, linear, usually less than 2mm wide, with long ligules and pale-bordered sheaths. Fruit 3-5mm. Common in brackish water. (Fruit × 4). K **D (Ma,** Mi, I) FE V 11

Other species possibly occurring in Mallorca:
Baldiella ranunculoides D. B (quotes Garcia, collecting 1905). Ll (Ma, Mi) Not Bl in FE V 2
Triglochin maritima K (quotes Willkomm 1873). ?D ?Ll (?Ma) Bl in FE V 6
Potamogeton natans Floating leaves present, up to 12.5cm, ovate to lanceolate with cuneate to subcordate base and a discoloured flexible joint in the petiole just below the lamina. Submerged leaves sessile, less than 3mm wide, often fugaceous. B D Ll (Ma, ?I) Bl excluded in FE V 9
P. nodosus Floating leaves up to 15cm, without flexible joint in petiole. Submerged leaves petiolate, at first minutely denticulate. B D Ll (Ma, Mi) Not Bl in FE V 9
P. lucens Floating leaves absent. Stipules of submerged leaves large, herbaceous. K (quotes Barceló 1867-1877) B D Ll (Ma) FE V 9
P. pusillus Floating leaves absent D Ll (Ma, Mi) FE V 10

In Minorca only:
Triglochin bulbosa subsp. *laxiflora* FE V 7

Plate 76

RUPPIACEAE: *RUPPIA*
POSIDONIACEAE: *POSIDONIA*
ZOSTERACEAE: *ZOSTERA*
ZANNICHELLIACEAE: (*ALTHENIA*), *ZANNICHELLIA*,
CYMODOCEA
NAJADACEAE: *NAJAS*

RUPPIACEAE: *RUPPIA*

1. *Ruppia maritima* Submerged perennial. Leaves less than 1mm wide. Sheaths of involucral leaves slightly inflated. Flowers in 2-flowered spikes on peduncles usually less than 6cm, flexuous in fruit. Fruit 2-3mm obliquely ovoid. Common in saline water. K **D** (**Ma**, Mi, I) FE V 11

2. *R. cirrhosa* As above, but leaves up to 1mm, usually rounded or obtuse. Peduncles more than 8cm, spirally coiled in fruit. Common. **D** (**Ma**, Mi) FE V 11

POSIDONIACEAE: *POSIDONIA*

3. *Posidonia oceanica* Submerged marine perennial. Rhizomes stout. Base of plant densely covered in fibrous remains of old sheaths. Leaves long linear with rounded apex. Peduncles up to 25cm with 3-6 flowers. Fruit 10mm, fleshy, ovoid. Shed fibrous material becomes matted together by action of sea to form balls up to about 8cm, common on beaches, as are massive deposits of rotting leaves. (Inflorescence and uncoloured enlarged detail of flower after Hutchinson 1959). **K D** (**Ma**, Mi, I) FE V 12

ZANNICHELLIACEAE

ZANNICHELLIA

4. *Zannichellia pedunculata* Reichenb. (*Z. palustris*) Horned Pondweed. Submerged monoecious perennial. Stems slender, leaves up to 2mm wide, subopposite on flowering branches, alternate on non-flowering branches. Sheaths free from leaf base, membranous when young, evanescent. Male flowers without perianth, peduncle simulating filament. Stamens 1 or 2. Female flower with cup-shaped perianth and 2-9 carpels (usually 4). Fruit laterally compressed, curved, toothed and beaked. Locally common in fresh or brackish water. (Enlarged detail of flower below main illustration after drawing in Hutchinson 1959). K **D** Ll (**Ma**, Mi) FE V 13)

CYMODOCEA

5. *Cymodocea nodosa* Submerged dioecious marine perennial. Stems with annular scars left by fallen leaves. Leaves 2-7 together on short shoots. Sheaths auriculate. Male peduncle 7-10 cm, simulating a filament. Stamens 2: anthers 11-15mm. Female flowers sessile with 2 carpels. Fruits 8mm, compressed, semicircular. (From Cretan specimen). K records from Mi only. **D** Ll (**Ma**, Mi, I) FE V 13

NAJADACEAE: *NAJAS*

6. *Najas marina* Brittle, submerged dioecious annual. Leaves up to 4.5cm, 1-6mm wide, prickly toothed on margins and back of midrib. Sheaths not or hardly auriculate. Male flowers with 2-lipped perianth, with 1 subsessile 4-locular anther. Female flower without perianth, with 1-locular ovary. Fresh or brackish water, not marine. (Main illustration from British specimen: enlarged details of fruit and male flower after drawing in Hutchinson 1959). K **D** Ll (Ma) FE V 13

Also recorded from Mallorca:
Zostera noltii Perennial submerged marine herb. Leaves linear, on non-flowering shoots up to 20cm × 1.5mm. Flowering stems about 10cm, lateral, simple or sparingly branched. Flowers with 1 sessile stamen, 1 unilocular ovary with a style and 2 long filiform stigmas. Ll (Ma, Mi, I) FE V 12
Zostera marina As above, but leaves on non-flowering shoots 20-50 × 2 12mm. Flowering stems up to 80cm, terminal, much-branched. K (quotes Barceló 1867-1877) D Ll (Ma, Mi, I) FE V 12
Althenia filiformis Submerged monoecious perennial. Stems slender, leaves linear, less than 0.5mm wide, setaceous. Sheaths adnate to leaf base, long-auriculate. Flowers axillary, solitary. Male flower with 3-toothed perianth with 1 stamen, female with 3 perianth segments and 3 carpels. Fruits ellipsoid, beaked. Brackish water. **D** ?Ll (?Ma) FE V 13

Plate 77

LILIACEAE (1): *ASPHODELUS, MERENDERA, GAGEA, (LILIUM), ORNITHOGALUM, URGINEA.*

ASPHODELUS

1. *A. aestivus* Robust perennial, usually more than 1m. Leaves flat. (× 1/10, detail × 1). Mar. - May. Common in cultivated areas, often a serious weed. **K D (Ma,** Mi, I) FE V 17
2. *Asphodelus fistulosus* Annual or perennial, usually about 50 cm. Leaves and stem hollow. (× 1/10, detail × 1). Apr. - May. Common in waste places. **K D (Ma,** Mi, I) FE V 17

MERENDERA

3. *Merendera filifolia* Perennial. Flowers solitary. Sept. Local in rocky places. **K D (Ma,** Mi, I) FE V 25

GAGEA

4. *Gagea mauritanica* Durieu Bulbous perennial. Perianth segments 13mm or more. Feb. - Mar. Very rare. (From sandy heath near sea). Ll (see Rita J. et al. (1985). **(Ma,** I) Not described in FE
5. *G. iberica* Terrac. (*G. nevadensis* Boiss.) Bulbous perennial. Perianth segments 10mm or less. Pedicel glabrous. Feb. - Mar. Rather rare. (From waste ground near Arenal). K (quotes Bianor 1910-1914). D **(Ma,** I) FE V 27

ORNITHOGALUM

6. *Ornithogalum narbonense* Bulbous perennial. Leaves without a white stripe. Flowers 30 or more in an elongated raceme. Apr. - May. Common in grassy places. **K D (Ma,** Mi, I) FE V 37
7. *O. umbellatum* Star of Bethlehem. Bulbous perennial. Leaves with a white stripe on upper suface. Flowers usually less than 20, in a compact raceme suggesting an umbel. Ovary green. Apr. - May. Rather local. K D **(Ma,** I) FE V 39
8. *O. arabicum* Bulbous perennial. Leaves with white stripe on upper surface. Flowers usually less than 20, in an elongated raceme. Ovary purplish black. Apr. - May. Common in grassy places around Alcudia. K D **(Ma,** Mi) FE V 40

URGINEA

9. *Urginea maritima* Perennial with large (up to 15cm) bulb, mostly above ground. Flowers small, very numerous, on stem up to 1.5m. Aug. - Oct. Common near sea in rocky places, including abandoned building sites. (× 1/10, detail × 1). **K D (Ma,** Mi, I) FE V 41

Also possibly in Mallorca:
Gagea arvensis K doubts. D and Ll omit. ?Bl in FE V 27
Lilium candidum D **(Ma)** Introduced, occasionally encountered in wild places. Bl not mentioned in FE V 34
Colchicum species:
C. lusitanicum (?Bl in FE) and *C. bivonae* (not Bl in FE). K saw a specimen of Bianor's purporting to be *C. bivonae* from near Deià, but doubted its actual provenance, and thought it was *C. lusitanicum* in any case. Ll lists *C. lusitanicum* for Ma. FE V 24

In other islands:
Asphodelus ramosus (A. cerasiferus Gay) Ibiza. Not Bl in FE V 17
Aphyllanthes monspeliensis ?Ibiza Bl in FE V 19
Ornithogalum collinum Ibiza Not Bl in FE V 38
O. orthophyllum subsp. *baeticum* Ibiza Not Bl in FE V 39
Urginea fugax Ibiza FE V 40

Plate 78

LILIACEAE (2): *SCILLA, BRIMEURA, MUSCARI, ASPARAGUS, RUSCUS, SMILAX.*

SCILLA

1. *Scilla autumnalis* Autumn squill. Bulbous perennial. Leaves very short or 0 at time of flowering. Sept. Local in dry, rocky places. K **D** (**Ma**, Mi, I) FE V 43

BRIMEURA

2. *Brimeura amethystina* Bulbous perennial. Mar. - May. Rare. (Specimen from Spanish mainland). Ll (Ma) Not Bl in FE V 44

MUSCARI Grape Hyacinth

3. *Muscari comosum* Bulbous perennial. Apr. - May. Dry grassland. Common. **K D** (**Ma**, Mi, I) FE V 47
4. *M. neglectum* Leaves linear, canaliculate. Fertile flowers blue to blackish-blue with white recurved teeth. Mar. - Apr. Dry grassland. (**Ma**, I) FE V 48
5. *M. parviflorum* Leaves narrowly linear or filiform. Fertile flowers pale blue, often absent. (Specimen from Rhodes, slightly enlarged: details × 3). Oct. Local. **K** D Ll (**Ma**) FE V 48

ASPARAGUS

6. *Asparagus albus* Shrubby rhizomatous perennial. Stems whitish with with bundles of 10-20 deciduous unarmed cladodes (up to 25mm × less than 2mm) in axils of straight spreading spines up to 12mm long. Flowers hermaphrodite. Aug. Roadsides, fairly common. **K D** (**Ma**, Mi) FE V 72
7. *A. acutifolius* Dioecious shrubby rhizomatous perennial. Stems up to 2m, flexuous and intertwined. Cladodes in bundles of 10-30, spreading, spiny. Spur on main branches usually developing into robust spine. July - Oct. Common in bushy places. (× 1, details × 2). K **D** (**Ma**, Mi, I) FE V 72
8. *A. stipularis* (*A. horridus* L. fil) Dioecious shrubby rhizomatous perennial. Stems up to 60cm, much ridged, woody. Cladodes solitary (rarely in fascicles of 2-3), 10-30mm, very spiny. Apr. - Sept. Common in bushy places. **K D** (**Ma**, Mi, I) FE V 72

RUSCUS

9. *Ruscus aculeatus* Butcher's Broom. Evergreen rhizomatous shrubby perennial. Flowering irregularly and infrequently. Common in scrub, especially in hilly places. (× 1, detail slightly enlarged). **K D** (**Ma**, Mi, I) FE V 73

SMILAX

10. *Smilax aspera* Sarsaparilla. Scrambling or climbing dioecious, woody perennial. Variable, plants in exposed situations often intricately branched, very prickly, and almost or quite leafless. (= endemic var. balearica.) Aug. - Sept. Common in bushy and exposed rocky places. (Specimens from four different plants × 1, and single flower × 2). **K D** (**Ma**, Mi, I) FE V 74

Also recorded for Mallorca:
Brimeura fastigiata **D** Ll (see Rita J. et al. (1985). (Ma, Mi) FE V 44

In Ibiza:
Scilla obtusifolia FE V 43
S. numidica Poiret (not described in FE)
Dipcadi serotinum FE V 46
Asparagus tenuifolius Not Bl in FE V 73

Plate 79

LILIACEAE (3): *ALLIUM*

(Illustrations all approximately × 1/2 - 3/4. Numbers appear between main illustration and enlarged details. Leaves sometimes shown green when usually withered at flowering time).

Note Stems: 2 and 5 have 3-sided stems, others are more or less terete.

Leaves: 12 ad 13 have fistular leaves, others are flat, keeled or canaliculate. 3,4 and 14 have all leaves basal or almost so.

Spathes: Spathes of 1 to 6, 9, 10, 11, 13 and 14 (sometimes 12) are 1-valved, though in 14 valve becomes split to base, and there may appear to be several valves. Spathes of 7, 8, and usually 12 have 2 valves. Valves of 1-6 and 14 have no beaks. Valves of 7-11 have long beaks, 12 and 13 short ones. Valves of 1-8 and 12-14 are persistent, those of 9-11 are caducous (sometimes the base of the valve may persist, giving appearance of two valves, but remaining stump lacks a beak; see illustration of no 12).

Stamens: 1-6 have simple, free stamens. Nos 7, 8 and 14 have simple stamens connate into an annulus: nos 9-13 have at least some stamens with a basal lamina supporting 3 cusps, only the central one bearing an anther.

1. *A. roseum* Up to 65cm, usually less. Stem smooth. Leaves 2-4, flat, sheathing lower 1/5 of stem. Bulbils often present: flowers long stemmed, usually pink. Umbel usually lax. Mar.June. Common. **K D (Ma,** Mi, I) FE V 56

2. *A. neapolitanum* Stem up to 50cm, 3-sided, with narrow wings on 2 of the angles. Flowers white, in lax umbel. Mar.May. Uncommon, waste places and roadsides. K D Ll **(Ma,** Mi, I) Not Bl in FE V 57

3. *A. subhirsutum* Stem up to 30cm, smooth. Leaves flat, almost basal, with cilia on at least part of margin. Flowers white. Stamens shorter than petals, anthers usually brownish. Mar. May. Uncommon. (From garden specimen). **K D** (Ma, Mi) FE V 57

4. *A. subvillosum* Very like 3, but stamens usually as long as more rounded petals, or longer. Anthers yellow. Mar. - May. Common, often growing through bushes in rocky places. K **D (Ma,** ?Mi) FE V 57

5. *A. triquetrum* Small plant, with three sided unwinged stems. Umbel lax, one-sided, with up to 15 mostly pendulous flowers. Mar. - Apr. Common, especially near streams. **K D (Ma,** Mi) FE V 58

6. *A. chamaemoly* Stem very short, umbel appears sessile. Nov. Mar. Local. (From herbarium specimen). K **D** Ll (Ma, Mi, I) FE V 58

7. *A. paniculatum* Stem smooth, up to 70cm. Leaves sheathing 1/3-1/2 stem. Longer valve of spathe up to 14cm, far exceeding pedicels. Perianth bell-shaped, becoming ovoid, lilac or whitish. Umbel with up to 70 flowers. Pedicels very variable in length, longest usually = 20cm, upper erect, outer curving. Stamens included or slightly exserted, anthers yellow. Apr. June. Locally common. **D (Ma)** Not Bl in FE V 60

8. *A. pallens* Often difficult to distinguish from 7, but umbel more compact. Perianth segments slightly wider above than below middle (in 7 they are ovoid). Pedicels all 20mm. Apr.June. Rare. (Specimen from Spanish mainland). **K** H Ll (Ma) FE V 61

9. *A. ampeloprasum* Wild Leek. Stem up to 150cm. Leaves canaliculate, with rough margin sheathing lower 1/3-1/2 stem. Umbel dense and globose, (up to 500 flowers), bulbils often present. Perianth bell-shaped, white to dark red, segments with large papillae on keel. Inner stamens have basal lamina 1.5-2.5mm wide, usually as wide as perianth segment, with elongated lateral cusps exceeding the central anther-bearing cusp and further exserted. Apr. - June. Very common. K D **(Ma,** Mi, I) FE V 63

10. *A. polyanthum* Leaves flat with smooth margin, sheathing lower 1/4 of stem. Umbel lax, many-flowered, pedicels unequal. Perianth pink, segments scabrid or slightly papillose on keel. Filaments on inner stamens tricuspidate, basal lamina narrower than perianth segment. Apr. - June. Common. K **D (Ma,** Mi, I) FE V 64

11. *A. commutatum* (*A. bimetrale* Gand). Up to 180cm. Leaves sheath lower 1/4 - 2/3 stem. Base of valve abruptly contracted into long 2-edged beak. Lateral cusps of inner stamens about equalling anther-bearing cusp, basal lamina < 1cm wide. Apr. - June. Local. (From Italian specimen). H Ll (Ma, Mi, I) Not Bl in FE V 64

12. *A. sphaerocephalon* Leaves fistular. Heads dense, usually egg-shaped. Perianth narrowly ovoid, often dark reddish or purple. Anthers reddish before opening, then greyish blue. Apr. - June. Uncommon. (From garden specimen). K D Ll (Ma, Mi) ?Bl in FE V 66

13. *A. vineale* Crow Garlic Leaves fistular. Umbel often with few flowers or none, and many bulbils (rarely no bulbils). Perianth bell-shaped, anthers yellow. Local. K D (Ma, Mi, I) FE V 67

14. *A. nigrum* Robust plant with flat basal leaves and smooth stem up to 90cm. Umbel very dense and more or less flat-topped. Perianth segments pinkish or dirty white, reflexed after flowering. Common weed of cultivated fields. Mar. - May. **K D (Ma)** FE V 68

Also in Mallorca:

A. antonii-bolosii Palau. Leaves filiform, slightly canaliculate, sheathing lower 1/3 - 3/4 of slender stem. Spathe 1-valved, persistent, tubular at base. Flowers 3-15 with very unequal pedicels. Perianth cylindrical, segments 5.5-9mm whitish or pink. Stamens included, filaments simple. H Ll list. (Ma, Mi) (cf. *A. cupani* subsp. *hirtovaginatum* in FE V 59)

A. oleraceum Leaves fistular in lower part, canaliculate above, sheathing at least lower half stem. Veins scabrid with minute teeth. Umbel with bulbils only, or up to 40-flowered. Pedicels unequal, slightly flattened or winged. Spathes 2-valved, valves unequal with long, slender appendage (longer up to 20 cm). Perianth bell-shaped, whitish, or tinged with other colours. Stamens simple, included in perianth, connate into an annulus. Ll lists. (Ma) Not Bl in FE V 61

In other islands:

Allium senescens Cabrera Not Bl in FE V 53
A. victorialis Cabrera Not Bl in FE V 56
A. grosii Ibiza, endemic. FE V 59
A. eivissanum Garbari & Miceli Endemic Ibiza (not described in FE)
A. ebusitanum Font Quer Endemic Ibiza (see under *A. vineale* FE V 67)

184

Plate 80

(AGAVACEAE: *AGAVE*)

AMARYLLIDACEAE: *STERNBERGIA, LEUCOJUM,*
NARCISSUS, PANCRATIUM
DIOSCORIEACEAE: TAMUS
IRIDACEAE (1): IRIS, GYNANDIRIS, CROCUS, (FREESIA)

AMARYLLIDACEAE

STERNBERGIA

1. *Sternbergia lutea* Oct. (Specimen from Rhodes). K (quotes Barceló 1867 1877) and Bianor (1914-1920) D lists. Ll treats as alien. (Ma) FE V 76

LEUCOJUM

2. *Leucojum aestivum* subsp. *pulchellum* Summer Snowflake. Feb. - Mar. Rather local by streams in mountain areas. **K D** (**Ma,** Mi) FE V 77

NARCISSUS

3. *Narcissus serotinus* Leaves appear in spring, and are absent at flowering time. Flowers 1-3 together. Sept. Locally common, roadsides and dry hills. **K D** (**Ma,** Mi, I) FE V 79
4. *N. tazetta* Leaves present at flowering time. March. Locally common sometimes pushing through tarmac surface of road margin. March. **K D** (**Ma,** Mi, I) FE V 79

PANCRATIUM

5. *Pancratium maritimum* Sea Daffodil. Sept. Fairly common on sandy and stony beaches. **K D** (**Ma,** Mi) FE V 84

DIOSCOREACEAE: *TAMUS*

6. *Tamus communis* Black Bryony. Dioecious climbing plant. Apr. - May. Common, roadsides and bushy places. **K D** (**Ma,** Mi, I) FE V 85

IRIDACEAE

IRIS

7. *Iris pseudacorus* Yellow Flag. Apr. - May. Occasional in marshy places. **K D** (**Ma,** Mi) FE V 88
8. *I. pallida* Pale Iris. Apr. - May. Spathes of flowering stems entirely scarious. Varieties of this species are cultivated here and may become established. (From cultivated Mallorcan specimen). K D (Ma, Mi, I) FE V 91

Other species may also be established. *I. albicans* and *I. germanica* both have spathes scarious only in the upper half at flowering time. The bluish-purple *Iris germanica* and its bluish white var. florentina usually have 4 flowers with the upper 2 very close together, while the pure white *I. albicans* usually has 3 well-spaced flowers. K considers Barceló's *Iris majoricensis* to be *I. albicans*, though the original specimen is lost.

GYNANDIRIS

9. *Gynandiris sisyrinchium* Barbary Nut. Feb. - Apr. Occasional in pinewoods and dry shady places. **K D** (**Ma,** Mi, I) FE V 92

CROCUS

10. *Crocus cambessedesii* Nov. - Mar. Rocky places and in mountains. Local. **K D** (endemic Ma, Mi) FE V 94

Also recorded from Mallorca;
Agave americana Widely cultivated, sometimes appearing wild. (**Ma,** I) FE V 74
Narcissus elegans, resembling *N. serotinus,* but with leaves 2-4.5mm wide, present at flowering-time, and flowers in umbels of 3-7, is established in several places. Ll (Ma, I) FE V 80
Freesia refracta. Corm with sword-like leaves. Secund spike of very sweetly scented zygomorphic flowers with creamish perianth segments, the lowest usually blotched with deep yellow. Native of S. Africa, much cultivated and frequently found on tips, also quite commonly as isolated apparently wild plants in fields etc. **D** (**Ma**) Not Bl in FE V 92

Plate 81

IRIDACEAE (2): *ROMULEA, GLADIOLUS*
JUNCACEAE: *JUNCUS*

IRIDACEAE.

ROMULEA

1. *Romulea ramiflora*. Scape elongating in fruit. Bract and bracteole herbaceous, bracteole with scarious margin. Perianth green outside. Feb. - Mar. (Side and top views of Portuguese plant × 1). The presence of this species in Mallorca has recently been questioned: see Rita (1990) K lists for Mi only. **D** ?Ll (?Ma, ?Mi) FE V 100

2. *R. columnae* subsp. *columnae* Bract herbaceous, bracteole almost entirely scarious. From British specimen: but the fruiting stem on the right of illustrations for *R. ramiflora* is from Mallorca (× ca 2/3), and was originally identified as *R. ramiflora*. However Dr Rita of the Universitat de les Illas Balears has studied this genus here, and finds that flowering plants all seem to be *R. columnae*, but the form and size of fruiting stems varies very much with the habitat, and is often not as described in FE in damp situations. (Personal communication). **K D** Common, especially in seasonally damp places. Ll (**Ma,** Mi, I) FE V 100

3. *R. assumptionis* Font-Quer and Garc. As 2, but perianth pure white with yellow and violet markings in the throat, about 6mm. Mar. - Apr. Locally common. **D** (**Ma,** Mi, I) Species not in FE: there is good reason to raise this as a new species and Balearic endemic. See Rita (1990) (cf. subsp. *R. columnae* FE V 100)

GLADIOLUS

The three species are very similar. Small specimens of 6 can easily be mistaken for 4, while specimens of 4 in cultivated fields can look like 6.

4. *Gladiolus illyricus* Generally small (but up to 50cm), with few leaves which hardly reach spike. Spike with 3-10 flowers, rarely branched. Anthers equal filaments or shorter. Seeds winged. Mar. - Apr. Common, dry scrubby ground, and fields. (Inflorescence, fruit and seeds × 1, also reduced plant to show typical habit). **K D** (**Ma,** Mi, I) FE V 101

5. *G. communis* (including *G. byzantinus*) More robust than 4, 50-80cm. Leaves reach above bottom of the 10-30-flowered spike, which is often branched. Anthers as 4, seeds winged. Mar. - Apr. Abundant in at least one site. (Part of spike and branch showing dark veined sheaths; also fruit, all × 1). In habit like 6. D Ll (**Ma,** Mi, I) Not Bl in FE V 101

6. *G. italicus* Robust plant, 50-100cm. Spike with 6-16 flowers, often branched. Flowers generally paler than in 4, but this is not constant. Anthers always longer than filaments or aborted. Seeds unwinged. Mar. - Apr. Fairly common field weed. (Lateral view of flower × 1, with petal removed to show relatively short filaments: much reduced plant to show habit). K **D** Ll treats as alien. (**Ma,** Mi, I) FE V 102

JUNCACEAE: *JUNCUS*

7. *Juncus maritimus* Sea Rush. Rhizomatous perennial up to 1m. Stems leafy. Mar. - Oct. Common in saltmarshes and damp places near sea. (Upper part flowering stem, detail capsule × 2). **K D** (**Ma,** Mi, I) FE V 104

8. *J. acutus* subsp. *acutus* Sharp rush. Densely tufted perennial, up to 1.5m or more. Stems leafy. Tip of lower bract very sharp. Inflorescence usually dense, but sometimes with long branches which may overtop tip of lower bract. Mar. - Oct. Common in sandy places near sea. (Top of small fruiting stem, capsule and flower × 2). **K D** (**Ma,** Mi, I) FE V 104

9. *J. inflexus* Hard Rush. Tufted perennial up to 1m or more. Stems slender with 10-20 prominent longitudinal ridges, leafless apart from brown basal sheaths. Apr. - June. Damp places, occasional. (Upper part flowering and fruiting stems slightly reduced, enlarged details of capsule and stem). **K D** (**Ma**) FE V 105

10. *J. subulatus* Rhizomatous perennial with leafy stems, up to 1m or more. May - July. Common in saltmarshes. (Inflorescence, enlarged details of flower and capsule). **K D** (**Ma,** Mi) FE V 105

11. *J. bufonius* Toad Rush. Annual, usually with many stems up to 50cm, usually less. Inflorescence branched, usually lax. Seeds obliquely ovoid. Apr. - May. Very common in wet places. (detail of capsule × 2, seed × 10). **K D** (**Ma**) FE V 107

12. *J. hybridus* (= *J. bufonius* L. subsp. *insulanus* (Viv.) Briq. Annual, resembling 11, but inflorescence with flowers in clusters: inner perianth segments shorter than outer and less acute. Seeds barrel-shaped. (See Cope T.A. and Stace C.A. 1980). Apr. - May. Occasional in damp saline habitats. (Seed × 10). ?K **D** (**Ma,** Mi, I) FE V 108

13. *J. subnodulosus* Blunt-flowered Rush. Rhizomatous perennial, up to 1m or more. Stems with 3-4 basal sheaths and 1-2 cauline leaves. Leaves bright green with longitudinal and transverse septa. May - July. Wet places, occasional. (Upper part of flowering stem slightly reduced, detail enlarged). **K D** Ll (**Ma,** Mi, I) FE V 108

14. *J. articulatus* Jointed rush. Tufted or rhizomatous perennial Stems with 0-2 basal sheaths and 3-6 cauline leaves. Leaves and longer bracts with transverse septa. Common in damp places. (Upper part of stem, details of flower, capsule and longitudinal section of stem enlarged). **K D** (**Ma,** Mi, I) FE V 111

Others recorded for Mallorca:
Romulea columnae subsp. *rollii* (= *R. rollii* Parl.) var *lutea* Palau seems to be very dubious here. See Rita (1990)
R. columnae subsp. *columnae* var *immaculata* Maire. See Rita (1990)
Juncus effusus K (quotes Rodríguez 1865-1904). D Ll (Ma, Mi). Bl specifically excluded in FE V 105
J. capitatus K (quotes Barceló 1867-1877). D and Ll list. (Ma, Mi). FE V 108
J. pygmaeus K lists for Mi only. D lists. Ll omits. (?Ma, ?Mi) Not Bl in FE V 108
J. bulbosus ?D. Ll lists *J. mutabilis* Lam., which may be this species here, for Ma, Mi. (?Ma, ?Mi) Not Bl in FE V 109
J. fontanesii D and Ll list for Ma, Mi. FE V 110

In Minorca:
Juncus littoralis (*Juncus acutus* L. subsp. *tommasii* (Parl.) Ascherson & Graebner) FE V 104

Plate 82

GRAMINEAE (1): *FESTUCA, LOLIUM, VULPIA, DESMAZERIA, CUTANDIA, (MICROPYRUM), (NARDUROIDES).*

FESTUCA

1. *Festuca arundinacea* Tall Fescue. Tussock-forming perennial. Inflorescence much branched. Lemmas rounded on back, with an awn or more or less awnless (2 subspecies here). May - June. Common in damp places. (Terminal part of inflorescence only, slightly reduced. Spikelet with awned lemmas × 2). **K D (Ma, Mi, I)** FE V 132

LOLIUM

Simple spike, spikelets lying edgeways on alternate sides of rhachis. Lower glume absent except in terminal spikelet.

2. *Lolium perenne* Rye-grass. Perennial. Young leaves flat or folded . Lemma usually unawned. Apr. - June. Common. **K D** Ll treats as alien. **(Ma, I)** FE V 154
3. *L. multiflorum* Italian Rye-grass. Usually annual. Young leaves rolled. Spikelets with (5-) 11-22 florets. Glumes not usually more than 1/2 length spikelet. Lemmas usually awned. Apr. - June. Common. **K D** Ll treats as alien. **(Ma, Mi, I)** FE V 154
4. *L. rigidum* Annual. Leaves rolled in young shoots. Spikelets with 5-8 florets. Glumes more than 1/2 length spikelet, often longer than spikelet. Apr. - June. Common. **K D (Ma, Mi, I)** FE V 154
5. *L. temulentum* Darnel. Annual. Lemma usually long awned, swollen when ripe. Apr. - June. Occasional. **K D (Ma, Mi)** FE V 154

VULPIA

Annuals. panicles (rarely racemes) often secund. Glumes very unequal. Lemma narrow, rounded dorsally, tapering into long straight awn. Main illustration slightly reduced, details of spikelets and glumes enlarged.

6. *Vulpia geniculata* Diffuse panicle. Pedicels dilated distally. Florets opening normally, anthers 2-5mm (all other species here are cleistogamous with anthers up to 2mm). Lower glume 2.5-5mm, 2/5 - 3/5 length of upper. Apr. - June. Rare. K D **(Ma, Mi)** FE V 155
7. *V. fasciculata* Pedicels dilated distally. Florets cleistogamous. Ovary pubescent at apex. Lower glume 0.1-2.6mm, less than 1/6 length upper. (Inflorescence typically partly included in uppermost leaf sheath, but not in this robust specimen, at first taken for *Bromus* species). Mar. - May. Occasional. **K D (Ma, Mi, I)** FE V 155
8. *V. membranacea* (*Vulpia pyramidata* (Link.) Rothm.) Dune Fescue. Like 7: small differences include anthers 0.6-0.9mm and ovary glabrous. Mar. - May. Local on sandy beaches. **D (Ma, I)** FE V 155

9. *V. bromoides* Squirrel-tail Fescue. Pedicels not dilated distally (nor in 10, 11, 12). Panicle usually smaller and less dense than other species here. Lower glume 2.5-5mm, 1/2 - 3/4 length upper. Mar. - June. ?Rare. (From British specimen). K lists for Minorca only. **D (Ma, Mi)** FE V 157
10. *V. muralis* Panicle usually well exserted from upper leaf-sheath. Lower glume 1-3 (-6)mm, 1/4 to 1/2 length upper. Mar. - June. Occasional. (Specimen from Spanish mainland). **D (Ma, Mi, I)** FE V 156
11. *V. myuros* Rat's tail Fescue. Resembles 10, but panicle usually partly included in uppermost leaf-sheath. Lower glume 0.4-2.5mm, 1/10-2/5 length upper. Lemmas of the 1-2 distal reduced florets usually glabrous, if ciliate might be confused with 12, but 12 has 3-7 distal sterile florets. Common. **K D (Ma)** FE V 156
12. *V. ciliata* Lower glume 0.1-1mm, less than 1/4 upper. Distal 3-7 lemmas sterile and long-ciliate. Mar. - May. Common. **K D (Ma, Mi, I)** FE V 156

DESMAZERIA

Hairless rather rigid annuals. Inflorescence spike-like above, often with branches below. In dry conditions whole plant often turns red.

13. *Desmazeria marina* Inflorescence usually unbranched. Lower glume acute, upper blunt. Mar. - June. Common. **K D** ?Ll **(Ma, Mi, I)** FE V 158
14. *D. rigida* Inflorescence usually branched below. Both glumes acuminate. Mar. - June. Common. **K D (Ma, Mi, I)** FE V 158
15. *D. balearica* Willk. (FE index equates with 14) seems to be particularly well-branched robust form of 14, often with axillary inflorescences. Detail as 14. (**D** also includes with 14). **(Ma, Mi, I)**

CUTANDIA

16. *Cutandia maritima* Like *Desmazeria*, but larger, with divaricate branches. Often prostrate, often turns deep blackish-purple. Mar. - June. Occasional, maritime sands. K **D (Ma, Mi, I)** FE V 159

Other species occurring in Mallorca:
Festuca ovina. D lists 'gr. *ovina*' L. B and Ll both list F. *ovina* L. Not Bl in FE V 145
Vulpia unilateralis (L.) Stace (*V. hispanica* (Reichard) Kerguélen) Ll lists. (Ma, Mi, I) Not Bl in FE V 156
Micropyrum tenellum ?D Ll Not Bl in FE V 157
Narduroides salzmanii D Ll Not Bl in FE V 158

Recorded from Ibiza:
Festuca heterophylla FE V 139

Plate 83

GRAMINEAE (2): *SPHENOPUS, (VULPIELLA), POA, PUCCINELLIA, DACTYLIS, (SCLEROCHLOA), CYNOSURUS, LAMARCKIA, PSILURUS, BRIZA.*

SPHENOPUS

1. *Sphenopus divaricatus* Hairless annual. Inflorescence a much-branched panicle, pedicels mostly 2 together, very slender, but quite distinctive in being gradually thickened distally (apart from this plant looks very like *Aira* species). Apr. - May. Local in salt marshes. K **D** (**Ma**, Mi, I) FE V 159

POA

Annuals or perennials with more or less pyramidal branched panicles. Spikelets compressed. Glumes keeled, lemmas keeled, usually awnless.

2. *Poa annua* Branches of panicle smooth, in pairs at least at lower nodes, deflexed after flowering. Lemma not lanate at base. All year. Very common in disturbed ground. K **D** (**Ma**, Mi, I) FE V 161
3. *P. trivialis* Stoloniferous perennial. Panicle branches 3-5 together at lower nodes. Ligule 3.5-10mm, pointed. Apr. - May. Common in damp places. K **D** (**Ma**, Mi) FE V 161
4. *P. angustifolia* Tufted perennial without stolons. Panicle resembles 3, but with branches rather shorter and more rigid. Ligule 1-3mm, truncated. Apr. - May. (Ligule only here, from British specimen). **D** (**Ma**) FE V 162
5. *P. flaccidula* Perennial, resembling 2, but panicle branches minutely scabrid (needs microscope), not deflexed after flowering. Lemma lanate at base. May - June. Occasional in NW mountains. **D** (**Ma**) FE V 164
6. *P. bulbosa* Tufted perennial with bulbous-based stem. Apr. Common in dry places. K **D** (**Ma**, Mi, I) FE V 165

PUCCINELLIA

7. *Puccinellia* species Perennial, panicle resembles *Poa* species, but lemmas rounded on back (keeled in *Poa*). Apr. - May. Common in saline marshes. **K D** (variously identified). Ll lists *P. fasciculata* (**Ma**, I). Bl not excluded for *P. distans*, (probably after Knoche's *Glyceria distans* Wahl.). Not Bl in FE V 168

DACTYLIS

8. *Dactylis glomerata* Cock's-foot. Coarse tufted perennial. May. Common in cultivated areas. **K D** (**Ma**, Mi, I) FE V 171

CYNOSURUS

Panicles dense, lobed, one-sided. Spikelets dimorphic, fertile (**F**) with relatively broad florets, the sterile (**S**) with widely spaced, comb-like, narrow glumes and lemmas.

9. *Cynosurus echinatus* Rough Dog's Tail. Annual. Leaves 3-9mm wide. Upper lemmas of sterile spikelets much the same shape as lower. Apr. - May. Common in dry grassy places. **K D** (**Ma**, Mi) FE V 171
10. *C. elegans* Similar to 10, but smaller. Leaves up to 3mm wide, upper lemmas of sterile spikelets shorter and wider than lower. Not common. (From Spanish specimen). **K D** (**Ma**) FE V 172

LAMARCKIA

11. *Lamarckia aurea* Golden Dog's Tail. Annual. Apr. - May. Common in cultivated areas. **K D** (**Ma**, Mi, I) FE V 172

PSILURUS

12. *Psilurus incurvus* Annual. Rare or possibly overlooked. (From Cretan specimen). **K D** (Ma, I) FE V 173

BRIZA

Annual. Spikelets broader than long, pendulous, often purplish, on long slender pedicels.

13. *Briza maxima* Quaking or Totty Grass. Annual. Apr. - May. Common in dry grassy places. **K D** (**Ma**, Mi, I) FE V 173
14. *B. minor* Annual. Apr. - May. Widespread but less common than 13. **K D** (**Ma**, Mi, I) FE V 173

Also recorded from Mallorca:
Vulpiella tenuis Knoche quotes Willkomm (collecting 1873). Also recorded from Minorca. FE V 159
Sclerochloa dura Ll lists. FE V 170

In Minorca:
Poa infirma Not Bl in FE V 161

Plate 84

GRAMINEAE (3): *SESLERIA, MELICA, BROMUS.*

SESLERIA

1. *Sesleria insularis* subsp. *insularis* Tufted perennial with shining more or less cylindrical inflorescence up to about 50mm, with toothed bracts at base. Spikelets with 2 or more florets. Glumes, palea and lemma all awned. April. Local in mountain areas. (Inflorescence × 1, lowest spikelet with bract × 3). **K D (Ma)** FE V 177

MELICA

Perennials. Inflorescence a panicle. Spikelets with a terminal club-like structure formed by sterile lemmas.

2. *Melica minuta* Lax inflorescence, little or much branched. Spikelets often purplish. Lemmas hairless. Mar. - May. Common. Easily confused with Piptatherum miliaceum (plate 88). (Main illustration × 1/2: details of spikelets slightly enlarged). **K D (Ma, I)** FE V 178

3. *M. ciliata* Panicle fairly dense, spike-like at least above, often with short branches below. Spikelets 4-8mm. Fertile lemma with long hairs on margin and veins, inflorescence softly hairy at flowering time. Mar. - May. Common. (Main illustration × 1/2, spikelet × 2). **K D (Ma, Mi)** FE V 178

4. *M. bauhinii* Resembles 3, but panicle (or raceme, as here) is lax. Spikelets 8-10mm, with lemma glabrous in distal 1/3. Mar. - May. Not common. (From garden specimen, reduced). **K D** Ll omits. (Ma) FE V 179

BROMUS

Annual or rarely biennial. Inflorescence a panicle with long many-flowered spikelets, drooping or erect on (usually) long pedicels. Lemma usually long-awned. Illustrations offer only very rough guide to identification, and keys in the FE or elsewhere do not seem to help here in distinguishing between nos 8, 9 and 10. General habit seems more significant. (Fatima Sales, private communication).

Main illustrations × 1/3 to 1/2, details × 1.

5. *Bromus diandrus* Panicle branches long, spreading, usually with single spikelet. Awn stout, scabrid, longer than lemma. Mar. - May. Common. K **D (Ma,** Mi, I) FE V 183

6. *B. rigidus* Panicle branches short, held stiffly erect. Spikelets resemble those of 5. Mar. - May. Occasional. **K D (Ma,** Mi, I) FE V 183

7. *B. sterilis* Like 5, but spikelets smaller, with a slender awn. Mar. - May. Rather dubious here. (From British specimen). Knoche includes many 'forms' now recognised as separate species. ?D. Ll omits. (?Ma, ?Mi, ?I) Bl not excluded in FE V 183

8. *B. madritensis* Panicle 3-15cm, erect but fairly lax, branches 10mm or more. Spikelets wedge-shaped, lax. Mar. - May. Common. (Panicle often denser than illustrated here, but peripheral spikelets at least usually distinct, not concealed among other spikelets as they usually are in 10). **K D (Ma,** Mi, I) FE V 184

9. *B. fasciculatus* Small plant. Panicle 4-5cm, with rigid branches. Lemma narrow. Mar. - May. Occasional. (Specimen from Spanish mainland). **K D** Ll (Ma, Mi, I) FE V 184

10. *B. rubens* Generally much larger than 9. Panicle usually dense, reddish. Mar. - May. Occasional. (Specimen from Spanish mainland). K **D (Ma,** Mi, I) FE V 184

11. *B. hordeaceus* (included in *B. mollis* L.) Soft Brome. Spikelets ovate, softly hairy. Awn of lemma straight, erect. Mar. - May. Common. **K D (Ma,** Mi, I) FE V 188

12. *B. lanceolatus* Spikelets up to 5cm, with up to 20 florets, the lemmas with long awns, which are flattened at the base, and twisted. Mar. - May. Rare. (From garden specimen). Could perhaps be confused with *Avenula bromoides* (a tufted perennial). K D (Ma, Mi) FE V 188

Also recorded for Mallorca:
Melica uniflora K (quotes Willkomm collecting 1873). Ll omits. Bl specifically excluded in FE V 178
Bromus squarrosus K (quotes Barceló, who records as 'rarísimo'). Ll lists for Ma, Mi. Bl in FE V 188
B. wildenowii Ibiza Not Bl in FE V 189 (recently collected in Mallorca by R. Palmer)

In Minorca:
Bromus arvensis Minorca: Bl in FE V 186

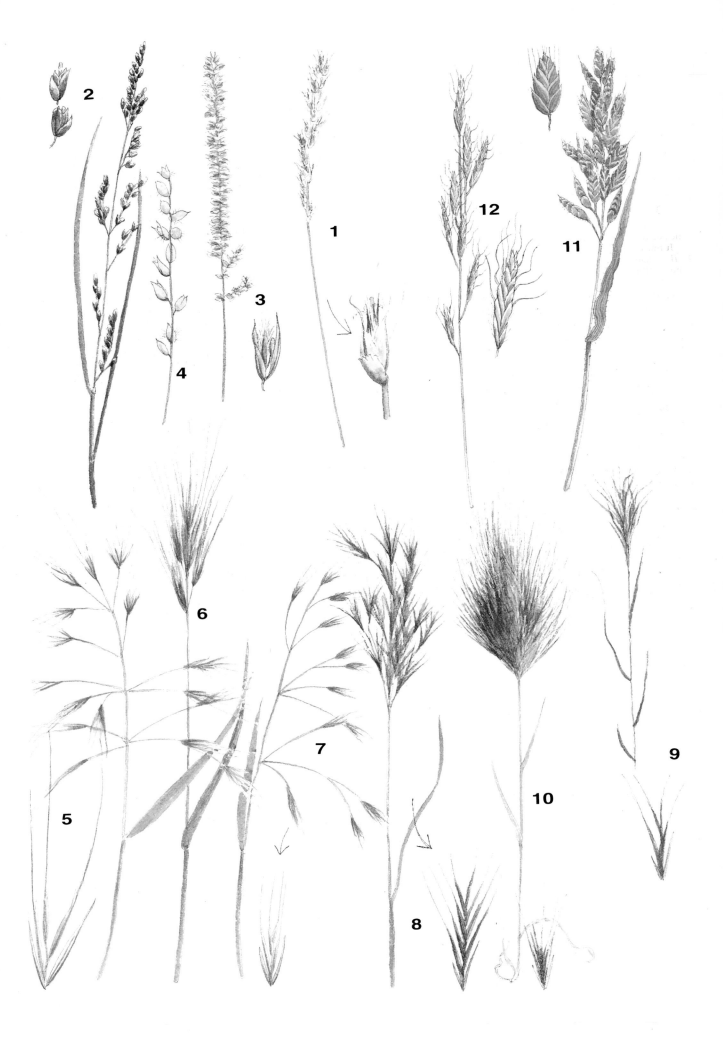

Plate 85

GRAMINEAE (4): *BRACHYPODIUM, ELYMUS, AEGILOPS, TRITICUM, (DASYPYRUM).*

BRACHYPODIUM
Inflorescence a raceme of long spikelets, inserted edgeways to rhachis.

1. *Brachypodium sylvaticum* Perennial. Leaves hairy. Spikelets not or hardly compressed. Lemma with awn at least 7mm. Apr. - June. Local. **K D (Ma,** Mi, I) FE V 189
2. *B. retusum* Wiry, stiff rhizomatous perennial. Leaves glaucous, becoming convolute. Raceme of 1-7 stiff spikelets, 20-30mm. Awns not more than 4mm. Common in dry places, chiefly in the mountains. Apr. - June. **K D (Ma,** Mi, I) FE V 190
3. *B. phoenicoides* Resembles 2, but less stiff and larger. Leaves flat or convolute. Raceme of 6-13 spikelets, often curved, 30-80mm. Awns up to 2.5mm or 0. Apr. - June. Common. **K D (Ma,** Mi, I) FE V 190
4. *B. distachyon* Annual. Upper leaves with characteristic twist. Spikelets laterally compressed. Lemmas awned. Mar. - May. Common. **K D (Ma,** Mi, I) FE V 190

ELYMUS
Inflorescence a spike, with spikelets solitary on alternating sides of rhachis, flattened side towards rhachis.

5. *Elymus elongatus* Tufted perennial, not rhizomatous. Rhachis tough, usually spinose-ciliate on angles, not disarticulating at maturity. June - July. Local. Salt-marshes and beaches. (Specimen from Spanish mainland). **K D** (Ma, Mi, I) FE V 195
6. *E. repens* Couch Grass. Rhizomatous perennial. Leaf-blades finely pointed but not hard and sharp. Rhachis not disarticulating at maturity. June - July. Common agricultural weed. (Green and glaucous forms shown). K D **(Ma,** Mi, I) FE V 196
7. *E. pungens* Sea Couch. Rhizomatous perennial. Leaf-blades with sharp hard-pointed tips. Rhachis not disarticulating at maturity. Uncommon. Dry soils, usually near the sea. (Specimen from Spanish mainland). K lists for Minorca only. **D** Ll (Ma, Mi, I) FE V 196

8. *E. farctus* subsp. *farctus* Sand Couch. Rhizomatous perennial. Rhachis disarticulating just above each spikelet (places where this occurs clearly visible before maturity). May - Sept. Common on beaches. K **D (Ma,** Mi, I) FE V 197

AEGILOPS
Annuals. Glumes swollen, leathery, rounded, with several teeth or awns.

9. *Aegilops ventricosa* Spike cylindrical, more than 10 × as long as wide. Glumes with teeth or very short awns. Common. Apr. - June. K **D (Ma,** Mi) FE V 201
10. *A. triuncialis* Spike up to 5+ as long as wide, gradually tapering upwards, wth one or 2 vestigial spikelets at base. Awns of lemma shorter than awns of glumes, which are 7-10mm on lowest spikelet, 30 - 60mm on terminal spikelet. May - June. Rare. (From garden specimen). K D Ll **(Ma)** Not Bl in FE V 201
11. *A. geniculata* Spike about twice as long as wide, awns of glumes about equalling awns of lemmas. Apr. - May. Common. **K D (Ma,** Mi, I) FE V 201

TRITICUM
Cultivated wheat. Many species are cultivated, and really outside the range of this book. They are annuals, usually with large spikes with awned or unawned glumes. T. aestivum is illustrated here as an example.

12. *Triticum aestivum* Commonly cultivated, sometimes found as a casual. **(Ma,** Mi, I) FE V 203

Also recorded in Mallorca:

Aegilops neglecta Resembles 10, but top of spike abruptly contracted, upper 1 or 2 spikelets sterile. Ll (Ma) Not Bl in FE V 202

In Minorca only:
Elymus pycnanthus FE V 196
Dasypyrum villosum FE V 203

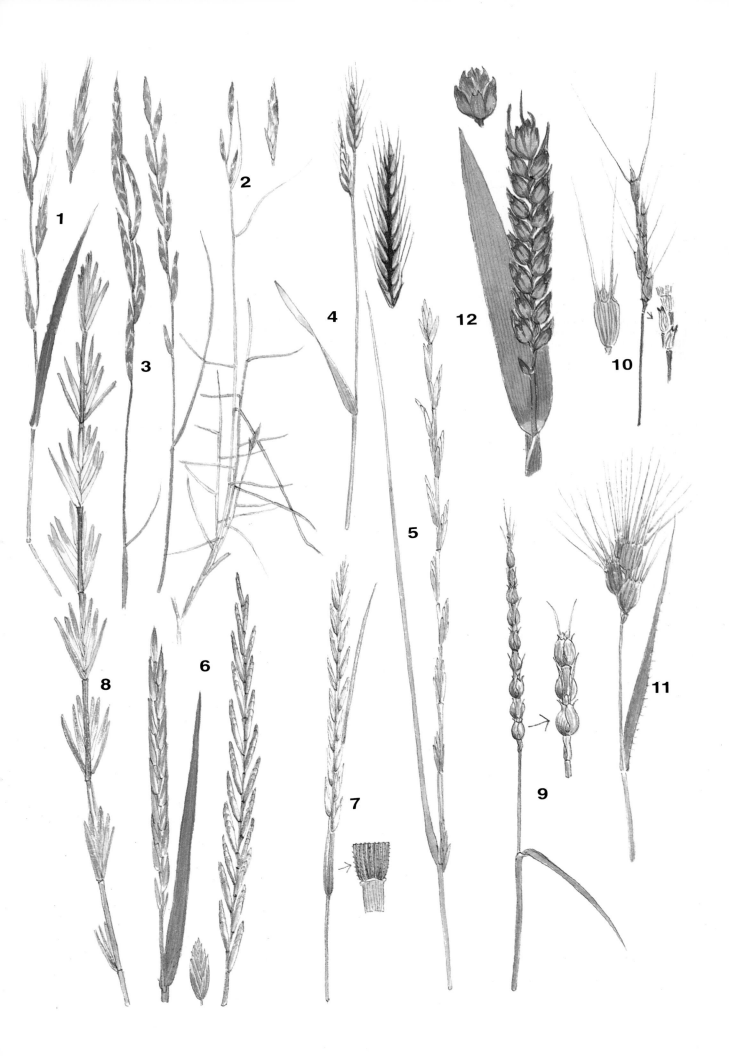

Plate 86

GRAMINEAE (5): *HORDEUM, AVENA, AVENULA,*
ARRHENATHERUM, GAUDINIA, (KOELERIA), LOPHOCHLOA,
TRISETUM, LAGURUS, AIRA.

HORDEUM

Annuals (here). Inflorescence a dense spike, with spikelets arranged in two rows of triplets, a central hermaphrodite spikelet between 2 vestigial or male spikelets. The glumes and lemmas have long awns.

1. *Hordeum murinum* (including *H. leporinum* Link) Wall Barley. Glumes of central spikelet long ciliate. Mar. - May. Disturbed ground. **K D (Ma,** Mi, I) FE V 204

2. *H. maritimum* Sea Barley. Glumes of central spikelet slightly rough, not ciliate. Inner glume of lateral spikelets winged at base. Apr. - June. Common in sandy places near sea. **K D (Ma,** Mi) FE V 205

AVENA

Annuals. Inflorescence branched panicle of drooping spikelets with long geniculate awns from lemmas. Cultivated species occur too, including *A. sativa* and *A. byzantina*, with spikelets not falling to pieces when ripe.

3. *Avena barbata* Bearded Oat. Spikelets 18-30mm. Lemma with woolly hairs up to insertion of awn, apex with 2 bristles 3-12mm long. Spikelet disarticulating above glumes and between florets. Apr. - May. Common. (+ 2/3, details × 1: smaller detail shows back of lemma without awn). **K D (Ma,** Mi, I) FE V 206

4. *A. sterilis* Winter Wild Oat. Like 3, but generally more robust. Spikelets 25-45mm without awns. Lemma with rigid hairs in lower 2/3, apex with 2 teeth 1-1.5mm long. Spikelet disarticulating above glumes. Apr. - May. Occasional. (Details only, × 1: smaller detail shows dorsum of lowest lemma). K D **(Ma,** Mi, I) FE V 208

AVENULA

5. *Avenula bromoides* Tufted perennial. Spikelets with 7-8 florets. Lemmas with divaricate awns. Apr. - May. Common. (Plants here differ from FE description in some ways: veins of lemmas become feint before margin. Panicles with more than 20 spikelets common. Glumes are acute, lemma regularly bifid at apex). **K D (Ma,** Mi, I) FE V 215

ARRHENATHERUM

6. *Arrhenatherum elatius* False Oat-Grass. Tufted perennial. Panicle of erect or spreading spikelets with 2 florets. Lower lemma with geniculate awn arising from lower 1/3 dorsum, upper with short fine bristle from near tip. Apr. - May. Not common. (Specimen from Spanish mainland). K lists for Minorca only. **D** Ll **(Ma,** I) FE V 216

GAUDINIA

7. *Gaudinia fragilis* Annual. Spike with spikelets appressed to rhachis in two opposite rows. Glumes unequal, lower short, narrow and acute, upper nearly as long as spikelet, broad and blunt with 7 strong veins. Lemmas with dorsal awns, geniculate and twisted when dry. Apr. - May. Occasional. **K** D **(Ma,** Mi, I) FE V 217

LOPHOCHLOA

8. *Lophochloa cristata* (*Rostraria cristata* (L.) Tzvelev) Annual. Inflorescence a panicle, usually dense, but very variable in shape and size. Spikelets with 2-5 florets. Lemma bifid, 5-veined with a short, straight awn from near apex. Mar. - May. Very common. **K D (Ma,** Mi, I) FE V 220

TRISETUM

9. *Trisetum aureum* Golden Oat-grass. Annual. Spikelets in fairly dense yellowish pyramidal or ovoid panicle. Lemma with slightly bent awn inserted slightly above middle of dorsum. Palea silvery, not enclosed by lemma at maturity. Apr. - May. Fairly common in sandy places. K lists for Minorca only. **D (Ma)** FE V 224

LAGURUS

10. *Lagurus ovatus* Hare's Tail. Annual. Soft woolly ovoid panicle easily recognised. Mar. - May. Common. **K D (Ma,** Mi, I) FE V 225

AIRA

11. *Aira cupaniana* Annual. Inflorescence a wiry, branched panicle of small spikelets (2-3.5mm), with pedicels thickened at apex. Apr. - May. Rather local in sandy places. **K D (Ma,** Mi, I) FE V 227

Other species recorded for Mallorca:
Hordeum hystrix (*H. geniculatm* All.) Resembles 2, but glumes of lateral spikes similar, unwinged. K **D** Ll **(Ma,** Mi) FE V 205
Avena fatua ?K (names ambiguous). ?D. Ll lists. (Ma). Bl not excluded in FE V 207
Koeleria macrantha A lot of room for confusion here, **K** records *Koeleria phleoides* Pers. (= *Lophochloa cristata* (L.) Hyl.) and *Koeleria cristata* Pers. (which includes *K. macrantha* (Ledeb.) Schultes & Schultes), but synonyms he gives would include at least 2 other species (according to FE index). D lists. Ll omits. FE V 219
Trisetum paniceum Ll (Ma, Mi) FE V 224

Aira caryophyllea Ll lists. **(Ma).** Not Bl in FE V 227
In other islands:
Avenula cincinnata ?Bl in FE V 215
A. crassifolia Ibiza (endemic) FE V 215
Arrhenatherum album Ibiza. Not Bl in FE V 216
Aira elegantissima Minorca FE V 227
Aira tenorii Minorca FE V 228

198

Plate 87

GRAMINEAE (6): *ANTHOXANTHUM, HOLCUS, AVELLINIA, TRIPLACHNE, AGROSTIS, GASTRIDIUM, POLYPOGON, AMMOPHILA, PHLEUM, ALOPECURUS.*

ANTHOXANTHUM

1. *Anthoxanthum odoratum* Sweet Vernal-grass. Coumarin-scented tufted perennial.Inflorescence dense pyramidal or cylindrical. Spikelets 7-9mm, with two sterile and one terminal hermaphrodite floret. Glumes very unequal, upper enfolding spikelet. Lemmas shortly awned. Apr. - May. Scattered in mountains. **K D (Ma**, Mi) FE V 230

HOLCUS

2. *Holcus lanatus* Yorkshire Fog. Softly hairy perennial. Spikelets 4-6mm, with 2-3 florets. Upper glume longer and broader than lower, usually shortly awned. Lemma of at least upper floret with hooked awn. May - June. Not common. (From British specimen). **K D (Ma**, Mi, I) FE V 230

AVELLINIA

3. *Avellinia michelii* Annual. Inflorescence elongated ovoid, often slightly lobed. Stems numerous, puberulent. Glumes very unequal, upper mucronate, almost as long as spikelet. Apr. - May. Common. (From Duvigneaud's specimen). **K D** (Ma, Mi, I) FE V 232

TRIPLACHNE

4. *Triplachne nitens* Annual. Panicle dense cylindrical to ovoid. Spikelets 3.5-4mm, glumes both exceeding single floret. Lemma (L) brown, geniculate awn from near base (awn almost hidden by glumes). Could be overlooked, resembling *Lophochloa cristata* and *Gastridium ventricosum*. (Specimen from Spanish mainland). **D** (Ma, Mi, I) FE V 232

AGROSTIS

Inflorescence lax, pyramidal, much-branched. Spikelets small, with one floret enclosed by glumes, which persist when the spikelet falls.

5. *Agrostis pourretii* Annual. Lemma less than half length lower glume, with long-excurrent lateral veins and a 3mm awn. Apr. - May. Rare. (Specimen from Spanish mainland). D Ll (Ma) Not Bl in FE V 234

6. *A. stolonifera* Creeping Bent. Tufted perennial with leafy stolons. Panicle patent only at flowering time. Spikelets 2-3mm, with one floret. Lemma at least 2/3 length glumes, usually unawned. Apr. - May. Common. **K D (Ma**, Mi, I) FE V 234

GASTRIDIUM

7. *Gastridium ventricosum* (including *G. scabrum* Presl.) Annual. Panicle narrow, spreading in flower, contracted before and after. Spikelets compressed, 1 floret. Lemma with geniculate awn. Occasional. **K D (Ma**, Mi, I) FE V 235

POLYPOGON

Resembles *Agrostis*, but inflorescence denser and spikelets fall entire.

8. *Polypogon monspeliensis* Annual. Panicle dense, silky, usually lobed. Glumes shortly ciliate and awned, lemma with apical awn up to 1.5mm. Apr. - May. Common in damp places. **K D (Ma**, Mi, I) FE V 235

9. *P. maritimus* (including *P. subspathaceus* Req.) Annual, panicle smaller and less silky than 8, often partly included in inflated sheath of upper leaf. Glumes long ciliate and awned, lemma unawned. Local in damp places near sea. K D (Ma, Mi, I) FE V 235

10. *P. viridis* Stoloniferous perennial. Panicle dense, deeply lobed, not silky. Glumes and lemma unawned. Damp places, or in water. Local. **K D (Ma**, Mi, I) FE V 236

AMMOPHILA

11. *Ammophila arenaria* subsp. *arundinacea* Marram Grass. Robust rhizomatous perennial. Leaves convolute. Panicle cylindrical, rigid. Spikelets of 1 floret, 12-14mm. Glumes and lemma about equal, lemma with short awn from near apexx. May - June. Common on coastal dunes. (Main illustration × 3/4). **K D (Ma**, Mi, I) FE V 236

PHLEUM

12. *Phleum arenarium* Sand Cat's Tail. Annual. Panicles dense, cylindrical to ovoid. Spikelets 2-4.5mm, with 1 floret. Glumes with stiff spreading hairs on keel; lemma truncated, about 1/3 length glumes. Local in sandy places. **D** Ll (**Ma**) Not Bl in FE V 240

ALOPECURUS

13. *Alopecurus myosuroides* Slender Fox-Tail. Panicle spike-like. Spikelets of 1 floret. Glumes connate for up to 1/2 length. Margins of lemma united below, long slightly bent awn from near base. Rare. (From British specimen). B D Ll (Ma) Not Bl in FE V 242

In other islands:
Anthoxanthum aristatum Minorca FE V 230
Corynephorus divaricatus Formentera Not Bl in FE V 231

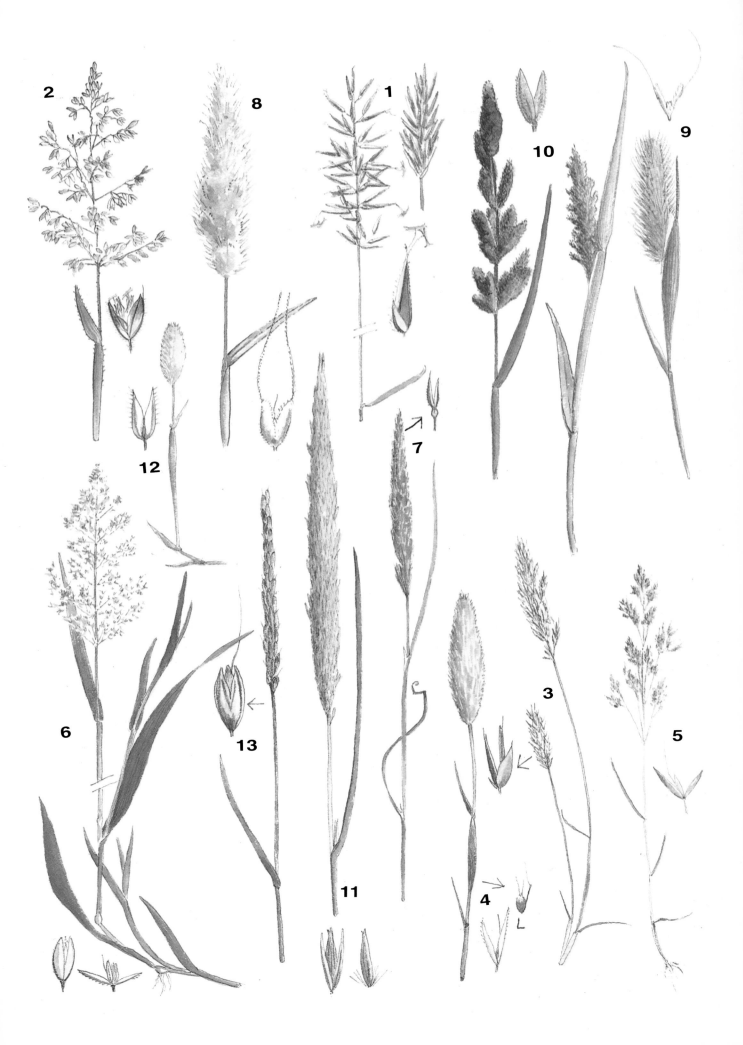

Plate 88

GRAMINEAE (7): *PARAPHOLIS, HAINARDIA, PHALARIS, PIPTATHERUM*

PARAPHOLIS

Annuals. Spikelets with 1 floret embedded in cavities of rhachis (1 fig. ii). Glumes 2, side by side (1 fig. i), covering cavity except in flower. Scarious outer margin (M) of glumes abruptly inflexed, so that keel (K) appears from outside to be outer margin. This may be winged (W) or not. Rhachis breaks when mature beneath each spikelet.

1. *Parapholis incurva* Annual. Spikes often strongly curved, with 10-20 spikelets, rather longer than internodes. Glumes unwinged. Apr. - June. Common, drier parts of saltmarshes, sandy or rocky places near the sea. (Detail ii × 3). K **D (Ma, Mi, I)** FE V 243

2. *P. filiformis* Sea Hard-grass. Resembles 3, but shorter. Spikelets not more than 1 1/3 × internode, glumes narrowly winged (fig. i). June - July. Local, saltmarshes. (Spike × 3: L is lemma appressed to rhachis). K **D (Ma, Mi, I)** FE V 243

3. *P. pycnantha* Tall straggling annual, up to 60cm. Spikes straight, with 15-30 spikelets, at least 1+ × internodes (twice here). Glumes unwinged. Apr. - June. Local, saltmarshes. (Upper half × 1, detail × 2.5). **D** Ll **(Ma)** Not Bl in FE V 244

HAINARDIA

4. *Hainardia cylindrica* Annual. Resembles *Parapholis* very closely, but only has one (upper) glume except in terminal spikelet, with 2. Except in flower, when the glumes of *Parapholis incurva* separate a little, they may be difficult to distinguish. There is a distinct white or yellowish line at junction between glumes in *P. incurva*. ?Rare: or overlooked because mistaken for 1. (Specimen from Spanish mainland). K **D** Ll (Ma, Mi, I) FE V 244 (Recently collected in Ma)

PHALARIS

Annual and perennial grasses. Panicle dense, ovoid or cylindrical. Spikelets strongly compressed, usually with 3 florets, the lower 1 or 2 reduced to small lemmas. Glumes large, flattened, papery with prominent green veins. (Shape and size of panicle very variable in all of these).

5. *Phalaris aquatica* Rhizomatous perennial up to 1.5m. Spikelets all hermaphrodite. Glumes acute with wing tapering to apex Apr. - May. Ditches and roadsides. Local. (From Mallorcan specimens: one has lobed panicle). K **D (Ma, Mi, I)** FE V 244

6. *P. canariensis* Annual. Panicle ovoid or oblong. Spikelets 7-9mm, persistent, mostly hermaphrodite. Glumes with entire wing. Sterile lemmas at least + length fertile. Apr. - May. Common casual. K **D (Ma,** Mi) FE V 244

7. *P. minor* Very like 7, but spikelets 4.5-5.5mm, glumes with a toothed wing, and sterile lemmas less than 1/5 × fertile. Apr.May. Common, usually field weed. (Name is misleading. Panicles 1.5 × 7 cm are not uncommon). K **D (Ma,** Mi, I) FE V 244

8. *P. brachystachys* Very like 7, but sterile lemmas both less than 1mm. Apr. - May. Field weed and ruderal. K D Ll **(Ma,** Mi, I) FE V 245

9. *P. paradoxa* Annual. Stems often branched at base. Panicle often partly enclosed in inflated sheath of top leaf. Spikelets in groups of 5-7, central sessile and hermaphrodite, 6-8mm, others male or abortive. Glumes with scabrid margin and single tooth near apex of wing. Spikes fall together as group, leaving bare rhachis at top of panicle. Apr. - May. Occasional field weed. K **D (Ma,** Mi) FE V 245

10. *P. coerulescens* Much like 9, but perennial, with swollen stem bases. Margins of glumes smooth, not scabrid, and wings with several teeth near apex. Apr. - May. Occasional. (Specimen from Spanish mainland). K **D** (Ma, Mi) FE V 245

PIPTATHERUM

11. *Piptatherum miliaceum* Perennial, up to 1.5m. Panicle up to 40cm, with (usually) 4-8 branches at each node. Spikelets with 1 floret, 3-4mm, often purplish. Glumes membranous. Lemma with awn 3-5mm. Apr. - May. Common. (Main illustration × 0.5, details × 1 and × 4). K **D (Ma,** Mi, I) FE V 246

12. *P. coerulescens* Perennial, up to 70cm. Panicle up to 20cm, with 1-2 branches at each node. Spikelets with 1 floret, 6-8mm, purplish or bright green. Glumes broad, membranous, lower broader than upper and enfolding it. Lemma with short awn, usually concealed by glumes. Apr. - May. Common in dry places in mountains. **K D (Ma,** Mi, I) FE V 246

Also in Mallorca:

Parapholis marginata, resembling *P. incurva* but with spikes not curved, glumes with winged keel, and (usually) inflated reddish leaf sheaths. (Not illustrated). D (Ma, I) FE V 243

Piptatherum thomasii Resembles 11, but has 20-50 short branches at lowest node of panicle which are sterile or bearing only a single spikelet. See FE V 246

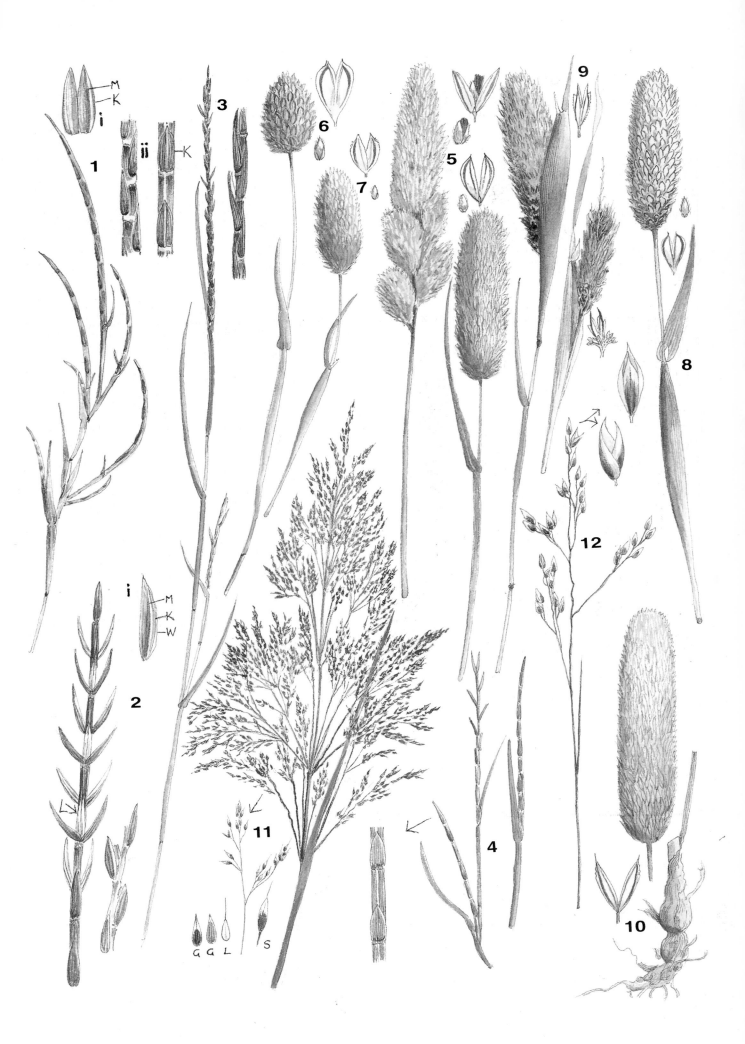

Plate 89

GRAMINEAE (8): *STIPA, AMPELODESMOS, ARUNDO, PHRAGMITES, AELUROPUS, ERAGROSTIS.*

STIPA

Leaves convolute, narrow, at least when dry. Inflorescence a slender panicle. Spikelets with one floret, the lemma with a very long awn.

1. *Stipa capensis* Annual or biennial. Lemma with awn 7-10cm, awns lying parallel to one another until ripe, so that dense, straw-coloured panicle resembles brushed hair. When ripe lemma becomes 2 geniculate, part above upper bend (the seta) remains straight, and rest (the column) becomes twisted, often round adjacent spikelets (unbrushed hair!) Apr. - June. Common. **K D (Ma,** Mi, I) FE V 250

2. *S. offneri* Caespitose perennial. Brownish panicle elongated, narrow and few-flowered. Lemma with awn 9-11cm, becoming twisted as in 1. Apr. - June. Locally common, mainly in the south. (Specimen from Spanish mainland: lemmas have fallen with grain. Seta of awn (detail enlarged) is more or less straight, shown curved here to indicate length in space available). **K D** (Ma, Mi, I) FE V 251

3. *S. bromoides* (Without close examination could easily be taken for *Vulpia* species). Caespitose perennial, resembling 2, but with awn 1.5-2.5 cm, also straight. Apr. - June. (Specimen from Spanish mainland). **D** Ll (Ma) ?Bl in FE V 252

AMPELODESMOS

4. *Ampelodesmos mauritanica* Robust tufted perennial, commonly up to 3m in flower. Inflorescence a panicle, up to 50 cm. Mar. - May. Common, often dominant in rocky scrub. (Much reduced, detail spikelet × 3). **K D (Ma,** Mi, I) FE V 252

ARUNDO

5. *Arundo donax* Giant Reed. Very large creeping perennial. Flowering stems up to 6m. Leaves flat. Panicle much branched, spikelets 12-18mm, with 3 florets. Lemma shortly awned. July - Oct. Wet places: planted for shelter, used formerly for roofing and manufacture of baskets and paper. (× 1/20, detail ×1). Introduced from SE Asia. K **D (Ma,** I) FE V 253

PHRAGMITES

6. *Phragmites australis* Common Reed. Similar to 5, but smaller. Spikelets with up to 10 florets. Glumes glabrous. Rhachilla with numerous long silvery hairs. July - Oct. Common in wet places. (Much reduced; detail of spikelet × 2). **K D (Ma,** I) FE V 253

AELUROPUS

7. *Aeluropus littoralis* Perennial with creeping rhizomes. Inflorescence 10-50mm, narrowly ovoid, 2-sided with almost sessile short spikes, each with about 20 spikelets, arranged broadside to the rhachis. Spikelets usually with 4-8 florets. April. Sandy places, usually maritime. Rare. (Specimen from Spanish mainland: detail of spikelet × 4: spike, front and side view, and arrangement of spikes also shown). K lists for Ibiza only. D Ll (Ma, I) FE V 256

ERAGROSTIS

Annual. Ligule a ring of hairs. Panicle loosely branched, of elongated many-flowered spikelets without awns. Glumes keeled, almost equal.

8. *Eragrostis cilianensis* Leaves glandular on the margin and midrib. June - Sept. (From Cretan specimen). **K D** (Ma, Mi, I) FE V 257

9. *E. barrelieri* Similar to 8, but leaves without glands, and spikelets generally smaller. June - Sept. Fairly common. **D (Ma)** FE V 257

Also recorded from Mallorca:

Arundo plinii D omits. Ll lists. Bl in FE V 252

Cortaderia selloana Pampas Grass Large tufted dioecious perennial, stems up to 3m. Panicle up to 100cm, branches erecto-patent in male plants, patent in female plants. Well established in Alcudia area. (**Ma:** introduced). FE V 253

In Ibiza only:

Stipa tenacissima FE V 251

Schismus barbatus Not Bl in FE except as 'occasional casual elsewhere' D FE V 254

Lygeum spartum FE V 255

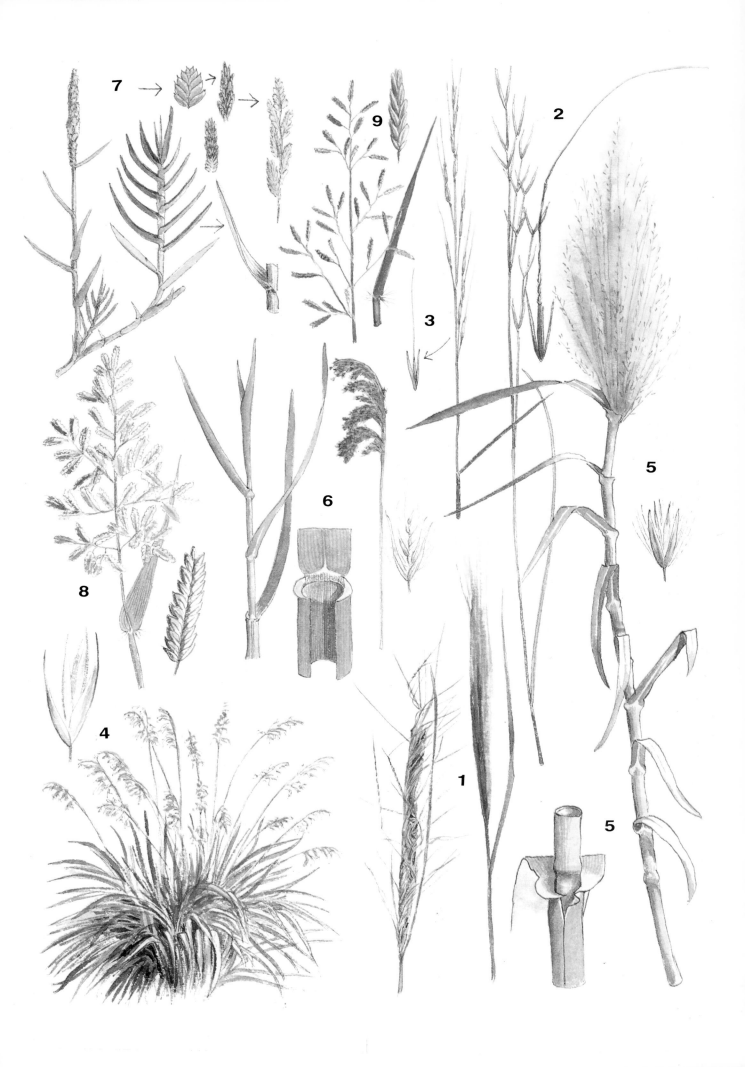

Plate 90

GRAMINEAE (9): *SPOROBOLUS (CRYPSIS), CYNODON (TRAGUS), PANICUM, ECHINOCHLOA, DIGITARIA, PASPALUM, STENOTAPHRUM, SETARIA, PENNISETUM, IMPERATA (SACCHARUM), SORGHUM (DICHANTHIUM), HYPARRHENIA, HETEROPOGON, (HEMARTHRIA).*

SPOROBOLUS

1. *Sporobolus pungens* Creeping, glabrous perennial. Leaf sheaths overlapping, ligule a row of hairs. Inflorescence a panicle, spikelets with a single floret. May - Aug. Common on beaches. (Small specimen × 1, spikelet ×4). **K D (Ma,** Mi, I) FE V 258

CYNODON

2. *Cynodon dactylon* Bermuda grass. Mat forming perennial. Inflorescence of 3-5 spikes arising from top of stem. Spikelets in 2 rows on one side of spike. July - Sept. Common in waste places. (Small specimen × 1, spikelet × 4, other details × 2). **K D (Ma,** Mi, I) FE V 259

PANICUM

3. *Panicum miliaceum* Millet. Robust annual with branched and eventually drooping inflorescence. Spikelets flattened with 2 florets, the upper fertile and lower sterile. June - July. Cultivated for fodder, sometimes naturalised. (Upper part small specimen × 1, spikelets × 4). D lists for Ib only. H and Ll list. Native China and SE Asia. (Introduced **Ma,** I) FE V 261
4. *P. repens* Creeping Millet. Rhizomatous perennial. Inflorescence an erect panicle of numerous tiny spikelets resembling those of 3. Stamens bright orange, anthers purple. July - Sept. Common, grassy places near the sea. (Upper part small specimen × 1, spikelet ×4). **K D (Ma,** Mi, I) FE V 261

ECHINOCHLOA

5. *Echinochloa colonum* Tufted annual. Leaf without a ligule. Inflorescence of several dense, 4-rowed unilateral racemes arranged along a central axis. Racemes up to 3cm, not branched. Spikelets in pairs, unawned. Lower glume much smaller than upper, which is as long as the spikelet. Sept. - Oct. Occasional. (Inflorescence of small specimen, slightly reduced: detail × 2). **K D** (Introduced **Ma,** I) ?Bl in FE V 262

DIGITARIA

6. *Digitaria sanguinalis* Crab-grass. Hairy annual. Spikelets in pairs, one with a longer stalk than the other, on an axes which are triangular in section. Fairly common in cultivated areas. **K D (Ma,** Mi, I) FE V 262

PASPALUM

7. *Paspalum paspalodes* Creeping stoloniferous annual, resembling 2 superficially. Leaf-sheaths ciliate on margin. Inflorescence with 2 (-4) terminal spikes, the spikelets in one row, but directed to alternate sides of the axis, so that they appear to be in 2 rows. Lower glume minute, upper herbaceous with a distinct mid-vein. Upper floret a sterile lemma, equalling spikelet. Upper hermaphrodite, with hardened lemma and exposed palea. Sept. Local in damp places. (× 1, spikelet × 3). **D** Ll **(Ma,** Mi, I) Not Bl in FE V 263

STENOTAPHRUM

8. *Stenotaphrum secundatum* Creeping stoloniferous perennial, rooting at the nodes. Leaves green even in very dry habitats, with broad linear blunt blades. Inflorescence spike-like, with spikelets, 1-3 together, embedded in a narrow, flattened rhachis. Native of tropics, frequently planted to form coarse drought resistant lawn, sometimes naturalised on coast. **D (Ma,** I) FE V 263

SETARIA

9. *Setaria pumila* Annual. Panicle spike-like, 1 - 15cm. Spikelets with 2 florets subtended by 4 -12 bristles arising from the stalk of floret and persisting when it falls entire. Upper glume + 2/3 length of upper lemma. Bristles usually pinkish to ginger coloured. June Sept. Roadsides, waste places. (× 1, back of spikelet × 5 showing upper glume and transversely wrinkled upper lemma). **K D (Ma,** Mi, I) FE V 263
10. *S. verticillata* Rough Bristle-grass. Resembles 9, but spike usually interrupted. Upper glume about equalling upper lemma. Bristles 1 or 2, retrorsely barbed, usually greenish. June - Sept. Common. (Small specimen × 1, spikelet × 2). **K D (Ma,** Mi, I) FE V 263
11. *S. viridis* Green Bristle-grass. Resembles 10, but spike very dense, not interrupted, and bristles antrorsely barbed. June - Sept. Not common. (Details only from small Cretan specimen × 1 and × 4). **K D** (Ma, Mi) FE V 263
12. *S. italica* Italian Millet. Robust annual, up to 1m or more. Panicle usually lobed. Bristles antrorsely barbed, 2-5 in each cluster of spikelets, not all spikelets having bristles from their stalks. Spikelet disarticulating above lower lemma at maturity. June - Sept. Occasional, cultivated for bird-seed and fodder. (From robust garden specimen: spike often narrower and less lobed. Inflorescence × 1/2, detail × 3). **D** (Introduced Ma, I) Not Bl in FE V 264

PENNISETUM

13. *Pennisetum villosum* Tufted perennial. Inflorescence a cylindrical panicle, with long feathery bristles arising below each spikelet, falling with spikelet. Aug. - Sept. Locally naturalised. (Inflorescence × 1, spikelet slightly enlarged). (Native of Ethiopia. **D** and Ll list. Introduced **Ma,** I) Not Bl in FE V 264

IMPERATA

14. *Imperata cylindrica* Rhizomatous perennial, stems up to 120cm. Panicle shining, silvery. Spikelets paired, each surrounded by long silky hairs. May July. Rare. (Specimen from Spanish mainland: detail × 2). K D Ll **(Ma,** I) FE V 265

SORGHUM

15. *Sorghum halepense* Johnson Grass. Robust perennial. Leaves broad, with white dorsal vein. Inflorescence a 10-30cm panicle, terminal branches racemose, with up to 5 pairs of dissimilar spikelets, one sessile and ellipsoid, sometimes awned, the other narrow lanceolate with a short pedicel, often purplish. July - Sept. Common casual. (Inflorescence × 1/4, details ×1 and 2). K D **(Ma,** Mi, I) FE V 265

HYPARRHENIA (CYMBOPOGON)

16. *Hyparrhenia hirta* Tufted perennial. Inflorescence with paired pedunculate racemes, one pedicellate, one sessile, the peduncle bracteate at the base. (There are often up to 30 pairs here, though FE gives 2-10). Spikelets paired, one sessile and awned, one pedicellate and unawned. Apr. - Sept. Very common. (Inflorescence × 1/2, detail ×1). **K D (Ma,** Mi, I) FE V 266

HETEROPOGON

17. *Heteropogon contortus* Tufted perennial. Inflorescence a raceme (usually solitary) with paired dissimilar spikelets, one sessile, one stalked in the upper part of raceme. Sessile spikelets with thick hairy awns. In lower part of raceme spikelets are similar and unawned. Rare. (Specimen from Spanish mainland). **D** Ll (Ma) FE V 266

Also recorded from Mallorca:
Crypsis aculeata Ll lists. Annual, up to 30cm. Leaves flat, villous on both sides, sheaths with tubercle-based hairs. Ligule a row of hairs. Inflorescence a spike-like panicle. Spikelets 4mm, of one hermaphrodite floret only, strongly laterally compressed. Glumes subequal, 1-veined, slightly shorter than lemma. Glumes and lemma with stout mucro or short awn. Ll lists. (Ma) Not Bl in FE V 258
Tragus racemosus Annual up to 40cm, decumbent or procumbent, rooting at nodes. Inflorescence spike-like. Glumes very unequal, the upper 7 - veined, exceeding spikelet, with hooked spines on the veins. K (quotes Barceló 1867-1877). D and Ll list. (Ma) FE V 260
Panicum capillare B. Ll omits. Not Bl in FE V 261
Echinochloa crus-galii Resembles 5, but longest racemes up to 10cm, usually branched at the base. Some spikelets usually long-awned. **K D** Ll (Also recorded from Mi). FE V 262
Setaria geniculata, resembling 9 but perennial, has recently been recorded from near Sóller. (Ann Boucher, personal communication 1990)
Saccharum ravennae Tufted perennial, stems up to 3m. Panicle 25-60cm, plumose and lobed. Spikelets with 2 florets dorsally compressed, enveloped in long hairs from the callus. Formerly cultivated. **K** (quotes Barceló, 1867-1877). Ll lists. (Ma, Mi. FE V 265
Sorghum bicolor Resembles 15, but annual with persistent spikelets. Cultivated for bird-seed. **D** Ll. (Ma, I). Not Bl in FE V 265
Dichanthium ischaemum Perennial. Inflorescence up to 100cm, subdigitate with 3-15 racemes. Racemes bear paired dissimilar spikelets, one sessile with a lower sterile lemma and an upper lemma with a 10-15mm geniculate awn, one stalked, awnless. **D** Ll Not Bl in FE V 266
Hemarthria altissima Not K, D or Ll. Bl in FE V 266
Paspalum vaginatum Very like 7, but leaf sheaths are glabrous at apex except on back of ligule. Lower glume nearly always absent. **D** (Also Ibiza) Not Bl in FE V 263

In other islands:
Setaria adhaerens Ibiza. See FE V 263

Plate 91

PALMAE: ARACEAE: LEMNACEAE: SPARGANIACEAE: TYPHACEAE

PALMAE: *CHAMAEROPS*

1. *Chamaerops humilis* Dwarf palm. Shrub or small tree up to 2m. Flowers numerous, in dense clusters at base of leaves. Mar. - June. Very common in hills and mountains around Pollensa, Andraitx and Arta, usually with *Ampelodesmos mauritanica.* (Illustrations much reduced). **K D (Ma,** Mi, I) FE V 267

ARACEAE

ARUM

2. *Arum italicum* Italian Arum. Fleshy, glabrous perennial with tuberous stock. Leaves appearing in autumn, persisting until flowering in spring. Spathe with margins overlapping at base. Mar. - Apr. Common in shady places, often near water. (× 0.5) **K D (Ma,** Mi, I) FE V 270

3. *A. pictum* Painted Arum. Leaves appearing shortly after inflorescence. Aug. - Oct. Locally common in stony scrub. K **D (Ma,** Mi) FE V 270

ARISARUM

4. *Arisarum vulgare* Friar's Cowl. Resembles *Arum*, but spathe with margins united to form closed tube. Mar. - June. Common in stony places. **K D (Ma,** Mi, I) FE V 271

DRACUNCULUS

5. *Dracunculus muscivorus* Tuberous-rooted perennial. Leaves compound. Spathe margins fused at base. Terminal part of spadix covered in filiform processes. Apr. - May. Occasional in stony places in northern mountains. (Detail of open spathe reduced). **K D (Ma,** Mi) FE V 272

LEMNACEAE: *LEMNA*

6. *Lemna gibba* Floating aquatic herb. Thallus grey-green to reddish, reticulate to the naked eye, usually swollen beneath. Inflorescence minute, on lower surface of frond, single stamen protruding above. Not common. (From British specimen: smaller illustration × 1). **K D** (Ma, Mi, I) FE V 273

7. *L. minor* As above, but thallus nearly flat on both sides, minute reticulation not visible to naked eye. (From British specimen: smaller illustration × 1). **K D** (Ma, Mi, I) FE V 273

SPARGANIACEAE: *SPARGANIUM*

8. *Sparganium erectum* Tall aquatic perennial. Apr. - May. Occasional in fresh water. (From British specimen). K D (Ma, Mi) FE V 274

TYPHACEAE: *TYPHA*

9. *Typha domingensis* Length of female part of spike 10 × width or more. Male and female parts spike separated by up to 6cm of bare rhachis. Scales of female flowers light brown, translucent. May - June. Occasional in marshy places. (× 1/4). **K D (Ma,** Mi, I) FE V 276

10. *T. latifolia* Reedmace, Bulrush. Length female part spike up to 6x width. Female part spike usually immediately below male, occasionally with up to 2.5cm bare rhachis between them. Female flowers without scales. May - June. (× 1/4). K **D (Ma,** Mi, I) FE V 276

Other possible species in Mallorca:

Arum majoricense (L.) Chodat. D Very rare, with purple-spotted spathe. Not described in FE.

Typha angustifolia Female part of spike dark brown as in 10, or reddish-brown and mottled. Male and female parts of inflorescence usually separated by 3-8cm of bare rhachis. Scales of female flowers dark brown, opaque. Ll. (Ma, Mi, I) FE V 275

Plate 92

CYPERACEAE (1): *SCIRPUS, ELEOCHARIS, CYPERUS, CLADIUM*

SCIRPUS

Glumes spirally arranged. Nut without a persistent style-base.

1. *Scirpus maritimus* Sea Club-rush. Rhizomatous perennial. Stems up to 120cm, trigonous, leafy. Longest bracts much exceeding terminal inflorescence. Spikelets 8-45mm, ovoid, in sessile bundle or at ends of rays up to 5cm. May. Common in saline mud. **K D (Ma,** Mi, I) FE V 278
2. *S. lacustris* subsp. *tabernaemontani* Bulrush. Rhizomatous perennial. Stems up to 3m, terete, leafless, or upper sheath with short blade. Lower bract appears to continue stem, usually shorter than inflorescence. Spikelets 3 - 10mm in bundles arranged in head, or in simple or compound umbel with unequal rays. Common in water. K D **(Ma,** Mi, I) FE V 278
3. *S. litoralis* Occasional at stream margins. Resembles 2, but stem up to 2m, trigonous. Lower bract equalling or exceeding inflorescence. Spikelets 5 - 15mm. May. Local, damp places, generally in brackish mud. **D (Ma,** Mi, I) Not Bl in FE V 278
4. *S. holoschoenus* Rhizomatous perennial. Stems up to 150cm. Bracts 1-2, lower appearing to continue stem, usually exceeding inflorescence. Spikelets 2.5 - 4mm, in globose heads, one or more sessile, the others on unequal simple or compound rays. Common in mud. **K D (Ma,** Mi, I) FE V 279
5. *S. cernuus* Tufted annual up to 30cm. Stems terete, sometimes leafy below. Bract continuing stem, not more than 1cm, often shorter than inflorescence of 1 sessile spikelet (occasionally up to 3). Apr. - Aug. Common in damp places. (Detail × 4). **K D (Ma,** Mi, I) FE V 279

ELEOCHARIS

Glumes spirally arranged. Nut with a persistent style-base.

6. *Eleocharis palustris* Rhizomatous perennial. Stems up to 1m, usually much less. Inflorescence a single terminal spikelet, without bracts, encircled at base by two empty glumes. Common in marshy places. K D **(Ma,** Mi) FE V 283

CYPERUS

Glumes (here) always arranged in two rows.

7. *Cyperus longus* Rhizomatous perennial: rhizomes 3-10mm wide. Stems up to 1.5m. Inflorescence a simple or compund umbel: spikelets tend to radiate to form more or less globular clusters. May - Oct. Very local. K D **(Ma,** Mi, I) FE V 286

8. *C. rotundus* Rhizomatous perennial, very like 7, but rhizomes about 1mm wide. Stems up to 60cm. Inflorescence a simple or compound umbel, spikelets usually more or less erect. June - Oct. Common. **K D (Ma,** Mi, I) FE V 286
9. *C. laevigatus* subsp. *distachyos* Rhizomatous perennial, often leafless. Stems up to 50cm, sheaths sometimes with blade. Inflorescence a bundle of 1-40 sessile elongated, spikelets, often curved. May - July. Occasional. **K D (Ma,** Mi, I) FE V 287

CLADIUM

Glumes spirally arranged. Nut with small, persistent style-base.

10. *Cladium mariscus* Fen Sedge. Rhizomatous glaucous perennial. Stems leafy, up to 2.5m. Blade of leaves rigid, keeled, with saw-like cutting margins. Inflorescence much branched, branches strict, ending in a panicle of 3-4mm ovoid spikelets in dense clusters. Apr. - May. Local in base-rich water. **K D (Ma,** Mi, I) FE V 288

SCHOENUS

Glumes arranged in two rows. Nut without a persistent style-base.

11. *Schoenus nigricans* Bog-rush. Tufted perennial. Stems up to 90cm. Leaves all basal. Inflorescence a terminal head of 5-10 spikelets. Lower bract usually exceeding inflorescence, green with a broad blackish-brown sheathing base. Apr. - May. Common in wet base-rich habitats. **K D (Ma,** Mi, I) FE V 289

Other records for Mallorca:
Fuirena pubescens Listed, but not seen, by Barceló (1879-1881). K D Ll omits. (?Ma) Bl in FE V 284
Cyperus fuscus D Ll (Ma, Mi, I) FE V 286
C. capitatus K (quotes Marès and Vigineix 1850-1880). D B Ll (Ma, Mi, I) FE V 287

and, more or less cultivated:

Cyperus esculentus D lists. Ll omits. Not Bl in FE V 286
C. eragrostis H and Ll list as aliens. 'Naturalised in S.W.Europe', Bl not mentioned specifically, in FE V 286
C. alternifolius D and Ll list as aliens. (Ma, I) Bl not specifically included in FE V 286

In other islands:
Eleocharis geniculata Ibiza Not Bl in FE V 282
E. uniglumis Minorca Not Bl in FE V 283

Plate 93

CYPERACEAE (2): *CAREX*

1. *Carex distachya* Densely caespitose perennial. Stems 15-45cm. Spikes 2-4, the lower very remote, shortly pedunculate with leaf-like bracts greatly exceeding inflorescence. Spikes lax, apex male with 2-5 basal female flowers. Female glumes exceeding utricle, the lower sometimes leaf-like and up to as long as spike. Utricles 4-6mm, pale greenish-brown with 1 prominent vein on each face, abruptly contracted into short, smooth beak. (Upper part stem. Details enlarged). Occasional in dry places. **K D** (Ma, Mi, I) FE V 296

2. *C. otrubae* False Fox Sedge. Tussock-forming perennial up to 1m. Stem trigonous with almost flat faces. Mar. - June. Common in damp places. (Inflorescence, and utricle and glume × 6).K (if his *C. vulpina* var.interrupta Bianor refers to this plant, as seems likely). **D** (**Ma**, Mi) FE V 297

3. *C. divulsa* (includes *C. leersiana* Rauschert) Grey Sedge. Inflorescence elongated, often with short lateral branches. Spikes all similar, the lowest at least well-separated. Apr.Aug. Common, often as a street weed in dryish situations. (Upper part of stem, utricle and glume × 6). **K D** (**Ma**, Mi) FE V 298

4. *C. divisa* Salt meadow Sedge. Rhizomatous perennial. Spikes 3-8, the upper often entirely male. Utricles 2.5-4mm, yellowish to dark reddish-brown, with prominent slender veins more or less gradually narrowed into a short, more or less scabrid beak. May - June. Common in saline soils. (Inflorescences from 2 specimens, utricle and glume × 6). **K D** (**Ma**, Mi, I) FE V 299

5. *C. flacca* Rhizomatous perennial. Leaves glaucous beneath, dark green above. Male spikes usually 2-3. Female spikes 1-5, the lowest sometimes pendent. Utricles broadly ellipsoid, rounded at the apex with a very short beak. Mar. - July. Common in damp places. (Upper part flowering stem, with utricle × glume × 6). **K D** (**Ma**, Mi, I) FE V 306

6. *C. hispida* Tall (up to 1m) rhizomatous perennial. Male spikes 3-5. Female spikes 2-5, often male above. Lowest bract usually exceeding inflorescence. Female glumes exceeding the 4-5mm utricles. Utricles plano-convex, with bristly teeth on margin. Beak 0.3-0.5mm. Apr. - May. Occasional in marshy places. (Inflorescence only - this specimen had upper 3 male spikes aborted: utricle and glume × 6). **K D** (**Ma**, Mi, I) FE V 306

7. *C. distans* Densely caespitose perennial. Very variable. Male spike usually solitary, female 2-3, distant with filiform peduncles, the lowest often pendent. Mar. - July. Fairly common in damp places. (Upper part of stem, utricle × 6). K **D** Ll (**Ma**, Mi, I) FE V 308

8. *C. extensa* Caespitose perennial. Male spike usually solitary. Female spikes 2-4, often overlapping male spike. Lowest bract greatly exceeding inflorescence. Utricle not shining, greyish or greenish brown, gradually narrowed into bifid beak. Mar. June. Common in damp places. (Flowering stem, utricle × 6). K **D** (**Ma**, Mi, I) FE V 309

9. *C. hallerana* Slender caespitose perennial, up to 40cm but usually less. Male spike solitary, Female spikes 1-3, the lowest on a long peduncle arising from base of stem. Apex of utricle abruptly contracted to short beak. Mar. - Apr. Common, usually in dry shady places. (Utricle and glume × 6). K records from Minorca and Ibiza only. **D** (**Ma**, Mi, I) FE V 311

10. *C. rorulenta* Like 9, but rhizomatous and more slender. Utricle gradually narrowed into longer beak. Mar. - June. Fairly common, often with 9. **K D** (**Ma**, Mi, I, endemic) FE V 311

Other possible species in Mallorca:
Carex depressa Not listed by K, D or Ll. ?Bl in FE V 312
Carex acuta Knoche (quotes Willkomm 1873). ?D ?Ll (?Ma) Bl in FE V 322

In Minorca:
Carex oedipostyla FE V 313

Plate 94

ORCHIDACEAE (1): *EPIPACTIS, CEPHALANTHERA, LIMODORUM, NEOTTIA, SPIRANTHES, (PLATANTHERA), (GYMNADENIA), (DACTYLORHIZA), NEOTINEA.*

EPIPACTIS

1. *Epipactis microphylla* Small-leaved Helleborine. May - July. Fairly common under *Quercus ilex*, but slender, greyish and inconspicuous. K **D** (**Ma**) FE V 328

CEPHALANTHERA

2. *Cephalanthera damasonium*. White Helleborine. Leaves broad ovate, bracts characteristically exceeding ovary, but in this specimen mostly much shorter than ovary. Apr. - May. Occasional in woods of *Quercus ilex*. (× 1/2). **D** (**Ma**) FE V 328
3. *C. longifolia* Long-leaved Helleborine. As 2, but at least lower leaves lanceolate, and bracts shorter than ovary. Uncommon, in similar situations to 2. (× 1/2). **K D** (**Ma**) FE V 328

LIMODORUM

4. *Limodorum abortivum* (including *L. trabutianum* Batt.) Mar. May. Formerly fairly common in woods, but decreasing as woods are destroyed for development. (Main illustration × 1/5, details × 1). **K D** (**Ma, Mi**) FE V 329

NEOTTIA

5. *Neottia nidus-avis* Bird's Nest Orchid. Apr. - May. Under *Quercus ilex*, locally common and increasing. Main illustration shows upper part of young stem × 1 1/2. The flowering stem persists for a long time, and overmature yellowish flowers with brownish edges (detail × 1 1/2) are more commonly encountered than the greenish-ochre young inflorecence. Not K. D and Ll list. (**Ma**) FE V 329

SPIRANTHES

6. *Spiranthes spiralis* Autumn Lady's Tresses. September. Locally abundant. (From British specimen × 1, details slightly enlarged). K D (reported to be abundant in at least one area, Sept. 1989). (Ma, Mi, I) FE V 330

NEOTINEA

7. *Neotinea maculata* Dense-flowered Orchid. Flowers small. Labellum usually held horizontally. Plants with slightly pinkish flowers have spotted leaves, those with greenish-white flowers have unspotted leaves. April. Occasional in scrub. (Illustrations × 3/4, details × 3 from photos taken recently in Mallorca by M. Thompson). K D (Ma, I) FE V 337

The following species have also been recorded from Mallorca, or as Bl in FE. Illustrations (flower only × 1) are not from Mallorcan specimens.

Epipactis palustris Marsh Helleborine (not illustrated). Not K, D, B, H or Ll. ?Bl in FE.

i. *Epipactis helleborine* Broad-leaved Helleborine. Stem leafy with broad ovate to orbicular leaves. K (quotes Bourgeau, collecting 1813-1877). ?D. Ll records without query. (Ma) ?Bl in FE V 327

ii. *Cephalanthera rubra* Red Helleborine. Resembles 3, but flowers bright pinkish-purple. K (quotes Barceló, who quotes Richard, collecting in 1761). D and Ll record without query. (Ma) Not Bl in FE V 329

iii. *Platanthera bifolia* Lesser Butterfly Orchid. Flowers small, fragrant, in a fairly dense spike. K (quotes Barceló 1867-1877). ?D. Ll records without query. (Ma) Bl included in FE V 331

iv. *Gymnadenia conopsea* Fragrant Orchid. Spike dense, cylindrial with numerous flowers. Not K. D and Ll record without query. (Ma) Not Bl in FE V 332

Dactylorhiza sulphurea Ll omits. ?Bl in FE V 334

v. *Dactylorhiza maculata* Spotted Orchid. Flowers numerous in a dense pyramidal raceme. Not K. ?D (lists '*D. maculata* subsp.'). ?H (lists 2 other species of *Dactylorhiza* with ?). Ll lists *D. maculata* without query. (Ma) ?Bl in FE V 336

In other islands:
Gennaria diphylla Ibiza. Not Bl in FE V 330

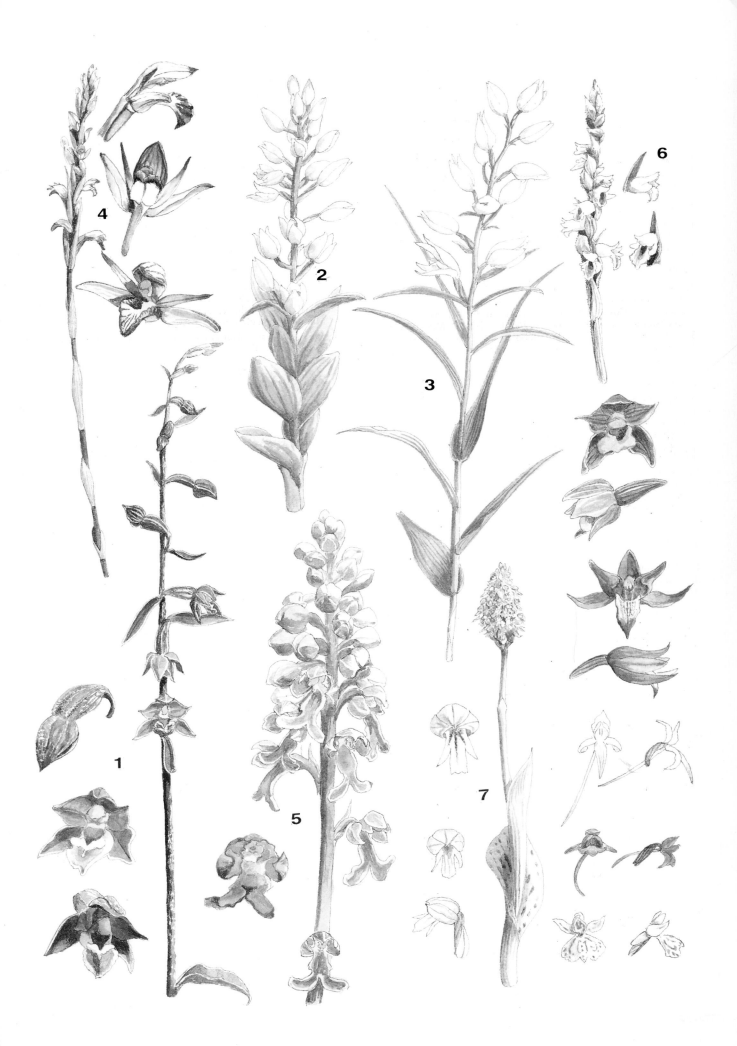

Plate 95

ORCHIDACEAE (2): *ORCHIS, ACERAS, BARLIA, HIMANTOGLOSSUM*

ORCHIS

1. *Orchis longicornu* Long-Spurred Orchid. Mar. - Apr. Very local, but often in large numbers. **K D (Ma)** FE V 339
2. *O. coriophora* subsp. *fragrans* Fragrant Orchid. Fairly common. Apr. - May. **K D (Ma, Mi, I)** FE V 339
3. *O. tridentata* and *O. lactea* Toothed Orchid and Milky Orchid. Mar. - Apr. Locally common, but not always clearly distinguishable here. Differences given in FE are:

O. tridentata	*O. lactea*
Stem 15-45cm	Stem 7-20cm
Flowers pale violet-lilac	Flowers white or greenish-pink
Middle lobes emarginate with or without apiculum in sinus.	Middle lobes usually not emarginate.
Spur half as long as ovary.	Spur sometimes longer than ovary.

   Both specimens shown here are probably *O. tridentata* **K D (Ma, Mi)** FE V 339
4. *O. italica* Naked Man Orchid. Not very variable. Mar. - Apr. Occasional, not common. K **D (Ma, I)** FE V 339
5. *O. mascula* subsp. *olbiensis* Early purple Orchid. Apr. - May. Occasional in hilly areas. **K D (Ma)** FE V 340
6. *O. laxiflora* subsp. *palustris* Jersey Orchid. May. Local in marshy places, becoming much rarer. **D (Ma)** FE V 341

ACERAS

7. *Aceras anthropophorum* Man Orchid. Apr. - May. Locally common in rocky places. **K D (Ma, I)** FE V 342

BARLIA

8. *Barlia robertiana* Giant Orchid. Jan. - Mar. Fairly common. **K D (Ma, Mi)** FE V 342

Other species possibly occurring in Mallorca (flowers only here, not from Mallorcan specimens):

i. *Orchis papilionacea* K (quotes Barceló 1867-1877). D and Ll list without query. (Ma) FE V 338
ii. *O. militaris* H (recorded 1983). Ll omits. (?Ma) Not Bl in FE V 340.
iii. *O. saccata* D and Ll list without query. (Ma) FE V 340
iv. *O. patens* **K** D ('groupe de *O. patens*'). Ll lists without query. (Ma) FE V 340
v. *Himantoglossum hircinum* H (recorded 1982). Ll omits. Not Bl in FE V 342
vi. *Orchis morio* subsp. *champagneuxii* (not illustrated) - Ll lists without query (Ma, Mi). FE V 338

In other islands:
Orchis simia Cabrera. Not Bl in FE V 339
O. mascula subsp. *mascula* Minorca. FE V 340

3

8

5

4

6

7

1

2

iv

iii

Plate 96

ORCHIDACEAE (3): *ANACAMPTIS, SERAPIAS, OPHRYS*

ANACAMPTIS

1. *Anacamptis pyramidalis* Pyramidal Orchid. Spike conical, with numerous flowers (commonly 100-200). Labellum deeply 3-lobed, with long, slender, downwards curved spur. Apr. June. Common in dry scrub. **K D** (**Ma,** Mi, I) FE V 343

SERAPIAS

2. *Serapias lingua* Tongue orchid. Labellum about twice length other perianth segments. Mar. - May. Occasional near the sea, often under pines. **K D** (**Ma,** Mi, I) FE V 344

3. *S. parviflora* Small flowered tongue orchid. Labellum not or hardly exceeding other segments, usually directed backwards. Apr. - May. Common. **K D** (**Ma,** Mi, I) FE V 344

OPHRYS

4. *Ophrys speculum* Mirror orchid. Heavily bearded lip and lateral lobes, with large central 'mirror'. Mar. - June. Common. **K D** (**Ma,** Mi, I) FE V 345

5. *O. lutea* subsp. *murbeckii* Yellow bee orchid. Sepals and petals green. Lip with broad yellow margin. Feb. - Mar. Local. K **D** (Ma, Mi, I) FE V 345

6. *O. fusca* Sombre bee orchid. A very variable species. Sepals green or yellowish. Dark lep is 3-lobed, with grey or bluish patches at base with w- or omega -shaped lower margin. Mar. - June. **K D** (**Ma,** Mi, I) FE V 346

There are 3 subspecies here:

a) subsp. *fusca* Lip up to 15mm long. Size of side lobes very variable. Median lobe indented at apex, sometimes with thin yellowish or white margin.

b) subsp. *iricolor* Large plant, with very dark lip up to 25mm. Markings large, iridescent metallic blue.

c) subsp. *dyris* (Maire) Soó Lip reddish, up to 14mm. Dark colour of peripheral part of lip continues as distinct narrow line between two basal markings of paler colour with cream margin.

d) and e) are other distinctive variants.

7. *O. sphegodes* subsp. *atrata* Early spider orchid. Mar. - May. Not common. **K D** (**Ma**) FE V 346

8. *O. bertolonii* Bertoloni's Bee orchid. Apr. - May. Fairly common, more so in the south. K **D** (**Ma,** Mi, I) FE V 347

O. bertoloniformis is probably a hybrid of this species with *O. sphegodes*. According to FE it is commoner than *O. bertolonii*.

9. *O. tenthredinifera* Sawfly orchid. Lip usually chestnut with broad yellow or greenish margin and small, white-edged blue pattern at base. There is a prominent forward-pointing distal appendage. Common. **K D** (**Ma,** Mi, I) FE V 349

10. *O. apifera* Bee orchid. Sepals pink to lilac or greenish white. Petals small, yellow or greenish. Lip deflexed at margins with prominent hairy side-lobes. Median lobes with violet or reddish-brown patch at base, surrounded by whitish or yellow lines, which are extended as lines or spots towards tip of lip. May - June. Fairly widespread. **K D** (**Ma,** Mi, I) FE V 349

11. *O. bombyliflora* Bumble-bee orchid. Small plant. Sepals broad, green, with variously patterned roughly circular dark brown labellum with shaggy lateral lobes. Mar. - May. Common, but inconspicuous. **K D** (**Ma,** Mi, I) FE V 349

12. *Ophrys hybrid.* Demonstrates the difficulties!. Mr J.J.Wood of the Herbarium at the Royal Botanic Gardens, Kew, suggests that this may be *O. speculum × O. fuciflora*, in which case *O. fuciflora* is probably about somewhere (though D and Ll only list this for Mi). There are also puzzling plants here which suggest a hybrid between *O. apifera* and *O. fuciflora*

Also recorded from Mallorca:
Ophrys insectifera (Hansen, recorded 1982). Ll lists without query. Not Bl in FE V 345

In Minorca:
Serapias cordigera FE V 343
S. vomeracea FE V 343
Ophrys fuciflora FE V 348

INDEX TO LATIN NAMES OF FAMILIES & GENERA

Where a family or genus occupies more than one plate, it is indexed only to the first.
If a family is represented in Mallorca by only one genus, from which the name of the family is derived, only the genus is given here.

Acanthus	PLATE 61	ARALIACEAE	43	Buxus	37	Clematis	13
Acer	37	Arbutus	47	CACTACEAE	42	Clypeola	18
Aceras	95	Arctium	68	Cakile	21	Cneorum	37
Achillea	67	Arctotheca	68	Calamintha	56	Colchicum	77
Acinos	56	Arenaria	10	Calendula	68	Coleostephus	67
Adiantum	1	Argyrolobium	25	Calicotome	25	COMPOSITAE	64
Adonis	13	Arisarum	91	Callitriche	54	Conium	45
Aegilops	85	Aristolochia	5	Calystegia	52	Conringia	20
Aeluropus	89	Arrhenatherum	86	Camelina	19	Consolida	13
Aeonium	22	Artemisia	67	Campanula	63	CONVOLVULACEAE	52
Aetheorhiza	73	Arthrocnemum	8	CAMPANULACEAE	63	Convolvulus	52
Agave	80	Arum	91	Capnophyllum	46	Conyza	64
Agrimonia	24	Arundo	89	Capparis	17	Coriaria	37
Agrostemma	11	Asarum	5	CAPRIFOLIACEAE	62	Coridothymus	56
Agrostis	87	ASCLEPIADACEAE	50	Capsella	19	Coris	47
Ailanthus	37	Asparagus	78	Cardamine	18	Coronilla	32
Aira	86	Asperugo	53	Cardaria	19	Coronopus	19
AIZOACEAE	9	Asperula	50	Carduncellus	71	Corrigiola	11
Aizoon	9	Asphodelus	77	Carduus	69	Cortaderia	89
Ajuga	55	ASPIDIACEAE	2	Carex	93	Corynephros	87
Alisma	75	ASPLENIACEAE	2	Carlina	68	Cosentinia	1
ALISMATACEAE	75	Asplenium	2	Carpobrotus	9	Cotula	67
Alkanna	53	Aster	64	Carrichtera	21	Crassula	22
Allium	79	Asteriscus	66	Carthamnus	70	CRASSULACEAE	22
Alopecurus	87	Asterolinon	47	CARYOPHYLLACEAE	10	Crataegus	24
Althaea	38	Astragalus	25	Catananche	71	Crepis	74
Althenia	76	Athyrium	2	Celtis	4	Cressa	52
Amaranthus	9	Atractylis	68	Centaurea	70	Crithmum	44
AMARYLLIDACEAE	80	Atriplex	7	Centaurium	49	Crypsis	90
Ambrosia	66	Avena	86	Centranthus	63	Crocus	80
Amelanchier	24	Avenula	86	Cephalanthera	94	Crucianella	50
Ammi	45	Avellinia	87	Cephalaria	63	CRUCIFERAE	17
Ammophila	87	Baldiella	75	Cerastium	10	Crupina	70
Ampelodesmos	89	Ballota	55	Ceratonia	25	CUCURBITACEAE	42
Anacamptis	96	Barlia	95	Ceratophylum	13	Cupressus	3
ANACARDIACEAE	37	Bassia	8	Cerinthe	53	Cuscuta	52
Anacyclus	67	Bellardia	60	Ceterach	2	Cutandia	82
Anagallis	47	Bellis	64	Chamaerops	91	Cyclamen	47
Anagyris	25	Bellium	64	Chaenorhinum	58	Cymbalaria	59
Anchusa	53	Berula	44	Chamaemelum	67	Cymodocea	76
Andryala	74	Beta	8	Cheilanthes	1	Cynanchum	50
Anemone	13	Bifora	44	Cheiranthus	18	Cynara	70
Anethum	45	Bilderdykia	6	Cheirolophus	70	Cynodon	90
Anogramma	2	Biscutella	19	Chelidonium	60	Cynoglossum	53
Anthemis	67	Biserrula	25	CHENOPODIACEAE	7	Cynomorium	5
Anthoxanthum	87	Blackstonia	49	Chenopodium	7	Cynosurus	83
Anthriscus	44	Bombycilaena	65	Chondrilla	74	CYPERACEAE	92
Anthyllis	32	BORAGINACEAE	52	Chronanthus	25	Cyperus	92
Antirrhinum	58	Borago	53	Chrozophora	35	Cystopteris	2
Aphanes	24	Bowlesia	3	Chrysanthemum	67	Cytinus	5
Aphyllanthes	77	Brachypodium	85	Cicendia	49	Dactylis	83
Apium	45	Brassica	20	Cicer	26	Dactylorhiza	94
APOCYNACEAE	50	Brimeura	78	Cichorium	71	Damasonium	75
Aptenia	9	Briza	83	Cirsium	69	Daphne	39
AQUIFOLIACEAE	37	Bromus	84	CISTACEAE	40	Dasypyrum	85
Arabidopsis	17	Buglossoides	53	Cistus	40	Datura	57
Arabis	18	Bunium	44	Citrullus	42	Daucus	46
ARACEAE	91	Bupleurum	45	Cladium	92	Delphinium	13

Descurainia 17
Desmazeria 82
Dianthus 11
Dichanthium 90
Digitalis 60
Digitaria 90
Dipcadi 78
DIOSCORIACEAE 80
Diplotaxis 20
DIPSACACEAE 63
Dipsacus 63
Disphyma 9
Dittrichia 66
Doronicum 67
Dorycnium 31
Dracunculus 91
Drosanthemum 9
Dryopteris 2
Ecballium 42
Echinochloa 90
Echinophora 43
Echium 53
Elaeoselinum 46
Elatine 41
Eleocharis 92
Elymus 85
Emex 6
Ephedra 3
Epilobium 43
Epipactis 94
Equisetum 1
Eragrostis 89
ERICACEAE 47
Erica 47
Erigeron 64
Erinus 60
Erodium 33
Erophila 19
Eruca 20
Erucastrum 20
Eryngium 43
Erysimum 17
Eschscholzia 16
Eucalyptus 42
Eupatorium 64
EUPHORBIACEAE 35
Euphorbia 35
Evax 65
Exacum 49
FAGACEAE 4
Fagonia 34
Fallopia 6
Fedia 63
Ferula 46
Festuca 82
Ficus 4
Filago 64
Foeniculum 44
Frankenia 41
Fraxinus 49
Freesia 80
Fuirena 92
Fumana 40

Fumaria 17
Gagea 77
Galactites 69
Galium 51
Gastridium 87
Gaudinia 86
Gazania 68
Genista 25
Gennaria 94
GENTIANACEAE 49
GERANIACEAE 33
Geranium 33
Gladiolus 81
Glaucium 16
Glaux 47
Globularia 61
Gnaphalium 65
Gomphocarpus 50
GRAMINEAE 82
GUTTIFERAE 39
Gymnadenia 94
GYMNOGRAMMACEAE 2
Gymnostyles 67
Gynandiris 80
Gypsophila 11
Hainardia 88
Halimione 8
Halimium 40
HALORAGACEAE 43
Hedera 43
Hedypnois 71
Hedysarum 32
Helianthemum 40
Helichrysum 65
Heliotropium 52
Helleborus 13
Hemarthria 90
Herniaria 11
Heteropogon 90
Hieracium 74
Himantoglossum 95
Hippocrepis 32
Hirschfeldia 20
Holcus 87
Hordeum 86
Hornungia 19
Hymenolobus 19
Hyoscyamus 57
Hyoseris 71
Hyparrhenia 90
Hypecoum 16
Hypericum 39
Hypochaeris 72
HYPOLEPIDACEAE 2
Iberis 19
Ilex 37
Imperata 90
Inula 66
Ipomoea 52
IRIDACEAE 80
Iris 80
Isoetes 1
Jasminum 49

Jasonia 66
Juglans 4
JUNCAGINACEAE 75
Juncus 81
Juniperus 3
Kickxia 59
Knautia 63
Kochia 8
Koeleria 86
Kosteletzkya 38
Kundmannia 45
LABIATAE 54
Lactuca 73
Lagurus 86
Lamarckia 83
Lamium 55
Lampranthus 9
Lappula 53
Lapsana 74
Laserpitium 46
Lathyrus 27
Launaea 73
Laurentia 63
Laurus 15
Lavandula 56
Lavatera 38
Legousia 63
LEGUMINOSAE 25
Lemna 91
Lens 26
Leontodon 72
Lepidium 19
Leucanthemum 67
Leucojum 80
Leuzea 70
Ligusticum 46
LILIACEAE 77
Lilium 77
Limodorum 94
Limonium 48
Linaria 59
LINACEAE 34
Linum 34
Lippia 54
Lithospermum 53
Lobularia 18
Loeflingia 11
Logfia 64
Lolium 82
Lonicera 62
Lophochloa 86
LORANTHACEAE 5
Lotus 31
Lupinus 25
Lycium 57
Lycopersicon 57
Lygeum 89
Lysimachia 47
Lythrum 42
Magydaris 45
Malcolmia 18
MALVACEAE 38
Malva 38

Mandragora 57
Mantisalca 70
Maresia 18
Marrubium 55
Marsilea 2
Matthiola 18
Medicago 29
Melica 84
Melilotus 28
Melissa 56
Mentha 56
Mercurialis 35
Merendera 77
Mesembryanthemum 9
Micromeria 56
Micropyrum 82
Minuartia 10
Mirabilis 9
Misopates 58
Moehringia 10
Moluccella 55
Monotropa 47
MORACEAE 4
Moricandia 20
Muscari 78
Myosotis 53
Myosurus 13
Myriophyllum 43
MYRTACEAE 42
Myrtus 42
Najas 76
Narcissus 18
Narduroides 82
Nasturtium 18
Naufraga 43
Neatostema 53
Neotinea 94
Neottia 94
Nepeta 56
Nerium 50
Neslia 19
Nicotiana 57
Nigella 13
Nonea 53
Notobasis 69
NYCTAGINACEAE 9
Nymphaea 13
Oenanthe 44
Oenothera 43
OLEACEAE 49
Olea 49
ONAGRACEAE 43
Ononis 28
Onopordum 69
Ophioglossum 1
Ophrys 96
Opuntia 42
ORCHIDACEAE 94
Orchis 95
Origanum 56
Orlaya 46
Ornithogalum 77
Ornithopus 32

222

Orobanche	94	Prunus	24
Osyris	5	Pseudorlaya	46
Otanthus	67	Psilurus	83
Oxalis	34	Psoralea	25
Paeonia	15	Pteridium	2
Pallenis	66	Pteris	2
PALMAE	91	Puccinellia	83
Pancratium	80	Punica	42
Panicum	90	Pulicaria	66
Papaver	16	PYROLACEAE	47
PAPAVERACEAE	16	Quercus	4
Parapholis	88	Radiola	34
Parentucellia	60	RAFFLESIACEAE	5
Parietaria	4	RANUNCULACEAE	13
Paronychia	11	Ranunculus	14
Paspalum	90	Raphanus	21
Pastinaca	46	Rapistrum	21
Pennisetum	90	Reichardia	73
Petasites	67	Reseda	21
Petrorrhagia	11	Rhagadiolus	71
Petroselinum	45	Rhamnus	37
Phagnalon	65	Rhodalsine	10
Phalaris	88	Ricinus	35
Phillyrea	49	Ridolfia	45
Phleum	87	Robinia	25
Phlomis	55	Roemeria	16
Phragmites	89	Romulea	81
Phyllitis	2	ROSACEAE	23
Phytolacca	9	Rosa	23
Picnomon	69	Rosmarinus	56
Picris	72	RUBIACEAE	50
Pilularia	2	Rubia	51
Pimpinella	44	Rubus	23
Pinus	3	Rumex	6
Piptatherum	88	Ruppia	76
Pistacia	37	Ruscus	78
Pisum	26	Ruta	36
Plantago	62	Saccharum	90
Platanthera	94	Sagina	11
Platanus	23	Salicornia	8
Platycapnos	17	Salix	4
Poa	83	Salsola	8
Podospermum	72	Salvia	56
Polycarpon	11	Sambucus	62
Polygala	37	Samolus	47
POLYGONACEAE	6	Sanguisorba	24
Polygonum	6	SANTALACEAE	5
Polypodium	2	Santolina	67
Polypogon	87	Saponaria	11
Polystichum	2	Sarcocornia	8
Populus	4	Satureja	56
Portulaca	9	Saxifraga	22
Posidonia	76	Scabiosa	63
Potamogeton	75	Scandix	44
Potentilla	24	Schismus	89
Prasium	55	Schoenus	92
PRIMULACEAE	47	Scilla	78
Primula	47	Scirpus	92
Prunella	56	Scleranthus	11

Sclerochloa	83	Thesium	5
Scolymus	71	Thlaspi	19
Scorpiurus	32	Thymelaea	39
Scorzonera	72	Thymus	56
SCROPHULARIACEAE	58	Tolpis	71
Scrophularia	58	Tordylium	46
Scutellaria	55	Torilis	46
Sedum	22	Trachelium	63
Sellaginella	1	Tragopogon	72
Senecio	68	Tragus	90
Serapias	96	Trapa	42
Sesleria	84	Tribulus	34
Setaria	90	Trifolium	30
Sherardia	50	Triglochin	75
Sibthorpia	60	Trigonella	29
Sideritis	55	Triplachne	87
Silene	12	Trisetum	86
Silybum	70	Triticum	85
SIMAROUBACEAE	37	Tropaeolum	34
Sinapis	20	Tuberaria	40
SINOPTERIDACEAE	1	Turgenia	46
Sison	45	Typha	91
Sisymbrium	17	Tyrimnus	69
Smilax	78	Ulex	25
Smyrnium	44	Ulmus	4
SOLANACEAE	57	UMBELLIFERAE	43
Solanum	57	Umbilicus	22
Soleirolia	4	Urginea	77
Solenopsis	63	Urospermum	72
Solidago	74	Urtica	4
Sonchus	73	Vaccaria	11
Sorbus	24	Valantia	51
Sorghum	90	VALERIANACEAE	63
Sparganium	91	Valerianella	63
Spartium	25	Verbascum	58
Spergularia	11	Verbena	54
Sphenopus	83	VERBENACEAE	54
Spiranthes	94	Veronica	60
Sporobolus	90	Vicia	26
Stachys	56	Viburnum	62
Staehelina	68	Vinca	50
Stellaria	10	Vincetoxicum	50
Stenotaphrum	90	Viola	39
Sternbergia	80	Viscum	5
Stipa	89	Vitex	54
Suaeda	8	Vitis	37
Succowia	21	Vulpia	82
Symphytum	53	Vulpiella	83
Tagetes	66	Withania	57
Tamarix	41	Xanthium	66
Tamus	80	Xeranthemum	68
Taraxacum	74	Zannichellia	76
Taxus	3	Zostera	76
Teline	25	Zygophyllum	34
Tetragonia	9		
Tetragonolobus	31		
Teucrium	54		
Thapsia	46		
Theligonum	43		